PURPOSE-MADE JOINERY

PURPOSE-MADE JOINERY

E. V. Foad

Principal Lecturer
Guildford College of Technology

Longman Scientific & Technical,
Longman Group UK Limited,
Longman House, Burnt Mill, Harlow,
Essex CM20 2JE, England
and Associated Companies throughout the world.

© E. V. Foad 1990

No part of this publication may be reproduced, stored in a retrieval system, or transmitted in any form or by any means, electronic, mechanical, photocopying, recording, or otherwise, without the prior written permission of the Publishers or a licence permitting restricted copying in the United Kingdom issued by the Copyright Licensing Agency Ltd, 33-34 Alfred Place, London, WC1E 7DP.

First edition published in 1990 by Van Nostrand Reinhold (UK) Co. Ltd

Second edition published 1990 by Longman Scientific & Technical

British Library Cataloguing in Publication Data

Longman
Scientific &
Technical

Longman Scientific & Technical
Longman Group UK Limited
Longman House, Burnt Mill, Harlow
Essex CM20 2JE, England
and Associated Companies throughout the world.

First edition published in 1982 by Van Nostrand Reinhold
Co. Ltd.
Second edition published in 1989 by Longman Scientific &
Technical.

British Library Cataloguing in Publication Data

Foad, E. V.
  Purpose-made joinery. – 2nd ed.
  1. Joinery
  I. Title
  694′.6

ISBN 0-582-41138-6

Set in Linotron 202 10/12pt Plantin
Produced by Longman Group (FE) Limited
Printed in Hong Kong

Preface

Purpose-made Joinery covers a very wide range of work, much of it of an individual nature, and some demanding considerable knowledge and a high degree of skill to produce.

The skills involved are based on the traditional techniques of working with natural timbers, but which need to be constantly examined to allow advantages to be gained from an ever-changing range of tools and equipment, and of manufactured materials.

The success of specially designed joinery for a specific job depends to a large extent on the manufacturer, who contributes a good deal to the design by his decisions on how the work will be constructed and by the standards of workmanship that he puts into it.

This book is concerned primarily with the work of the joiner in producing work that has been designed elsewhere, and covers the range of topics that are essential to interpreting the design, and to setting-out and production processes. The contents are designed to provide subject material for practical and theoretical studies at Advanced Craft Level and are presented in a way that makes the book a very useful source of reference to students following Architectural and General Building courses.

The first chapter is concerned with the design of Purpose-made Joinery, and shows that considerations of Function, Aesthetics and Manufacture are all vital to the design process, and each is discussed at some length.

Communications, their objectives and methods employed are the subject of Chapter 2, where some reference is made to the links between the joinery works and external bodies. A closer examination follows on communications and the methods employed between the specialists within the joinery works.

Chapter 3 is devoted to Workshop Geometry, which is seen as a very important part of joinery manufacture not only at setting-out stage but throughout manufacturing and fixing stages. Selected aspects of applied geometry are included, without repetition of items that form part of basic craft studies. Some topics are also omitted from the chapter to be applied more effectively to the work of succeeding chapters.

Chapters 4 to 8 are each devoted to particular areas of joinery where the related subject matter is discussed in considerable depth and well supported by illustrated details. At the end of each of these chapters, a number of joinery projects are given in the form of drawings with a brief specification, and these are intended to bring together the principles and features that have been discussed, in realistic items of joinery. Each project is capable of being used as a workshop exercise and presents an opportunity to apply the technology, geometry, science and calculations of the craft.

Acknowledgements

The author would like to express his appreciation to the following companies
and organisations for the help they have given in allowing reference to be
made to their products in this book.

Her Majesty's Stationery Office, Norwich – the Building Regulations

JKO Cutters Ltd, High Wycombe – the 'Lamello' jointing system

Pyromaster Ltd, Pampisford, Cambridge – intumescent and smoke seals

Westland Engineers Ltd, Yeovil – 'Unique' spiral sash balances

Contents

Preface   v

Acknowledgements   vi

1 THE DESIGN OF PURPOSE-MADE JOINERY   1

Functional Design   3
    Aims   3
    Evolution   3
    Ergonomics   3
    Performance   3
    Terotechnology   3
    Analysis   4
  Differential Movement   5
  Protection of External Joinery   15
  Timber Selection   16
    Manufactured Boards   17
      Plywoods   18
      Blockboards   19
      Laminboards   19
      Particle Boards   19
      Other Manufactured Boards 20
      Glues   20
Aesthetic Design   22
  Geometrical Work – and aesthetics   25
  Materials – and aesthetics   26
  Jointing – and aesthetics   29
  Some Other Working Processes – and
aesthetics   31
    Moisture Movement   31
    Changes in Colour   31
    Worked Finishes   32
    Transport and Handling   34
    Softwood Grounds   36
Production Design   37
  Materials – and productivity   38
  Operations – and productivity   41

2 COMMUNICATIONS   49

External Communication   49
  Statutory Contacts   50
  Operational Contacts   50
  Working Contacts   51
Internal Communication   52
  Scaled Drawings   54
    Small-scale Drawings   54
    Assembly Drawings   55
    Detail Drawings   55
  The Specification   56
  The Bill of Quantities   58
  The Workshop Rod   59
  Cutting Lists   61
  Labour Costs   63
  Patterns   65

3 WORKSHOP GEOMETRY   69

4 WINDOWS   97

Functions   97
  Light Admission   97
  Ventilation   97
  Draught Exclusion   97
  Through Vision   98
  Obscurity   98
  Ease of Operation   98
  Weather Resistance   98
  Security   99
  Thermal Insulation   99
  Sound Insulation   99
  Appearance   99
  Ease of Maintenance   100
Construction   100
  Putty and Glazing Beads   100

Weather Resistance Features   101
Fixed and Opening Windows   101
Louvres   104
Curved Members   108
Bay Windows   112
Bow Windows   114
Vertical Sliding Sashes   114
Double Glazing   118
Curtain Walling   120
    Weather Resistance   122
    Strength Requirement   122
    Moisture Movement   122
    Spandrel Panels   122
Joinery Projects   124
Project I: Splayed Bay Window   126
Project II: Bullseye Windows   137
Project III: Elliptical Borrowed Light 140
Project IV: Bow Window   142
Project V: Louvred Frames   147

5 DOORS AND FRAMES   150

Door Frames and Linings   150
    A Door Frame   150
    A Door Lining   150
Frames that incorporate Architraves 156
Linings that incorporate Architraves 157
Doors – design criteria   158
    Access   158
    Weather Protection   158
    Security   159
    Light Admission   159
    Appearance   159
    Fire Resistance   159
Basic Forms of Door Construction   159
    Panelled Doors   161
Glazing   164
    Part-Glazed Doors   165
Flush Doors   166
Swing Doors   169
Fire-resisting Doors   170
    Intumescent Seals   172
Joinery Projects   174
Project VI: Vestibule Doors and Frames 175
Project VII: Hardwood Doors with
Enriched Panels   183
Project VIII: Emergency Exit Doors   186
Project IX: Inward Opening 'Stable
Door'   189

Project X: Industrial Sliding Doors with
Wicket   192

6 WALL PANELLING, WORK
SURFACES
AND COUNTERS   195

Wall Panelling   195
    Cover Fillets   197
    Pellets   197
    Slot Screwing   197
    Slotted Plates   197
    Interlocking Blocks   197
Framed Panelling   198
Strip Panelling   201
Sheet Panelling   204
Work Surfaces   207
    Strength   208
    Accuracy   208
    Slip Resistance   208
    Wear Resistance   208
    Spillage Resistance   208
    Heat-Resistance   208
    Hygiene   208
    Heat Conductance   208
Counters   212
Joinery Projects   220
Project XI: Wall Panelling to Reception
Area   221
Project XII: Strip Panelling to Isolated
Pier   225
Project XIII: Table-Mounted Lectern
Design 1   228
Project XIV: Table-Mounted Lectern
Design 2   231
Project XV: Curved Portion to Bar
Counter   234

7 STORAGE AND DISPLAY
FITMENTS AND SEATING   236

Storage and Display Fitments   236
    Sliding Doors   241
    Drawers   245
Seating   248
    Offices   250
    Dining Rooms   250
    Lecture Rooms, Churches and
    Waiting Rooms   250

Public Outdoor Seating   250
Lounge   251
Joinery Projects   254
Project XVI: Seating to Reception Area   255
Project XVII: Enquiry Hatch with
Sliding Doors   261
Project XVIII: Refectory Tables   264
Project XIX: Credence Table   267
Project XX: Wall-mounted Cross   270

8 STAIRS   273
Function and Design   273
Private Stairs   281
Common Stairs   281
Rise and Going Dimensions – Tapered
Steps   282
Checking the Ratio of Rise to Going   282
Checking the Goings of the Tapered
Steps   282
Checking the Ratio of Rise to Going   284
Checking the Goings of the Tapered
Steps   284

Landings and Limitations in Lengths
of Flights   284
Headroom   285
Guarding and Handrails   285
Construction Details and Features   286
Step Details   286
Spring Details   288
Shaped Steps   289
Cut Strings   291
Wall Strings at Winders   293
Wreathed Strings   294
Open-riser Stairs with Strings or with
Carriages   296
Wall-fixed Handrails   298
Handrail Scrolls   299
Wreaths in Geometrical Handrailing   301
Joinery Projects   306
Project No. XXI: Open-riser Domestic
Stairway   307
Project No. XXII: Glazed Balustrade to
Domestic Stairs   312

Index   315

Chapter 1

THE DESIGN OF PURPOSE-MADE JOINERY

In most building work, the design of joinery is principally the responsibility of the architect who, with a broad overall knowledge of the principles of construction and with particular skills in design, is able to furnish each specialist in the construction team with detailed instructions on the work. Positive details are presented to the joinery producer mostly in the form of scaled drawings and in some cases by sketches to convey the essential features of the work. The DRAWINGS provided will generally include detailed sections through the members concerned, but *are unlikely to include details of the jointing necessary to frame the work together*. A worded description or specification will normally accompany the drawings to set standards and control the general approach to the work and this must be interpreted by the craftsman through his own specialised knowledge of production and materials to determine the more intimate features of manufacture.

From the craftsman's point of view, some design knowledge is necessary to appreciate the design aims of the architect and to process the instructions to the best possible effect. His contribution to the design may be very necessary and can have a noticeable effect on the finished product. In some cases the joiner may become more involved with design when he is in direct contact with a customer who has not employed a specialist designer, and he will then be called upon to design and produce items of joinery with very little information provided from elsewhere.

Courses in purpose-made joinery and the qualifying examinations at advanced craft level are largely concerned with problem solving related to joinery design.

There is no doubt that the architect and the joinery manufacturer will each perform his work more effectively with an understanding of the problems of the other, and it follows that effective communication between the two will be highly beneficial to both.

The design of an item of joinery should be the result of a number of considerations following the original idea or recognition of a need and it is these that are the subject of this chapter; they are concerned with *function, aesthetics* and *manufacture*. Depending on the nature and type of joinery to be produced, priority may be given to either of these considerations; but in any item of work they will all be worthy of some thought and attention.

FUNCTIONAL considerations are concerned with the effectiveness or efficiency of the piece of joinery in use, and would be most important in the design of an item intended principally to fulfil certain working functions.

AESTHETIC considerations are concerned with appearance, and these would be most important in the design of joinery required primarily to fulfil a decorative role. These considerations can probably be satisfied most fully where function and economy are less important, although it has sometimes been observed a purely functional design can result in a thing of considerable beauty.

MANUFACTURE is a vital consideration in the design of joinery if the work is to be produced in a satisfactory and economical manner. By failing to consider the manufacturing problems the designer may, sometimes unknowingly, cause unnecessary wastage of materials and introduce unnecessary operations, which restrict the speed of production and add considerably to the cost of the work.

Each of the design considerations seen in Fig. 1.1 as part of the overall design is sufficiently important to justify its examination in some detail so that the subject of purpose-made joinery can be more fully appreciated; this chapter therefore is devoted to those topics and the influence each may have on the work of the joiner.

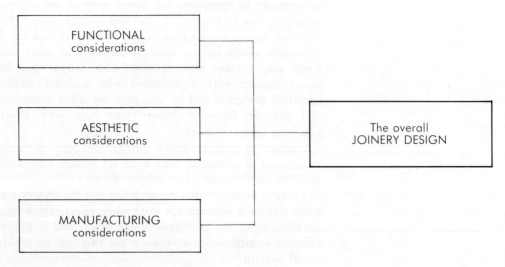

Fig. 1.1
Considerations leading to
joinery design

FUNCTIONAL DESIGN

Aims.   The item of joinery must effectively *do the work expected of it and perform for an economical life-span under the conditions of service in which it will be placed.* To satisfy these aims, the finished work will need to have certain well defined characteristics and properties which will allow it to perform satisfactorily, and to be constructed in such a way and be of such materials that it will survive the environmental conditions likely to affect it.

Evolution.   Most common items of joinery to be produced will be based on functional designs that have evolved over the centuries, as joinery as a craft has developed. Such work follows earlier examples, which were made to satisfy needs as seen by the craftsman himself and whose design may have been limited by the knowledge and skills, materials and equipment available at that time. As these things change, the design of even the most basic items of joinery should be revised, without necessarily any loss of efficiency.

Ergonomics.   A major consideration in the functional design of modern joinery is the need to relate the dimensions and shapes of the product to the physical characteristics of the people expected to use it. This study of *anthropometrics* concerns safety and comfort and the avoidance of unnecessary fatigue in the user through the design of furniture and equipment.

It is of course rarely possible to design an item of joinery to suit an individual's physical characteristics and while in some cases it is possible to incorporate adjustable parts in the design it is more likely that the dimensions will be standardised to be used in reasonable comfort by the limited range of people concerned. Common items of joinery where such consideration is necessary in the determination of dimensions and shapes include seating, tables, workbenches, shelving, counters and stairs; examples of these, together with appropriate dimensions, are shown in later chapters.

Performance.   The effectiveness of joinery cannot be anticipated without considering the environmental conditions in which it will exist and which may adversely affect its durability and performance. In some cases the performance of an item of joinery in a particular environment is ensured by the *statutory control* of its design and there is a need to be aware of current legislation, e.g. in the design of stairs and fire-resisting components.

Terotechnology.   Of growing concern in the design of joinery is the economy of resources, which can be wasted not only during manufacture but also through the life-span of the product.

These things have always been of some concern to the true craftsman who will economise, as far as the design will allow, in his manufacturing methods, with due concern for the durability of his work. Increasing costs and the scarcity of many natural resources are resulting in a growing awareness, under the heading of terotechnology, of the need to design and manufacture responsibly, to reduce as far as possible the need for maintenance, repair and replacement. Short-term economies, particularly in design and manufacture, can very easily be lost in the resultant increase in 'cost-in-use' of the product.

Analysis. Where a design is to be as original as possible, the functional aspect should be considered from first principles by questioning firstly 'What will be its functions?' and secondly 'In what conditions will it exist?' Answers to these questions, which the designer may put to himself, and compliance with any relevant Statutory Regulations, will lead to the properties and characteristics necessary in a good functional design. It should be noted that, in considering the environmental conditions, the designer is interested not only in the more obvious problems, such as humidity, temperature, sunlight and weather conditions, but also in the likelihood of exceptional wear and tear, carelessness, or vandalism which may be expected in a particular situation and should therefore influence the design.

The analysis is therefore concerned with effectiveness and durability, and will involve dimensions, shapes, materials selection, construction details, treatments and finishes, and this design process can be seen graphically in Fig. 1.2.

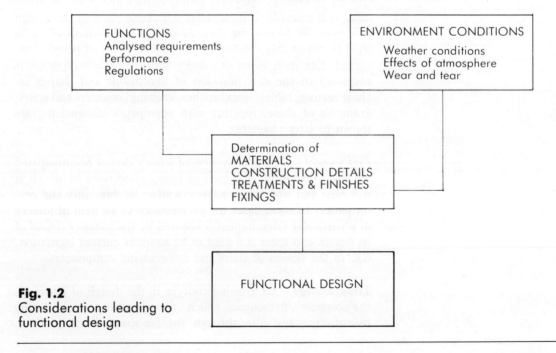

Fig. 1.2
Considerations leading to functional design

Such an analysis can be applied even to a simple common item of joinery such as the rear entrance door and frame required for a new house as seen in Table 1.1, although this could well be a mental process by the designer as he commits his drawing to paper.

A second example, requiring rather more thought, is shown in Table 1.2, where the greater number of points to be considered is by no means exceptional.

To illustrate some problems associated with the functional design of joinery, the following diagrams and notes are intended to illustrate a number of points of interest to the designer.

Differential Movement

Fig. 1.3 shows the range of moisture content levels, reaching a state of equilibrium with the atmosphere in which joinery exists. Changes in moisture content in joinery timber will result in dimensional changes in the material. Loss of moisture results

Table 1.1
Requirement: Rear Entrance Door and Frame to a New Dwelling House

Considered functions	Easy personal access — kitchen to garden Occasional passage of household effects Vision through Light admission Weather exclusion Security
Derived features	Normal, standard door height Possibly wider than average Half glass. Clear glass Solid rebated frame with cill 3-lever mortice lock
Environment	Normal domestic usage Internal space very restricted Adequate space externally Exposed to weather
Further derived features	Lock to include latch and furniture Open outward Protective porch desirable Weather resistant construction, door and frame Hardwood cill Softwood to be painted Hardwood to be oiled
Functional design	of both the door and frame is largely fixed by the above, but some consideration should now be given to aesthetics and production

Table 1.2
Requirement: Internal Door and Frame Between Classroom and Corridor in a New School

Considered functions	Frequent access to and from the room by children Frequent passage of furniture Borrowed light required in corridor Security of room when not in use
Derived features	Door height standard throughout building Width to be greater than in domestic situation Glazed area to be included Roller latch, push plate and pull handle Mortice dead-lock and escutcheons
Environment	Heavy usage by large number of children Corridor is a designed escape route Need for cleanliness Building is centrally heated
Further derived features	Consider use of hardwood throughout Possibly plywood-faced flush door with hardwood elsewhere Glass to be clear, wired and situated to allow vision Robust construction and hardware Kicking plates required Open inward Kiln-dried timber Painted finish
Functional design	Determined from the above information, leads to the necessary consideration of aesthetics and production

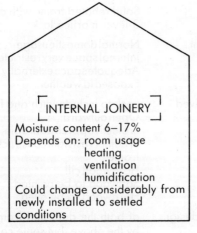

INTERNAL JOINERY
Moisture content 6–17%
Depends on: room usage
           heating
           ventilation
           humidification
Could change considerably from newly installed to settled conditions

EXTERNAL JOINERY
Moisture content fluctuates
12–20% July–November

Fig. 1.3
Equilibrium moisture content levels in joinery

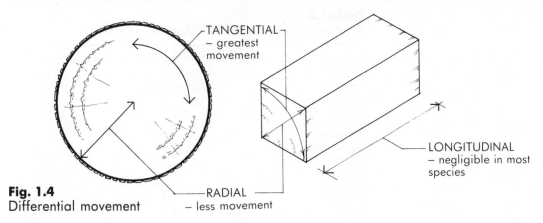

Fig. 1.4
Differential movement

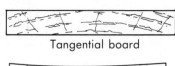

Tangential board

Cupping and loss of width
– as timber dries

Fig. 1.5
Tangentially cut board – the
least stable

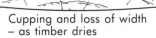

Radial board – stable but
wasteful conversion

Quarter-sawn – a good
compromise with
economic
conversion

Fig. 1.6
More stable sections

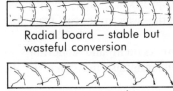

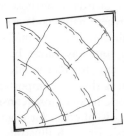

Fig. 1.7
Diamond effect – distorted
section from loss of moisture

in shrinkage. and an increase will result in swelling. If the problem were as simple as that the joiner would not have to contend with what is probably the greatest single problem related to joinery manufacture and this is the problem of *differential movement*. The amount of movement differs relative to the growth structure of the tree, and directions of movement are expressed as tangential, radial and longitudinal (Fig. 1.4).

The effects of differential movement in any one piece of timber, depending on the way it is cut from the tree, may result mainly in:

1. Movement in the face width;
2. Loss of 'square' in a sectional right-angle;
3. Cupping.

A board cut tangentially from the tree (Fig. 1.5) will suffer considerable loss of width on drying and is also likely to cup. A radially cut board (Fig. 1.6), or more economically a quarter-sawn board, will move less in its width and is more stable. A square or rectangular section as in Fig. 1.7 will lose its squareness because of differential movement as the moisture content changes.

The amount of movement, whether it be swelling or shrinking as humidity fluctuates, also varies with species. Table 1.3 shows for comparison a range of common timbers and their radial and tangential movements expressed as percentages of the board width as their moisture content varies from 12 to 20%. It will be seen, for example, that a piece of European redwood 100 mm wide would be expected to fluctuate in width by 2.3 mm if cut tangentially, but only 1.0 mm if cut radially as the moisture content fluctuates from 12 to 20%. Another common timber that presents particular movement problems is Parana pine, which could be expected to move considerably more than amounts indicated for redwood. It must be remembered that, while these fluctuations are occurring, movement in length will be negligible, and this presents further problems.

Table 1.3
Relative Movement 12–20% Moisture Content

Species	Movement (mm/100 mm)	
	Tangentially	Radially
Afrormosia	1.4	0.6
Douglas Fir	1.5	1.0
European Redwood	2.3	1.0
Iroko	1.0	0.5
Sapele	1.8	1.2
Keruing	2.5	1.5
Teak	1.2	0.8
Utile	1.7	1.4
Western Red Cedar	0.8	0.5
Yang	3.3	2.0

These notes on moisture movement generally, and differential movement in particular, illustrate that without due care and attention to detail the designer and producer of joinery may well produce an item that will quickly become unsightly or even useless. It will be seen that careful consideration must be given to:

1. The selection of an appropriate species of timber, and if possible its mode of conversion (the way it is cut from the tree);
2. The specification of a moisture content and conditions of manufacture and fixing that will minimise movement in the completed work;
3. The use of construction details that will minimise the effects of movement, yet allow inevitable movement to take place without damage.

It is rarely possible to specify to a timber supplier material which has been converted from the log in a particular way, but it is possible to select the most suitable boards from those available. A very good example of this is where hardwoods are purchased in the common form of 'slab sawn' or 'through and through' boards. Pieces produced in this way range between the extremes of completely radial cut to tangential, with quarter-sawn boards in between and it is therefore important to select those most suitable for the work in question (considerations other than moisture movement, visual effect for example, may be more important in some cases). Fig. 1.8 illustrates the range of boards produced in this way.

Other methods of conversion, however, may produce pieces all of which have similar movement characteristics, and an ex-

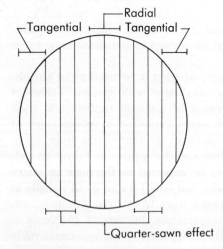

Fig. 1.8
Through-and-through – the varying boards produced

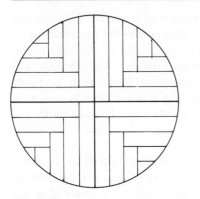

Fig. 1.9
Quarter-sawn – uniform boards
produced

ample of this is shown in Fig. 1.9, where every board is defined as quarter-sawn.

Specified moisture contents in joinery are aimed at the equilibrium moisture content at which the work will settle in use. To avoid the damaging effects of movement in the finished work, it is important to achieve as near as practicable the final moisture content in the material before it is framed together. Table 1.4 gives typical moisture content ranges for a number of joinery situations.

Difficulties in controlling the moisture content during manufacture and fixing are bound to arise where the specified moisture content is in the lower levels and achieved by artificial or kiln seasoning. The environment in the normal joinery workshop and in the new building at joinery-fixing stage is likely to be such that the material will absorb moisture. Work of a critical nature, having a low moisture content, demands humidity control in the workshop or, as a more positive approach, manufacture and assembly of the joinery on site in its final situation when the humidity has stabilised.

Table 1.4
Moisture Contents in Timber for Joinery

Situation	Moisture content range (%)
Radiator casings duct covers, items near to heat source, casings to electronics equipment	6–10
Furniture and fitments in schools, libraries and public buildings	10–14
Kitchen fitments, bathroom furniture, bakehouse, equipment	10–16
Domestic internal joinery, central heated	10–15
Domestic joinery, intermittent heating	14–17
External joinery	15–20
Carcassing, structural timbers as in trusses, prefabricated work	15–18

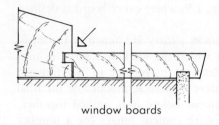

window boards

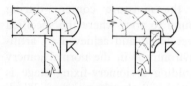

Treads & risers

Fig. 1.10
The masking of shrinkage

In addition to these considerations in materials selection and seasoning, various construction details may be incorporated to allow the inevitable movement to occur and to conceal the unsightly effects it would otherwise produce. Wide boards will obviously present greater movement problems than narrower ones. Fig. 1.10 shows examples in window boards and stair members where the work demands considerable widths of material. Tongued joints or cover mouldings mask the effect of shrinkage.

Made-up widths involving edge-jointed boards as in flooring, strip panelling and in certain types of door are designed to allow movement to take place in free-moving joints that are tongued and grooved together to retain a flush surface. Three features employed here are:

1. The use of narrow boards in preference to wider ones to minimise the effect of movement on each joint;
2. The avoidance of glued joints to allow free movement; and
3. The inclusion of a decorative feature to conceal movement at the joints.

Note too that in the case of external work, where seasonal absorption will take place, the over-camping of boards having a low moisture content may exert considerable pressure against framing when swelling at a later stage and damage will result. In Fig. 1.11, note that (a) illustrates the obvious and unsightly effects of opening joints as shrinkage occurs, and the advantage of using narrower boards to minimise the effect on each joint, (b) shows some common decorative joints and (c) shows a case where absorption and swelling can be damaging.

In some work it would of course be inappropriate to use edge joints which open with shrinkage; e.g. in various door panels, table tops, shelving and wide members in cupboard fitments. Joints in such work will be glued together in various ways and the resulting made-up board will in effect become one wide solid piece. The effects of movement will, however, be affected by the selection of boards employed and the method of fixing the panel to adjoining work. Fig. 1.12 illustrates, for example, that the use of wide pieces can result in considerable distortion due to cupping (in addition to the expected shrinkage) and that by using narrower pieces or 'ripping' and reversing alternate pieces greater stability is achieved.

Fluctuations in width must be allowed to take place, yet the member must be held firmly in place. A table top (Fig. 1.13) is a good example, and it will be seen that wood buttons or metal shrinkage plates offer alternative solutions. Similarly, the full-width door panel shown in Fig. 1.14, although restrained within grooves, would suffer considerably from movement and this would be dealt with most effectively by the inclusion of a muntin in the centre. This would reduce the visual effect of mois-

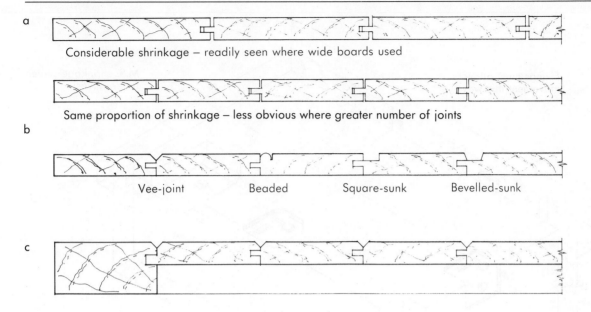

a

Considerable shrinkage – readily seen where wide boards used

Same proportion of shrinkage – less obvious where greater number of joints

b

Vee-joint   Beaded   Square-sunk   Bevelled-sunk

c

Fig. 1.11
Moisture movement in tongued & grooved boards
(**a**) Significance of board widths on noticeable shrinkage
(**b**) Decorative features 'conceal' shrinkage
(**c**) Problems also from swelling if boards confined

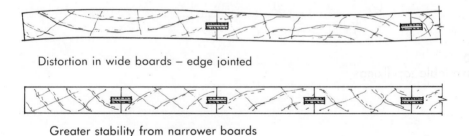

Distortion in wide boards – edge jointed

Greater stability from narrower boards

Fig. 1.12
Stability of glued edge-jointed
boards

ture content changes as the movement would be distributed between four moving joints instead of two.

One of the greatest problems related to movement in joinery is that of differential movement in work where it is necessary to join members together in such a way that the grain runs in opposing directions. Where the natural movement in one piece is restricted by the differing characteristics of the next, serious damage can result. It is essential always to anticipate the effects of such movement and give due attention to construction details. Figs 1.13 and 1.14 show the importance of allowing

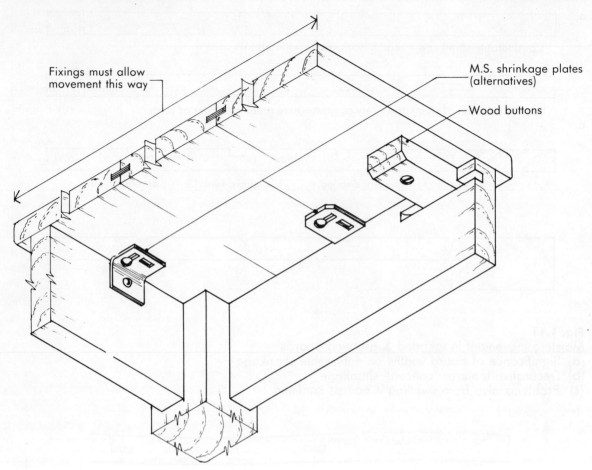

Fig. 1.13
Alternative table top fixings

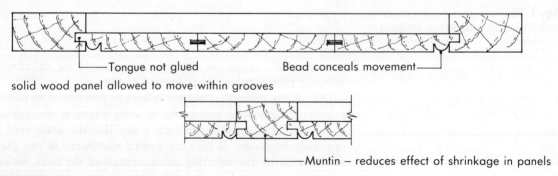

Fig. 1.14
Moisture movement in door
panels

members to move independently of each other; the door panel relative to a rail, and the solid table-top relative to the crossrail beneath it.

A further example is shown in Fig. 1.15 and concerns a cupboard fitment having ends and divisions made from solid edge-jointed timber. Members such as drawer runners and shelf-bearers which are fixed to these boards must allow freedom to expand or contract, and this is achieved by screw fixings through slotted holes. It should be noted that one end of each member may be positively fixed, to control where movement is allowed to occur.

A further problem related to moisture movement in solid boards concerns the bonding of laminated plastic sheets or any other veneer that will prevent one face of the board having contact with the atmosphere. The resulting imbalance in the conditions surrounding the timber causes excessive distortion. The fixing of a balancer veneer on the reverse side has long been practised by cabinet makers and is still a sound principle in using any modern facing material. A more positive means of

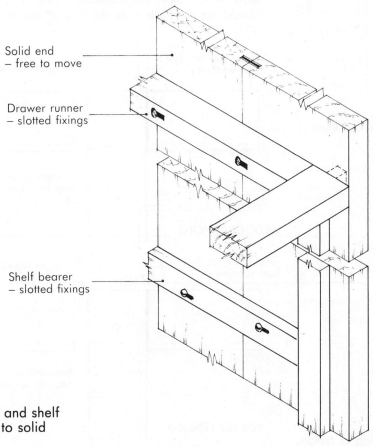

Solid end
– free to move

Drawer runner
– slotted fixings

Shelf bearer
– slotted fixings

Fig. 1.15
Drawer runners and shelf bearers – fixed to solid cupboard end

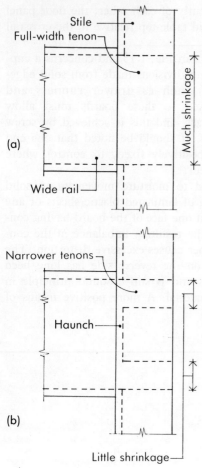

(a)

Stile
Full-width tenon
Much shrinkage
Wide rail

(b)

Narrower tenons
Haunch
Little shrinkage

Fig. 1.16
Haunched tenons to wide rails

retaining a flat surface, however, is to use one of the 'reconstructed' timber boards instead of solid timber when any form of veneering is to follow, but even with these balancer veneer is often specified.

One further concern for moisture movement should be the effect on any joints employed in framed joinery. Most traditional joints have evolved through observation of their behaviour in use and are now based on tried and tested design features and craft procedures. Shrinkage can result in loosening joints, opening shoulders and possibly the splitting of material and some of these points can be seen in the mortice and tenon joints in a door. Fig. 1.16a, for example, shows that the wide tenon to a middle rail would suffer considerable shrinkage and Fig. 1.16b indicates the value of reduced tenon width by haunching. The shoulders of a tenon should remain tight regardless of any shrinkage, and this is ensured by the correct gluing and wedging or pinning (Fig. 1.17).

Details occur in joinery where adjoining members are dry-fixed to each other by screwing or nailing without the use of glue, e.g. in glazing beads or certain securing fillets which may need to be removed occasionally. Without glue, such members should not be flush with the face of the work since moisture

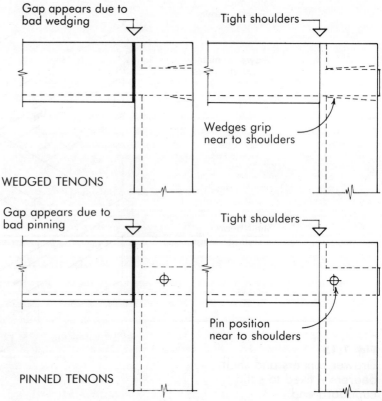

Gap appears due to bad wedging

Tight shoulders

Wedges grip near to shoulders

WEDGED TENONS

Gap appears due to bad pinning

Tight shoulders

Pin position near to shoulders

PINNED TENONS

Fig. 1.17
The proper securing of tenons

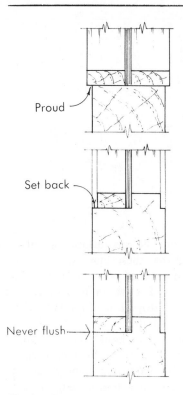

Fig. 1.18
Movement in glazing beads

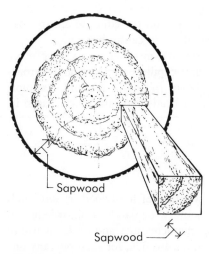

Fig. 1.19
Sapwood in timber

movement will produce an unsightly effect. Glazing beads and the like should therefore either stand proud or be set back positively from the face of the work as illustrated in Fig. 1.18.

Protection of External Joinery

External joinery is also affected by contact with rainwater, which can produce more extreme problems than the atmospheric conditions already discussed. Water in contact with joinery, in addition to being absorbed by the material itself, can penetrate between members and behind applied finishes, resulting in discolouration of material, corrosion of metal fixings, breakdown of glued joints and fungal decay of timber. The selection of timber, glue, fixings, treatments and finishes is an important part of the design of external joinery; so too is an appreciation of the need to detail the work so as to encourage water to pass quickly over it, with the least possible harmful effects. Contributing to the problems, particularly in softwood joinery, is the fact that almost every piece of softwood in use today includes some sapwood, and this is responsible for the increasing incidence of wet rot in relatively new work (Fig. 1.19).

Sapwood has very little resistance to fungal decay, so there is a good case for the preservative treatment of softwood exterior joinery regardless of any applied finish to follow. The natural durability of hardwoods can be very good indeed, but varies according to species, some being little better than softwoods. In an increasing number of cases, preservative-treated softwoods are being used rather than the more expensive durable hardwoods.

Preservative treatments in use for timbers are of three classes:

1. *Tar oils or creosotes.* These are not generally suitable for joinery because of their odour and the fact that they cannot be painted over. Their effectiveness as a preservative depends on the thoroughness of application, which is most effectively done by vacuum/pressure methods.
2. *Inorganic salts in water solution.* Copper/chrome/arsenic salts as a waterborne solution, applied by vacuum pressure methods, result in distortion of the timber and therefore are not ideally suited to joinery.
3. *Organic solvents.* Fungicides and possibly insecticides in petroleum solvent or white spirit, applied by vacuum treatment or immersion, do not cause distortion, and readily accept paint, putty, glue and mastics. They are most widely used for joinery timbers.

Weathering details designed to cope with water in contact are illustrated in the following notes and diagrams. Fig. 1.20 shows

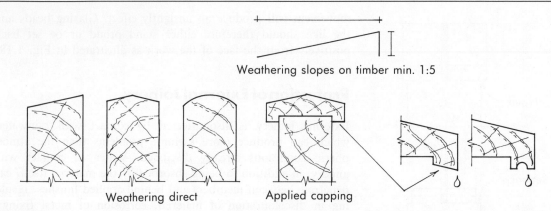

Weathering slopes on timber min. 1:5

Weathering direct   Applied capping

Fig. 1.20
Weatherings to upper surfaces
(continuous members or posts)

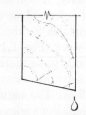

Speedier drying of bottom edge
with sloping under-surface

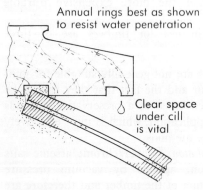

Annual rings best as shown
to resist water penetration

Clear space
under cill
is vital

Fig. 1.21
Weathering bottom surfaces

details designed to shed water from the top surfaces of rails or posts, and it should be observed that these may not be ideally suited to the more absorbent end grain of posts or stiles.

Applied cappings can be more effective in protecting end grain and in projecting the water to drip clear of the face of the work, and examples of these are included.

Under-surfaces are often not given enough consideration. Water may cling to the bottom of a cill or rail for long periods, and this should be discouraged by employing sloping surfaces or drip grooves. A sloping surface on a bottom edge can be almost as important as one on a top surface. A clear space for the water to fall freely is also important, as may be seen in Fig. 1.21.

Ventilation also plays an important part. A clear open space may well be more effective than a tight joint in excluding water. An example of this is shown in Fig. 1.22, which shows details at the side and bottom edges of a boarded panel within a window frame. The boards are fixed to a softwood sub-frame, and have clear ventilating space around the edges to ensure that water is not held between members to cause damage.

Adequate projections to horizontal members, so as to protect work below, together with anti-capillary grooves and throatings, as at a transom, are shown in Fig. 1.23, and common causes of deterioration at glazing beads and rails may be seen in Fig. 1.24.

Timber Selection

The specification of timber, whether of hardwood or softwood, for a functional design in joinery demands a knowledge of timber's availability, working characteristics and performance in use. Under the classification of hardwoods, for example, any one species may offer particular merits in beauty, stability, workability, finishing characteristics or durability, but will rarely be

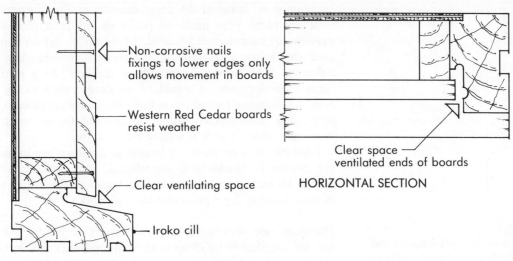

Non-corrosive nails
fixings to lower edges only
allows movement in boards

Western Red Cedar boards
resist weather

Clear ventilating space

Iroko cill

VERTICAL SECTION

Clear space
ventilated ends of boards

HORIZONTAL SECTION

Fig. 1.22
Further weathering features

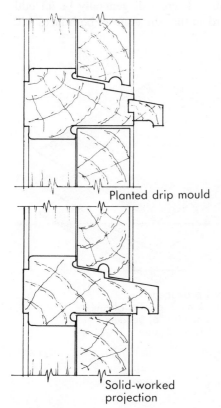

Planted drip mould

Solid-worked
projection

Fig. 1.23
Weathering to transoms

ideal in all these respects. If strength is important, it is necessary to determine whether the material is to resist bending, impact, indentation, cleavage or abrasion, because a material that offers strength against one of these may be particularly weak against another. A broad knowledge of common timbers is very valuable, and some research into the properties of any lesser-known species before specifying it is essential.

With all its inherent faults, timber continues to offer considerable appeal as a material to live with, and evidence of this can be seen in its use as a 'luxury' finish in some of the most expensive buildings and manufactured items. Reconstructed wood in various types of manufactured board is designed to retain a number of the desirable properties of the natural material, yet at the same time dispense with some of its problems. A manufactured board is likely to have more predictable qualities both in strength and in stability, and it will be available in greater widths than its natural counterpart. The designer can employ a manufactured board with more confidence in its properties, and the joinery producer will generally be involved in less manufacturing processes than with solid timber. On the other hand, reconstructed boards will have lost the natural appearance that we have come to recognise in sawn solid planks converted directly from the log, and to regain this appearance sliced veneers of chosen material must be applied to the faces of the board. A further problem associated with manufactured boards is that they are likely to be abrasive to the cutting edges of tools and machines, demanding either special cutters, or more frequent maintenance.

Manufactured Boards

Manufactured boards should not be treated as inferior substitutes for natural solid timber, as in some ways they may be

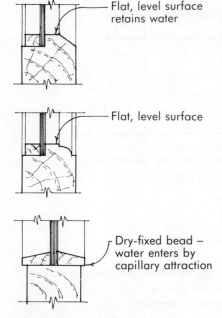

Flat, level surface retains water

Flat, level surface

Dry-fixed bead – water enters by capillary attraction

Fig. 1.24
Problem sources – external mouldings and glazing beads

superior to it. Some of the finest items of antique furniture in existence today were made up partly on the principles of our present-day manufactured boards, where the craftsman appreciated the value of laminating, veneering, cross-banding and balancing for reasons of strength or stability. As a result of further development, it would be no exaggeration to say that some high-quality reproduction furniture being produced today, employing reconstructed timber, is superior to, and may well last longer than, that it is setting out to copy.

Examples of manufactured boards in common use in joinery are plywood, blockboard, laminboard and chipboard, each having its own properties and characteristics which may make it most suitable for a particular item of work.

Plywoods are manufactured from veneers peeled from a log, bonded together to build up to the required thickness and with the grain of each veneer at right angles to the next as in Fig. 1.25. Depending on the type of timber, the log will have been stored in water, boiled or steamed prior to peeling. The veneers, clipped to size, selected for face or core, dried to about 8% moisture content, are bonded together to form thicknesses of 3, 4, 5, 6, 9, 12, 18 or 25 mm. There will generally be an odd number of veneers in a board so that the grain of both faces will

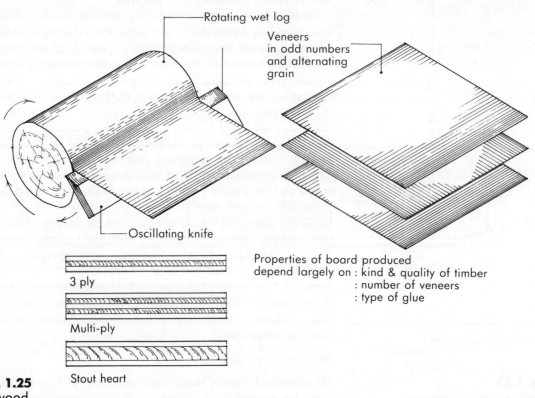

Rotating wet log

Veneers in odd numbers and alternating grain

Oscillating knife

3 ply

Multi-ply

Stout heart

Properties of board produced depend largely on : kind & quality of timber
: number of veneers
: type of glue

Fig. 1.25
Plywood

run the same way and the board will be 'balanced'. Where the number of veneers exceeds three, the board is referred to as 'multi-ply', and the cheaper alternative where the core is thicker is known as 'stout-heart'.

The quality of the board, and its performance characteristics, will depend on the selection of the material and on the glue employed to bond it together. In earlier plywood the weaker part of the composition was the glue line, which would most commonly fail in the presence of moisture. In modern plywood the glue may well be the most durable part and some glues may also penetrate the veneers to give them more resistance to fungal or insect attack.

Blockboards are intended as a more economical alternative to the thicker plywoods. They are likely to be slightly less stable than plywood but are very effective for interior joinery demanding unframed rigid flat panels, as in cupboard carcase construction. Blockboard is particularly suitable where the faces are to be veneered with plastics or decorative hardwoods, although some moisture movement can be evident where surfaces are finished in high gloss materials. Visible edges need to be lipped as the cores are not of the best quality timber and some gaps are likely to be evident. In thicknesses of 12–38 mm, blockboard consists of a core of softwood or low-density hard-wood in strips 18–25 mm wide laid side by side and generally glued together. Face veneers of rotary-cut hardwood are glued each side, singly to form 3-ply or in two layers each side (grain the same way) to form 5-ply. In 5-ply blockboard the face veneers are occasionally laid at right angles to those beneath and are therefore the same way as the cores. Fig. 1.26 indicates the composition of blockboard.

Blockboards are not suited to external application since the cores are generally glued with UF resin (see below), and are sometimes only spot glued. Even when the veneers are PF bonded, the cores are likely to be sensitive to changes in moisture content.

Laminboards are similar to blockboards except that the cores are made up from veneers 3–7 mm thick, resulting in a heavier, more stable panel. As a material this is likely to be more expensive, but it is fully justified where high-quality surface veneers are to be applied. Fig. 1.26 also shows a typical laminboard section.

Particle Boards (Chipboard) are produced from wood chips or particles derived from forest thinnings or joinery production. Some sheets have finer graded chips near the surface for a denser finish, with coarser chips forming the core. Particles are glued

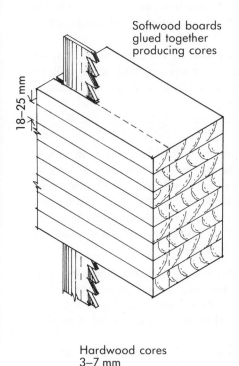

Softwood boards glued together producing cores

18–25 mm

Hardwood cores 3–7 mm

Laminboard

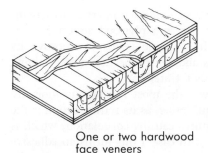

One or two hardwood face veneers

Fig. 1.26
Blockboard and laminboard

with UF adhesive and the sheet is formed by hot pressing. Since there is no continuity of natural wood fibres in the material, its strength characteristics differ from those boards previously mentioned. Several densities are produced for different applications, from furniture to flooring. In joinery, chipboard will normally be veneered. Some difficulties arise in fixings to edges although special fixing devices and tools have been developed to overcome these. Thicknesses available are 6, 9, 12, 15, 18, 21 and 25 mm. BS 5669 covers the manufacture of this material.

Other manufactured boards   are used by the joiner as facings, for fire resistance or for insulation purposes, and these will be referred to in later chapters in relation to particular items of joinery.

Glues

Glues used in the manufacture of plywood and joinery in general are of various types, some of which have been in use for centuries and others being quite recent developments. The choice for any particular application will depend partly on the production methods to be employed and partly on the conditions of service for which the work is intended. The following is a summary of the types in use. 'Natural' glues include:

1. *Animal glue* is spread and pressed (or cramped) in a hot state and sets by loss of heat followed by loss of moisture. The setting action is reversible at each stage, so this glue is suitable only for interior use. Manufactured to BS 745. Classified INT (interior).
2. *Casein* is a derivative of soured skimmed milk with chemical additives and is produced as a powder to be mixed with water. Its alkaline nature causes staining in certain hardwoods, notably oak and mahogany types, and it is irritant to the skin. The setting action is partly by loss of moisture and partly chemical. It is slightly more resistant to moisture than animal glue but is suitable only for interior use. Classified INT (interior).
3. *Soya bean* produces a glue of similar properties to casein, which has found popular use as a plywood adhesive. It is sometimes combined with synthetic resins to improve its resistance to moisture. Its alkaline properties cause staining in hardwoods. Classified INT (interior).
4. *Blood albumin* as a glue was the most resistant to moisture prior to the use of synthetic resins, as its setting action is the result of elevated temperatures causing coagulation, which is not reversible. Combined with casein this forms an adhesive that has been widely used in plywood manufacture but by present-day standards is not suited to external use. Classified INT (interior).

Synthetic resins can be compared to the 'plastics' that are so familiar in various manufactured items. As glues, these are applied in a liquid state to harden between the two timber surfaces and form a glue line that will be, to varying degrees, superior to those already mentioned. Five types in common use are:

1. *Polyvinyl acetate emulsion* (PVA). This is purchased as a ready-to-use white creamy liquid which is clean and easy to apply by brush or spatula in general joinery work though not suitable for plywood manufacture. Its moisture resistance is similar to that of casein but it does not give the same problems of staining hardwoods. Manufactured to BS 3544. Classified INT (interior).
2. *Urea formaldehyde* (UF) is available as a powder to be mixed with water, or as a syrup. It is activated by a catalyst at the time of application, although some powders include this, and used as a hot-setting adhesive in plywood, but otherwise used cold. This and the following are manufactured to BS 1203 (for plywood) or otherwise to BS 1204. Classified MR (moisture resistant).
3. *Melamine formaldehyde* (MF) is similar to UF in the forms available and in its application, but it has a higher performance classification. Classified BR (boil resistant).
4. *Phenol formaldehyde* (PF) is the adhesive used to produce the highest quality plywood since it is very resistant to water, other solvents, fire and most acids. Classified WBP (weather and boil proof).
5. *Resorcinol formaldehyde* (RF) is little used in plywood manufacture, but is valuable in assembly work, where it has all the qualities of PF glues but with better gap-filling properties and can bond wood to wood, or to many other materials. Applied cold. Classified WBP (weather and boil proof).

It should be noted that a proprietary glue purchased for joinery manufacture may be a combination of some of the above. In identifying the suitability of such a glue, reference should be made to its durability classification and to any British Standard specification number it may be manufactured to. The term 'gap-filling' applied to the description of a glue means that the glue will be effective in a glue line up to 1.3 mm in thickness and is therefore suitable for general joinery work where the connecting faces within a joint may be in less intimate contact than those in plywood manufacture.

It will be seen that the quality of any particular plywood will be determined very largely by the glue employed in its manufacture, and each sheet will be marked to show its quality, generally by giving its glue classification. The terms EXTERIOR or MARINE are also used; the latter, as its name suggests, is of the highest quality and is probably better than most joinery work demands. It will not only employ a WBP adhesive, but the timber will be highly durable and the jointing throughout will be to the highest standard. Such boards are manufactured to BS 1088 *Plywood for Marine Craft.*

Of the timbers most commonly used in plywood manufacture, the following are selected to indicate their durability and resistance to decay:

Poor	Alder, Beech, Birch, Elm, Gaboon, Limba, Obeche, Parana Pine, Poplar, Ramin
Moderate	Lauan, African Mahogany, Meranti, Sapele, Seraya, Douglas Fir
Good	Utile, Makore

It should also be noted that provided the plywood is WBP bonded it may be treated with preservatives even by pressure impregnation methods. Painting or varnishing may also extend its life and it is recommended that even the protected face of an external panel should be given at least a protective coat of priming paint.

Finally on the subject of plywood, the quality of the face veneers can vary from very poor to very good, each being suitable in certain situations. Classifications that group the qualities of face and reverse sides are generally indicated by letter codes which vary slightly with the country of manufacture but are generally on similar lines and these are indicated below. Letters given indicate firstly the face side, then the reverse, as for example A/B.

A	Unjointed, free from defects. Sanded.
B	Jointed, some small sound defects. Sanded.
BB	Well made plugs permitted. Scraped.
BBB	Broken knots, gaps, splits. Rough finish but well glued.

The foregoing notes and diagrams have indicated some of the principal points of concern in the functional design of joinery. It is seen that it is important to consider both the function of the item of work and its anticipated environmental conditions. It is necessary to have a knowledge of the characteristics of materials and construction details before the design can be determined. The subject is of course a very wide one which has by no means been extensively covered here.

AESTHETIC DESIGN

The 'aesthetics' or beauty of an item of joinery concerns the experience it imparts by sight, and to some extent by touch. In judging the beauty of a piece of work we are most concerned with its appearance, but also with the 'feel' of the materials and finishes used in its manufacture. The aesthetic success of joinery is very largely dependent upon its design, but it does also depend very much on the craftsman's part in its production, and this is shown diagrammatically in Fig. 1.27.

Aesthetics will be of some importance in any class of work. At the very least it will be required only to be acceptable, to be compatible with its surroundings without giving offence in any way and not to be particularly noticeable as an item of work. In such a case, where compatibility with surroundings is the keynote, it is likely that the joinery is intended to perform some function of more importance than to give a visual impression. It should be noted that an item of joinery that is right and acceptable in its designed situation can be quite wrong and unacceptable in another. Examples of such incompatibility can be seen too often where replacement windows are fitted to an existing building in an attempt to 'modernise' the property.

Aesthetics will be more important where the joinery is positively required to be visually pleasing, to be the subject of enjoyment through its beauty. This is putting greater emphasis on the appearance of the work, where visual appeal may be as important as any functional requirement that the joinery is to fulfil. Work of this kind is likely to be more expensive than the more functional examples, as a result of the choice of materials and the higher production costs that are generally involved.

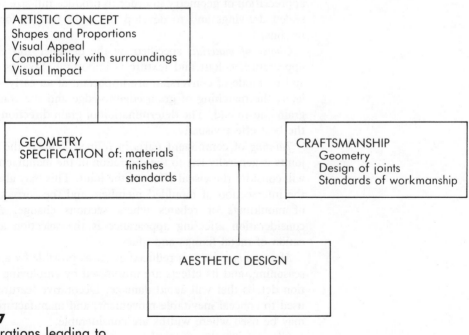

Fig. 1.27
Considerations leading to
aesthetic design

Occasionally there are more extreme cases where, through its aesthetic design, the joinery is required to create visual impact or excitement. The accent here will be on originality, with less concern for tradition, fashion or compatibility with surroundings. Such work is stimulating to the designer (who may have to accept as much criticism as praise) and will appeal to the creative instincts of the craftsman, particularly because it is likely to be 'one-off' or small-quantity work.

Aesthetics in joinery is of course more likely to be fully understood and appreciated by the designer or architect than by the craftsman. The architect has the artistic attributes that led him into his chosen profession, and the benefit of having studied in depth the underlying principles and traditions of aesthetic design. He will therefore exercise subtleties of line, proportion and shape to produce forms designed to please the most discerning eye. He will anticipate the effects of light and shadow when considering shapes, mouldings, enrichments, textures and finishes and beyond this may even employ principles of design that are intended to correct optical error or illusion.

There are many more fundamental aspects of aesthetic design concerned with manufacture and having a significant effect on the beauty of the work and which the designer will endeavour to control through his scaled drawings and specifications, and these are listed below.

Interpretation of geometric design by the producer, who will need to understand the design intentions, demands a good appreciation of geometry in order to produce full-size work from scaled drawings and to develop the work further for practical reasons.

Choice of materials specified by the designer and chosen for appearance, colour and texture is important. Species of timber and its mode of conversion are important at an early stage, and later, the matching of grain edge-to-edge and the continuity of grain end-to-end. The determination of grain direction is to give the best effect visually.

Jointing of component parts in framed joinery: the design of joints is generally left to the discretion of the manufacturer, who will consider the visual effect of the joint. This may also concern the intersection of moulded members and the correct stopping of mouldings or rebates where sections change. A further consideration affecting appearance is the selection and application of metal fixings and glues.

Moisture movement is reduced as far as possible by appropriate seasoning, and its effects are minimised by employing construction details that will avoid damage. Decorative features may be used to conceal inevitable movement, and manufactured boards may be used where widths are considerable.

Changes in colour in timber as a result of sunlight or atmosphere, seen as darkening or fading, should be anticipated.

Increasing contrast between heartwood and sapwood and between timber and matched stopping may result.

Accidental staining of timber as a result of contact with certain metals, glues and wet plaster can be very unsightly. Avoidance of contact between some materials is vital, to avoid staining.

Worked finishes in surfaces prepared by the joiner will determine the effectiveness of applied finishes to follow. Standards and methods of preparation differ according to whether the final finish will be clear or opaque, matt or gloss.

Applied finishes are not the direct concern of the joiner beyond his need to know what type of finish will follow. Finishes will be selected to perform effectively in the anticipated environment, to show the material to its best advantage and to protect it.

Corrosion of metal in fixings or applied hardware can seriously spoil the appearance of the work. Corrosion may be due to the interaction between the metal and the timber in contact or to atmospheric conditions. Specification of an appropriate metal and its finish is important.

Transport, handling and storage of joinery is best done under the supervision of the producer, who will have the greatest sympathy with his product. Serious damage to the appearance can result from carelessness between the manufacturing and fixing stages.

Fixing or building-in of joinery is an important part of the craft since its final appearance will be judged on the completed work. However well the joinery is produced, it can be ruined by a poor standard of work at this stage.

Standards of craftsmanship generally are largely the result of the personal interest, attention to detail and expertise exercised by the craftsman at each stage of production.

From the foregoing list of features of production affecting the appearance of the work it will be seen that it is difficult for the designer to control completely the outcome of his design and that he will rely to a considerable extent on the craftsman's contribution. Areas where the craftsman or producer makes the greatest contribution are those that are most difficult to control by drawings and specifications, and concern features on which the aesthetic appeal of the work, in respect of craftsmanship or 'quality', will be judged.

It is worth examining each of these in more detail to see how the joinery producer may contribute to the aesthetics of the work.

Geometrical Work – and aesthetics

Geometrical work having a direct effect on the appearance of joinery occurs at the setting-out stage, when the architect's documents are interpreted and full-size 'rods' or working draw-ings are produced. It concerns, too, the work involved in marking-out the prepared timber for machine or hand-worked operations to follow and there could be some geometry involved in the processes of manufacture and fixing. The first essential is accuracy, and, even though the finest graduation on the joiner's rule is probably one millimetre, it is possible and necessary to work to much finer limits of tolerance. Accurate working comes partly from the use of high quality tools kept in good condition, but also from an attitude of mind that demands precision as a habit.

It would be reasonable to assume that those studying purpose-made joinery will have a knowledge of basic geometry including the properties of angles, triangles and other plane figures such as the circle and the ellipse, all of which have their applications to joinery. The production of purpose-made joinery also involves the application of three-dimensional or solid geometry, often as a means of determining lengths, bevels and shapes of members at setting-out stage. The craftsman will employ the principles of such geometry in a practical manner more suited to the work-shop or site than to the drawing board.

Even in simple linear measurement, as for example in the measuring of material thickness being prepared through a thick-nessing planer, by measuring the overall thickness of several pieces side by side any error will be magnified and greater accuracy can be achieved. Similarly, on a large item of work comprising a number of measured smaller parts, the cumulative, overall dimension is a good check on the accuracy of the smaller ones.

Chapter 3 is devoted to examples of plane and solid geometry that are commonly met in the setting-out of joinery, and their proper application can have a marked effect on the appearance of the finished work. Some geometry is also included in the work of other chapters, as applied to particular items of joinery.

Materials – and aesthetics

Materials and their decorative appeal will depend initially on the type and quality specified by the architect or designer. In the case of solid timber he may also specify the mode of conversion for the desired effect. We have come to recognise the radial and tangential faces of the common species and the peeled face of some used in plywood manufacture (most of which are not considered to be decorative). Some show their most decorative or distinctive effect on a radial face, notably Oak, in which the medullary rays are exposed as 'silver grain' and Sapele which because of its alternating spiral growth shows alternate stripes of fibres lying in opposite directions to reflect the light in a

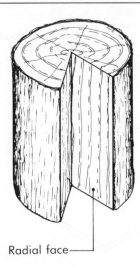
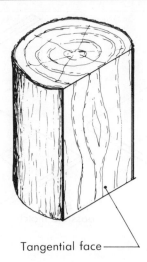
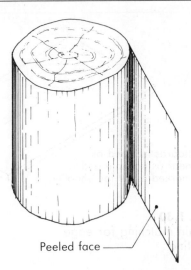

Radial face

Tangential face

Peeled face

Fig. 1.28
Decorative faces cut from the log

Avoid this

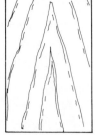

Better this way

Fig. 1.29
Grain direction in a panel

manner similar to a newly rolled lawn. A tangential face is distinctive in Beech, where the end view of medullary rays shows as the familiar red flecks and is very effective in timbers having the greatest contrast in colour between spring wood and autumn wood in the annual rings. Redwood, Douglas fir and Elm are particularly effective on this face. Few timbers are considered to show their best on a peeled face, but notable exceptions are Birdseye Maple and Oregon Pine. Fig. 1.28 illustrates the faces referred to.

For economy, decorative faces are frequently achieved by the application of veneers of selected timbers or other materials, which for reasons already discussed should preferably be bonded to manufactured boards rather than solid timber.

The craftsman will make the best of timbers specified by applying his own particular expertise in a number of ways. Considering the direction of grain, for example, any distinctive arch-like features in a panel or door stile should be the right way up for the best effect, as in Fig. 1.29.

Edge-jointed boards, as in panels, counter-tops and the like, will be matched as well as possible, and marks applied prior to machining the edge joints. The best possible matching of two boards edge-to-edge is to 'deep' a thicker board to produce a pair (see Fig. 1.30). Another example where matching is very important is in a pair of clear-finished doors. The meeting stiles in particular will be the centre of attention at all times. Rails, too, should be from a continuous piece for continuity of grain, as shown in Fig. 1.31. Similarly, the panels in a clear-finished door should be cut from a continuous piece of material for the best effect, as shown.

Fig. 1.32 shows a similar approach to drawer fronts where continuity of grain will enhance the appearance of a cupboard fitment.

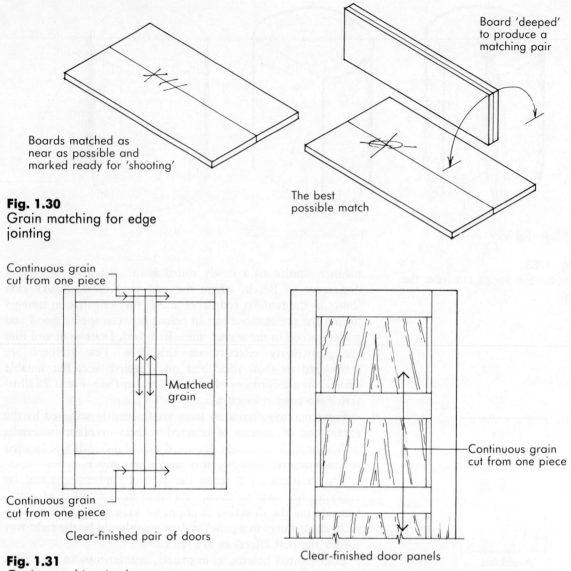

Fig. 1.30
Grain matching for edge jointing

Boards matched as near as possible and marked ready for 'shooting'

The best possible match

Board 'deeped' to produce a matching pair

Continuous grain cut from one piece

Matched grain

Continuous grain cut from one piece

Clear-finished pair of doors

Continuous grain cut from one piece

Clear-finished door panels

Fig. 1.31
Grain matching in doors

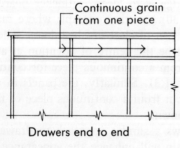

Continuous grain from one piece

Drawers end to end

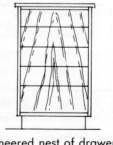

Veneered nest of drawers

Fig. 1.32
Grain in drawer fronts

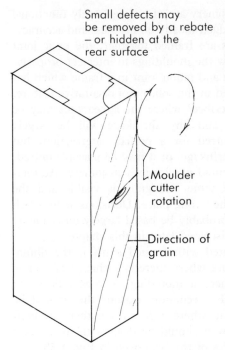

Small defects may be removed by a rebate – or hidden at the rear surface

Moulder cutter rotation

Direction of grain

Fig. 1.33
Direction of grain and cutter rotation

At marking-out stage the face-marking of members will dictate on which faces any rebates or moulded features will occur, and it is good practice to observe carefully the direction of grain and any natural defects that may be present. By the placing of a facemark it is possible to influence the standard of finish produced, as illustrated in the moulded member in Fig. 1.33, and to 'position' any defect so as to get the best from the material.

Jointing – and aesthetics

Jointing, and the craftsman's concern for getting the best visual effect from what is necessary in bringing together the designed sections is illustrated here.

The mitre, as has already been shown, is a very effective means of bringing together two moulded members so that their features intersect properly. It is also a means of avoiding end grain being visible on a face. An unfortunate aspect of a mitred joint, however, is that it exaggerates the effect of shrinkage, particularly in wide members, so some alternative should be sought in forming angles in window boards, counter-tops and the like. The problem is illustrated in Fig. 1.34.

Housed joints as in hardwood door linings, book shelves and cupboard carcass construction are generally concealed from the face by notching back from the front edge. At the corners a mitre is generally formed for neatness, as in Fig. 1.35.

Dovetailed joints have always been evidence of true skill in the craftsman, but there are some cases where such joints are concealed from the face of the work, as shown in Fig. 1.36, where a top rail joins a cupboard end and a drawer side is fitted to a drawer front.

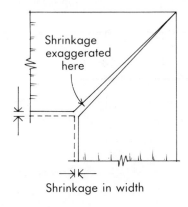

Shrinkage exaggerated here

Shrinkage in width

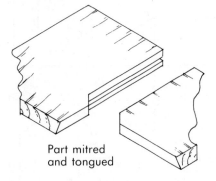

Part mitred and tongued

Fig. 1.34
Mitres in wide boards

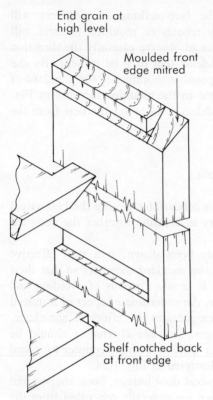

End grain at
high level

Moulded front
edge mitred

Shelf notched back
at front edge

Fig. 1.35
Joints in bookshelves

Joints used in framed joinery are of course largely functional and their appearance is judged mostly on neatness and accuracy. Where moulded members are framed together, the basic joint has added features to allow the mouldings to intersect properly. Fig. 1.37 shows a mortice and tenon joint in a frame which has a 'stuck moulding' (worked in the solid) as a decorative feature. Such a feature may be 'scribed' where the appearance may be very similar to a mitre and any shrinkage will be largely concealed. It may be mitred for a perfect intersection, but subject to opening with shrinkage, or it may be mason's mitred, a technique which has limited applications in joinery. Aesthetically this is poor, since some end grain is visible and the shoulder line appears in the wrong place. Decisions as to which approach to employ will probably be based largely on economy of production, which is discussed later in this chapter.

Another feature associated with framed joints is the diminished shoulder. This occurs where there is a change of section at the joint position, where a moulding or rebate does not continue past the joint. For economy reasons this should be avoided where possible, but where it does occur there are craft principles involved in how it should be dealt with to the best visual effect. Two examples of this are given in Fig. 1.38.

In some cases the design of a shoulder is dictated by the shaping of members resulting from features like radiused corners to glazed openings, and these may result in weakness

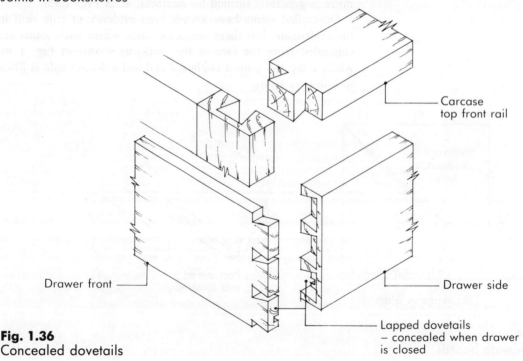

Drawer front

Carcase
top front rail

Drawer side

Lapped dovetails
– concealed when drawer
is closed

Fig. 1.36
Concealed dovetails

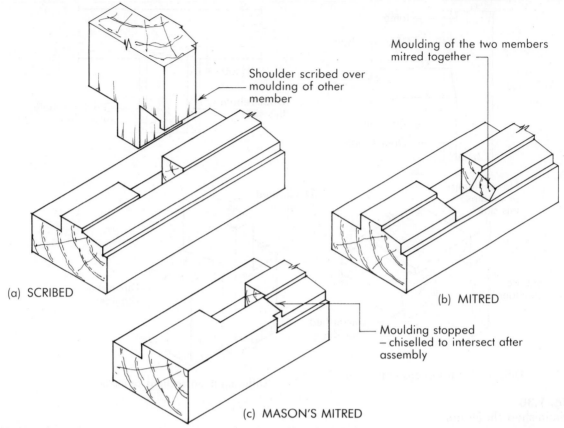

Shoulder scribed over moulding of other member

Moulding of the two members mitred together

(a) SCRIBED

(b) MITRED

(c) MASON'S MITRED

Moulding stopped – chiselled to intersect after assembly

Fig. 1.37
Intersection of mouldings in frames

due to short grain. Fig. 1.39 shows two examples where the glazed opening to a door has rounded corners where the treatment depends upon the size of the curve and the amount of short grain resulting from it.

Some Other Working Processes – and aesthetics

Moisture Movement. A good deal has already been said on this subject (and shown in Figs 1.10–1.18) related to design and manufacture, and the craftsman will treat the work sympathetically from both points of view. Additional benefits will come from his using materials in sequence, cutting, preparing and possibly assembling 'dry' then delaying the gluing for as long as possible. Beyond that will be the need to determine the most appropriate protection methods and time of delivery.

Changes in Colour in clear finished timbers as a result of contact with daylight cannot be avoided. Clear varnish or polish

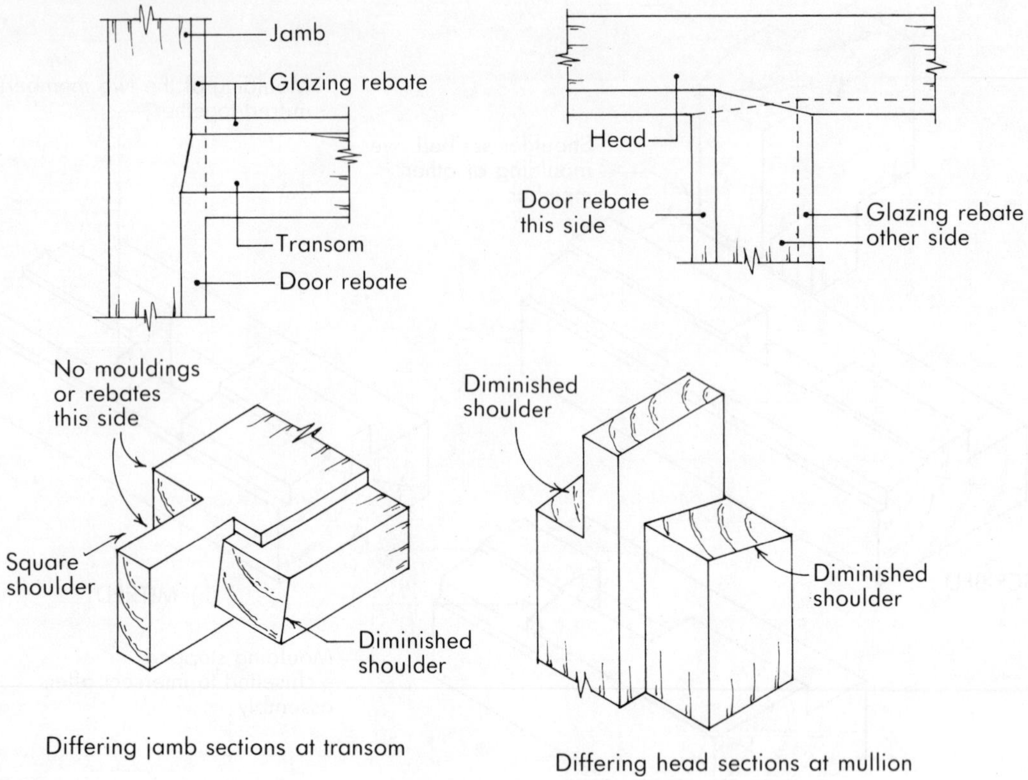

Jamb

Glazing rebate

Head

Door rebate this side

Glazing rebate other side

Transom

Door rebate

No mouldings or rebates this side

Square shoulder

Diminished shoulder

Diminished shoulder

Diminished shoulder

Diminished shoulder

Differing jamb sections at transom

Differing head sections at mullion

Fig. 1.38
Diminished shoulders

has little effect in this respect, although where stains are used prior to varnishing some of these are claimed to be fade resistant. Observation of timbers in use may lead to the specifier avoiding certain species like Utile or Iroko, which change in colour very quickly. The craftsman will use stoppings sparingly, but it can be very unsightly where the timber has changed and the stopping has retained its original colour. Where the work is to be stained, care is needed in avoiding excessive glue from sealing the grain around joints and affecting the regularity of the stain. The joiner will also, for the same reason, leave any necessary stopping to the following trade who will probably apply it after staining. Also to be avoided as far as possible is the use of iron in fixings to Oak, casein glue for clear-finished work and contact between wet plaster and any unprotected joinery.

Worked Finishes refer to the prepared surfaces of the work by the joiner in preparation for the applied finishes to follow. It is rare for joinery not to have an applied finish, since the surface will become soiled by the atmosphere and through handling. The timber may be concealed by a painted finish, or exposed through a clear finish, in which case it may be changed in colour

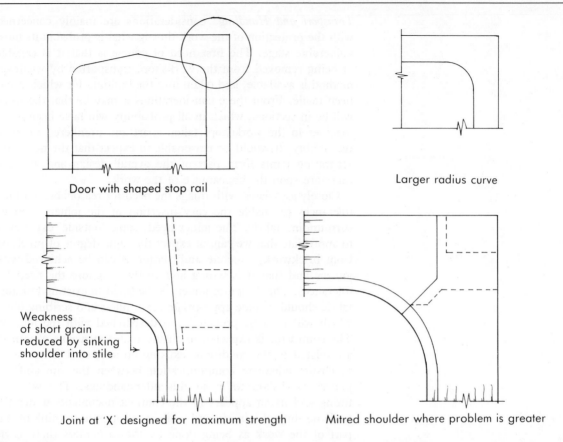

Door with shaped stop rail

Larger radius curve

Weakness
of short grain
reduced by sinking
shoulder into stile

Joint at 'X' designed for maximum strength

Mitred shoulder where problem is greater

Fig. 1.39
Joints adding to visual appeal

before finishing by applied bleaches or stains. Whatever the chosen material, it may be finished in gloss, matt or semi-matt.

The most essential point regarding the preparation of surfaces is that the higher the gloss to follow, the more perfect must be the preparation. Blemishes are seen far less in a matt finish than in a gloss. Gloss finishes do not hide blemishes, they highlight them. A second essential point is that where the finish is to be clear (whether stained or not) there must not be scratches across the grain, so final glass-papering must be parallel to the grain.

The aims in preparing the surface of joinery, whether by hand or by machine methods, expressed here in the order in which they are approached in the workshop, are flatness, freedom from tool marks, and the right degree of smoothness depending on the finish to follow. Ideally the whole surface is of consistent quality throughout and, depending on the quality of the work, pieces may have been repaired by having knots removed and matching inserts glued in, or have been rejected and replaced. Arrises in clear finished hardwood are generally lightly papered to appear crisp and clean, but in softwood, which is more easily damaged, and in painted work they are usually removed more positively.

Transport and Handling   considerations are mainly concerned with the protection of the work during what is probably its most vulnerable stage. The first need of course is that it is capable of being removed from the workshop, transported by whatever method is available, and taken into the building for which it has been made. From these considerations it may be that the work will be in sections, which in all probability will have been fitted together in the workshop, taken apart and numbered for final reassembly. It would be reasonable to expect that the necessary separating joints form part of the overall design and will not therefore spoil the appearance of the work.

Closely associated with this is the need for reasonable working tolerances to enable the easy insertion of the joinery into its surrounding fabric. The joiner needs some 'outside' experience to appreciate that we cannot expect the same degree of precision from brickwork, concrete and plaster as can be achieved with joinery and that it is wrong and costly to ignore the need for tolerances. The design of joinery to be fitted to existing building fabric should include appropriate cover fillets and scribing fillets which will then be prepared and despatched with the joinery. The contractor is expected to ensure that dimensions of joinery are related to the conditions existing on site, so it is necessary to ensure adequate communication between the site and the joinery workshop to avoid misunderstandings. The work of fitting and fixing appears in the contract documents under the trade heading of joinery, and while it is common to think of this part of the work as being done by the carpenters there is no doubt that high-class joinery is best fixed by the joinery craftsman.

The work may involve levelling and scribing to the floor, and the joinery must be put in its exact position before levelling with temporary packs or wedges. The contours of the floor are now scribed with dividers or a small block of wood, which produces a cutting line that follows exactly the shape of the floor surface. In work of this nature it is common practice when making the joinery to leave surplus material at the bottom for scribing purposes, and the assumed 'floor line' is clearly marked on the work to convey the fact that this is intended to be cut at approximately this level. Similarly, plumbing and scribing to a wall entails the accurate positioning of the work, ensuring that it is perfectly plumb before scribing as already described. Both of these processes are shown in Fig. 1.40.

It will be seen that these operations involve the cutting of the work itself, which may involve awkward handling and difficult cutting, often in confined spaces, and for these reasons it is generally better not to attempt to scribe the work itself, but to use scribing fillets which are scribed neatly to the wall, floor or ceiling and fixed to the face of the joinery. Examples are shown in Fig. 1.41, where it will be seen that this approach is particu-

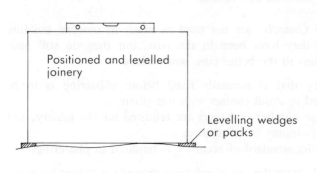

Positioned and levelled joinery

Levelling wedges or packs

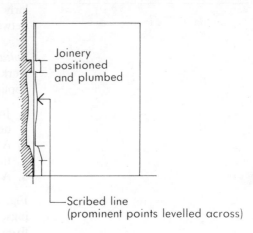

Joinery positioned and plumbed

Scribed line (prominent points levelled across)

Scribing to the wall

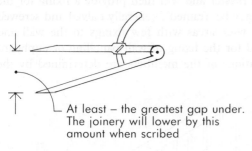

At least – the greatest gap under. The joinery will lower by this amount when scribed

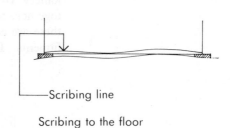

Scribing line

Scribing to the floor

Fig. 1.40
Scribing to floors and walls

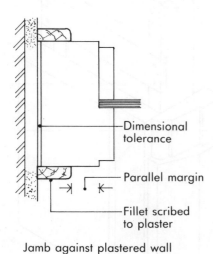

Dimensional tolerance

Parallel margin

Fillet scribed to plaster

Jamb against plastered wall

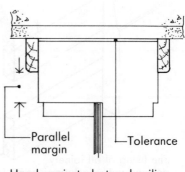

Parallel margin

Tolerance

Head against plastered ceiling

Fig. 1.41
Scribing fillets

larly useful where the work is to be fitted between walls or between the floor and ceiling.

Softwood Grounds are not used as much in modern building work as they have been in the past, but they do still have applications in the better-class work where:

1. Joinery that is normally fixed before plastering is to be delayed to avoid contact with wet plaster;
2. A large number of fixings are required for the joinery, and their positions are critical; or
3. A higher standard of accuracy is required in plastering.

Fig. 1.42 shows the use of softwood grounds as fixings for skirtings, linings and architraves. It will be seen that the grounds, fixed accurately before plastering, will determine the thickness and flatness of the plaster and will then provide a fixing for the joinery. Grounds may be 'framed', generally halved and screwed together, to cover wide areas with few fixings to the wall and these are employed for the fixing of wall panelling or cupboard fitments. The positions of the members are determined by the

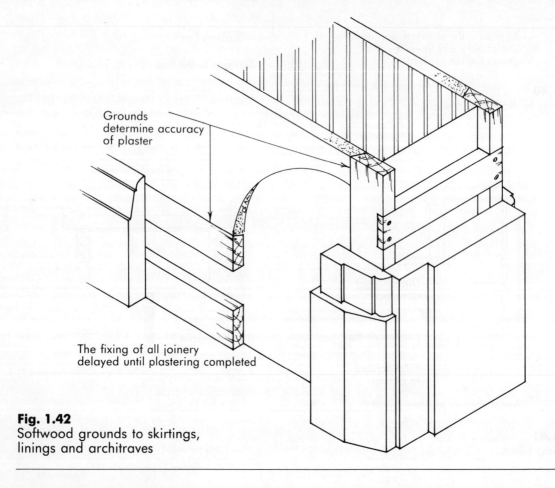

Grounds determine accuracy of plaster

The fixing of all joinery delayed until plastering completed

Fig. 1.42
Softwood grounds to skirtings, linings and architraves

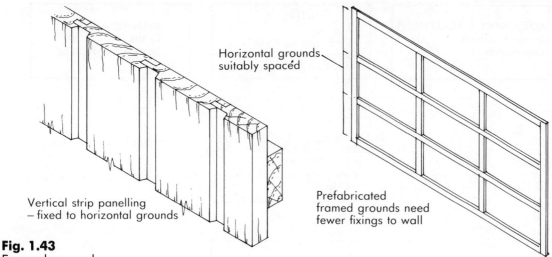

Horizontal grounds
suitably spaced

Vertical strip panelling
– fixed to horizontal grounds

Prefabricated
framed grounds need
fewer fixings to wall

Fig. 1.43
Framed grounds

fixings necessary for the joinery. An example may be seen in Fig. 1.43.

Also of importance in the aesthetic appeal of the joinery is the way in which it is fixed to the grounds. In high-class work there will be an attempt to conceal the fixings. Figs 6.2 and 6.3 and associated notes in Chapter 6 show a number of approaches to concealed or 'secret' fixings as applied to wall panelling.

An attempt has been made here to show that the aesthetic success of joinery depends to a considerable extent on the craftsman's contribution in its manufacture, and on the designer's awareness of the detailed work involved. The third element in joinery design, to be pursued in some detail now, is that concerned with manufacture, and it is in some respects as important as the two already discussed.

PRODUCTION DESIGN

As has already been described, the designer will give considerable thought to the functions and appearance of the finished product, but without giving due consideration to the manufacturing problems he could find that the work is at the least unnecessarily expensive, and in some cases even impossible to bring together properly. As a result of his design he may create problems related to:

1. The availability of specified materials;
2. The working characteristics of materials;
3. The operations dictated by the design.

These considerations, leading to Production Design, are shown graphically in Fig. 1.44.

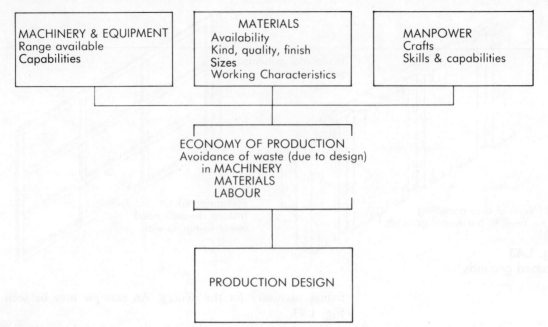

Fig. 1.44
Considerations leading to
production design

Materials – and productivity

The experienced designer, before specifying a material, will have some knowledge of its availability and will have ensured that it is obtainable in the type, quality and sizes required. By comparing alternatives he will have avoided as far as possible the considerable wastage that can be associated with purchasing and with production processes related to some materials. He will have determined, too, whether the chosen material will present any production problems due to its working characteristics and might therefore have rejected materials that are known to be particularly abrasive to cutters or in any way difficult to machine or finish.

Softwoods for joinery, imported mostly from Northern Europe and some from the North American continent, are purchased as sawn planks in a number of standard sizes broadly equivalent to the Imperial sizes they replace. In the past the planks were shipped loose in random lengths but the growing practice is to transport in packages or bundles comprising pieces of equal length for economy of handling.

Depending on the size of order placed by the joinery manufacturer, quantities and prices will be expressed in linear measure, per 50 or per 100 m 'run', or in volume per cubic metre. While prices may be less per unit as the size of order increases, a given volume of timber is likely to cost more where the sawn sections are smaller, as a result of the amount of sawing involved. Table 1.5 shows the range of metric sizes listed as

Table 1.5

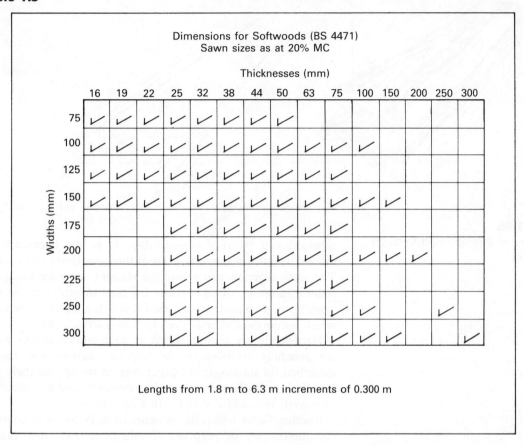

Dimensions for Softwoods (BS 4471)
Sawn sizes as at 20% MC

Widths (mm) / Thicknesses (mm)

Widths (mm) \ Thicknesses (mm)	16	19	22	25	32	38	44	50	63	75	100	150	200	250	300
75	✓	✓	✓	✓	✓	✓	✓	✓							
100	✓	✓	✓	✓	✓	✓	✓	✓	✓	✓	✓				
125	✓	✓	✓	✓	✓	✓	✓	✓	✓	✓					
150	✓	✓	✓	✓	✓	✓	✓	✓	✓	✓	✓	✓			
175				✓	✓	✓	✓	✓	✓	✓					
200				✓	✓	✓	✓	✓	✓	✓	✓	✓	✓		
225				✓	✓	✓	✓	✓	✓	✓					
250				✓	✓		✓	✓		✓	✓			✓	
300				✓	✓		✓	✓		✓	✓	✓			✓

Lengths from 1.8 m to 6.3 m increments of 0.300 m

standard in the softwood trade, and this applies to the majority of softwood used in this country, and which is of European origin.

Softwoods imported from the American continent are still expressed in Imperial units (feet and inches) and most merchants sell to the consumer in the same units. This is to avoid discrepancies between the 'foot' lengths they buy in and the 300 mm increment of the metric system.

Hardwoods, too, are still listed in Imperial units, this being the long-established practice in the much greater number of countries involved in this market. Depending on the species and the country of origin a particular hardwood may be marketed in the form of 'slab-sawn' or 'through-and-through' planks in a range of Imperial thicknesses with quantities and prices expressed in cubic feet. It should be noted that in this case the purchaser is buying waney-edged planks with sapwood so there will be considerable waste in material terms and there will be additional sawing within the joinery works in removing sapwood and producing the necessary 'straight-line edge' before any other operation can follow. Fig. 1.45 illustrates that the proportion of

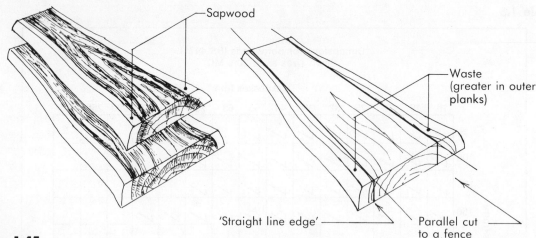

Fig. 1.45
Waste in through-and-through planks

sapwood can be very considerable. It is not uncommon to discard as much material as is used; this constitutes 100% waste. The same diagram also shows the straight-line edge located to remove sapwood. (This is either fed freehand through the saw, working to a chalk line or passed through a straight-line edger which automatically feeds the plank in a straight line.)

Hardwoods are also marketed as square-sawn planks which are generally available in the Imperial sections and lengths described for softwoods but depending on the species there may be a limit to the lengths and widths available, and it is necessary to consult merchants' lists for this information.

Another factor which the designer must be aware of concerns the dimensions in prepared (finished) sections that can be achieved from the sawn (nominal) dimensions. Planing entails the removal of some material in producing an accurate surface, and the amount removed depends upon the accuracy of the sawn material beforehand. Longer pieces are likely to be reduced most in straightening, so material in door stiles or long members in door or window frames is likely to present the greatest problem in this respect. The designer, when committing sectional details to paper, should make realistic allowances for reduction due to planing, but he will at the same time need to exercise some control over the manufacturer, who might reduce sections excessively.

The Standard Method of Measurement recommends that 'limits on planing margins shall be given' but does not suggest a figure. Earlier editions have suggested a maximum of 3.2 mm ($\frac{1}{8}$ inch) for each prepared face, which is of course 6.4 mm ($\frac{1}{4}$ inch) reduction on each dimension when material is 'prepared all round'. Certainly a limit of 5 mm reduction for planing or 6 mm in the assembled and sanded work is not excessively wasteful where long members are involved. Fig. 1.46 illustrates these points where (a) shows the sawn or 'nominal' size of the

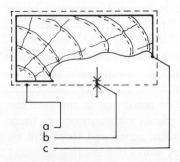

Fig. 1.46
Nominal and finished sizes

material, (b) shows the amount of material removed, or 'planing margin', and (c) shows the prepared or 'finished' size.

Sheet materials can be a very big source of waste, particularly in 'one-off' or small-quantity production, where special sizes cannot be readily obtained. A wide range of sizes is available in many of the sheet materials, provided that the order is in large quantities; otherwise the smaller consumer will have to accept the more readily available popular size of sheet. In the smaller works it is not uncommon to waste more of a sheet than is used, and the cost of the product must include the cost of the waste.

Operations – and productivity

Operations involved in the workshop in the production of joinery depend on the design of the work, and for economy of production the designer should have an appreciation of the practical processes and the implications of the details that he commits to paper.

The basic operations usually involved in the small-scale production of joinery, most of which are carried out by machine, follow the same sequence as that followed by the craftsman working by hand. These processes, listed in the sequence in which they apply in the workshop, are described briefly in Table 1.6. For each of the woodcutting operations, there is a machine

Table 1.6

Operation	Brief description	Typical machines used in smaller works
1. Setting out	Interpretation of the design. The production of workshop drawings or 'rods', and cutting lists.	
2. Cross-cutting	Selection and cutting to length of listed timber.	Pullover crosscut saw
3. Ripping	Cutting timber to width and thickness.	Circular saw bench
4. Surface planing	Accurately preparing the face side and edge.	Combined surfacer and thicknesser planer
5. Thicknessing	Reducing the material to gauged width and thickness.	
6. Marking-out	Referring to workshop rods, marking the timbers for exact positions of joints, mouldings, rebates and shapes. Face-marking, pairing and matching.	
7. Morticing	Cutting mortices and haunchings.	Chain or chisel morticer
8. Tenoning	Cutting tenons to fit mortices. Producing scribed shoulders or diminished shoulders.	Single end tenoning machine
9. Moulding	Working mouldings and rebates, to fit scribed shoulders where applicable.	Spindle moulder

designed to carry out that function. In some cases one machine is capable of more than one function. Typical machines selected to perform these operations in the smaller joinery works are also shown. The range will be so positioned as to provide a logical flow of work (based on the normal sequence already mentioned) and to achieve economic routes of travel for most work passing through the workshop, and this is shown diagrammatically in Fig. 1.47. The actual layout in any workshop will be dictated also by local conditions, two vital aspects of which will be the position of the timber store at one end of the flow and the position of the joinery (assembly) shop at the other. These two features could exist at the same end of the building, or on different floor levels. Consideration will also be given to the easy access of long lengths of timber to each machine and to intermittent storage, between machines, of work in progress.

Other machines beyond the basic range, and outside the common flow of operations may be required in the smaller works for some items of joinery. These include:

- Narrow band saw for curved cutting
- Dimension saw for the precision-cutting of prepared materials and sheets
- Vertical panel saw for cutting sheets to size
- Narrow-belt sander for general finishing work
- Drum sander (two or three drums) for flatting and finishing wide panels or assembled frames
- Wide-belt sander, which has largely superseded the last for the same purposes
- High-speed router for shaping and moulding in a wide range of applications

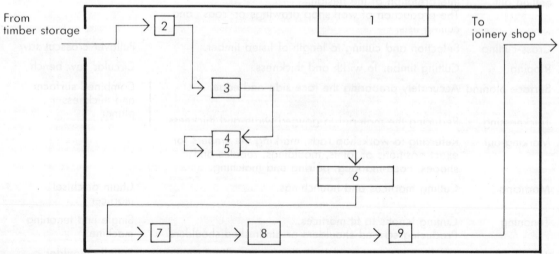

Fig. 1.47
Layout – basic machines

Also to be accommodated in association with joinery production are hardwood and softwood racks, storage of sundry materials, sheet materials storage, machined components storage and, of course, the joinery workshop itself with the necessary equipment for fitting, assembling and finishing the work. Facilities for the storage of finished work and possibly the application of finishes may also be included within the premises. Some additional facilities are likely to be added to the workshop layout already shown, as seen in Fig. 1.48 where a narrow bandsaw could usefully be located at (a), a dimension saw at (b) would serve joinery production and the plywood racks at (c) and a narrow belt sander at (d) would be accessible to both machinists and joiners.

As an important part of machine shop layout, it would be necessary to consider the extraction of waste from machine woodworking processes, to ensure the efficient operation of machines and to minimise the health hazard and fire risk that is likely to result when such waste is not removed at source. Typically, most of the machines shown would be linked to a system of extraction trunking leading to collection and disposal facilities. Although secondary to the actual machinery processes, waste extraction and the necessary equipment to perform it is an essential factor in the selection and location of machinery and equipment in the joinery workshop.

Most purpose-made joinery will involve a large proportion of machine operations in preparing the component parts, followed by benchwork carried out by joiners using hand or power tooled methods in fitting, assembling and finishing the work. The proportion of machine work to benchwork varies from job to

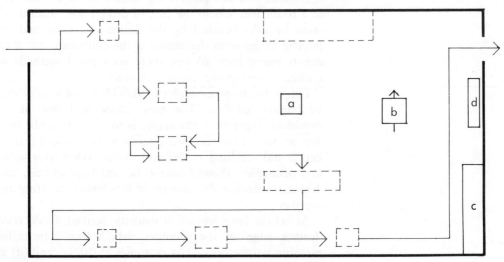

Fig. 1.48
Common additions and their location

Feather edge

Shoulder
left for bench fitting

(a)
Large 'round'

(b)

(c)

(d)

Undercut mouldings

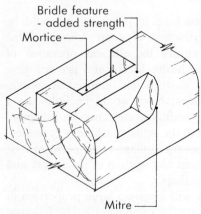

Bridle feature
- added strength

Mortice

Mitre

(e) The hand-finished joint

Fig. 1.49
Mouldings demanding bench
fitting

job, but machinery will be employed whenever it is practical and economical to do so, in order to gain as much as possible from the machine capabilities in consistent repetitive production.

Non-standard or intricate skilled operations, whether in setting-up the machine or in benchwork, will lead to high unit costs. Repetitive operations, particularly by machine, where the proportion of productive running to machine setting is high, result in lower unit costs.

Some operations in small quantities might be more economically carried out by hand, because the setting-up time would be disproportionately high.

At setting-out and at marking-out stages, design details will lead to decisions on the kind of joints to employ, the working procedures to be adopted and the machinery and equipment that will best carry out the work.

The following examples show some details that will demand operations that are particularly skilled or labour-intensive and as a result will add to the cost of production. Such details will often be fully justified by the design intentions and will add interest to the work demanded of the craftsman, but alternative details might have allowed more economical methods without noticeable loss in the finished product.

Fig. 1.49 shows examples of mouldings in joinery that is to be framed together. The most economical way of bringing mouldings together at the angles is to machine-scribe the shoulders as part of the tenoning operation, so avoiding fitting at the bench and resulting in the same visual effect as a mitre. The four examples shown cannot be machine-scribed, and will demand a considerable amount of benchwork in fitting members together.

At (a) the large 'round' if machine scribed would result in a 'feather edge' at the shoulder, which would be difficult to machine satisfactorily. The examples at (b), (c) and (d) are also incapable of being scribed because they all have an undercut feature. In all four cases it would be necessary to machine the shoulder square to its longest point, to be finished as a bench

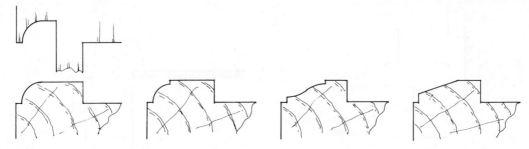

Fig. 1.50
Mouldings that can be scribed

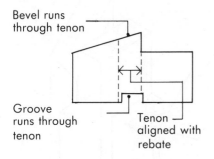

Bevel runs
through tenon

Groove
runs through
tenon

Tenon
aligned with
rebate

Sectional details affecting tenon

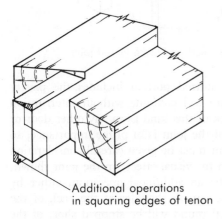

Additional operations
in squaring edges of tenon

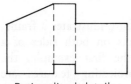

Rationalised details
reducing operations

Fig. 1.51
Moulding details affecting
tenons

fitting operation. The most likely approach at the bench will be to mitre the moulding, possibly bridled as shown at (e) for additional strength. The alternative of employing a mason's mitre is usually restricted to the simpler mouldings such as rounds and chamfers of small dimension where the exposed end grain is acceptable.

Fig. 1.50 shows a number of mouldings that can be framed together more economically because the joint shoulders may be scribed. Where the numbers justify the preparation of cutters the joints will be machine scribed ready for assembly. If a very small number of joints are to be prepared then the shoulders may be left square to be scribed by hand methods, part-way through to produce the same effect.

The sectional shape of the material can also affect the position of the tenon, and its width. Fig. 1.51 shows firstly a rebated and splayed section, typically found in door and window frames. The tenon thickness illustrated is selected from the range of standard chisel sizes available, and its position located so as to be in line with the rebate and to achieve the greatest possible tenon width. It is seen that the splay and the mortar groove will pass along the edges of the tenon and will necessitate additional operations to square its edges. A further result is that there is a reduction in the width of the tenon, as illustrated in the second diagram.

The third diagram shows that by making some changes to the sectional details the work is simplified, will be less costly to produce, and a greater width of tenon is achieved.

A frame is sometimes designed to stand proud of the surrounding fabric, in which case the projecting portion may create jointing problems which will add cost to the work. In Fig. 1.52 the internal door frame shown in section is designed to eliminate the need for an architrave by projecting beyond the face of the plaster, and incorporating a plaster groove.

The joiner will attempt to avoid showing end grain at the joint, and in painted work this may be achieved by allowing the jamb to 'run up' so that the end grain will appear above eye level. Clear finished work would require the projecting portion to be mitred as shown in the pictorial view of the joint where

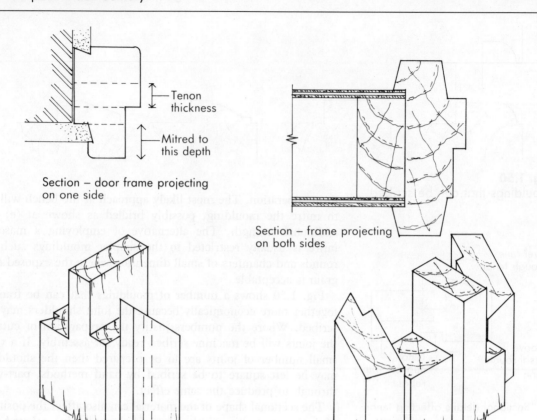

Tenon
thickness

Mitred to
this depth

Section – door frame projecting
on one side

Section – frame projecting
on both sides

Tenoned and mitred joint

Tenoned and twice-mitred joint

Fig. 1.52
Joints in projecting frames

it will be seen that the mitred portion includes the plaster rebate, so that this feature will continue without interruption around the frame. In work of this kind as in any other door or window frame, strength of the joint is of prime importance, so the mortice and tenon joint must be given careful consideration in addition to the concern for visual effect. In the joint shown, the mitred portion will be an additional operation, either by machine or by hand. The square shoulder at the back of the joint shows that the pencil round will be stopped short of the joint, to be mason's mitred.

The second example shown in the Figure illustrates a frame, most likely of hardwood, which projects on both sides of a plywood-faced stud partition. As in the first example, the additional labours created by the projecting features are considerable and should be carefully weighed against alternative details that might be less costly to produce.

Another important aspect of design and its effects on production is where the sectional shapes of members are required to change within their length. Additional labours and

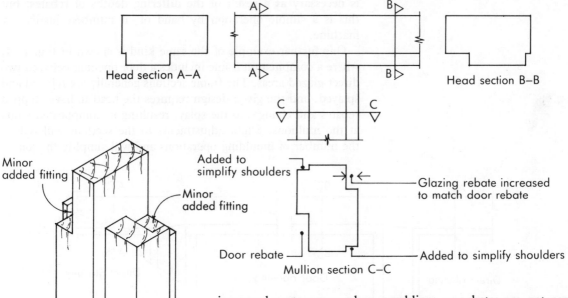

Head section A–A

Head section B–B

Minor added fitting

Minor added fitting

Added to simplify shoulders

Glazing rebate increased to match door rebate

Door rebate

Added to simplify shoulders

Mullion section C–C

Tenon to mullion

Fig. 1.53
Modified sections to simplify joints (1) (see also Fig. 1.38)

increased costs occur when mouldings or rebates are not continuous, or when the width or thickness of a member changes.

Items of joinery that commonly involve these problems include 'combination' door and window frames, and part-glazed doors. The changes in section occur at joints with intermediate members such as the transoms and mullions of frames, and intermediate rails of doors. The increased production costs result from the interruption of moulding operations, and the special joints that are required to accommodate any change from one section to another, usually in the form of diminished shoulders.

Details of the kind described are often a necessary feature of purpose-made joinery, but it is important to avoid unnecessary complications by ensuring that as far as possible the dimensions and sectional shapes of a member are continuous throughout its length.

Fig. 1.38 earlier in the chapter gave two examples of differing sections, one at a transom and one at a mullion where diminished shoulders produced the best visual effect in satisfying given details. Both of these could have been avoided by minor changes in the design. In the first, the face width of the glazing rebate above the transom could have been made to match that of the door rebate below, so allowing a square shoulder. Fig. 1.53 shows how the second example could have been made to avoid the need for diminished shoulders on both sides. The face width of the glazing rebate has been adjusted, and a moulding (in this case a square recess) of the same width as the rebates has been added. The need for diminished shoulders has been removed, and the tenon can be almost completed in one operation. In the pictorial view it will be seen that some minor fitting is necessary as a result of the differing depths of rebates, but this is a simple operation by hand or, if numbers justify, by machine.

One further example of the same kind is shown in Fig. 1.54, where a combination frame includes a door opening between two direct-glazed areas. The frame sections generally are rebated and splayed, and the given design requires the head to have stopped rebates and changes to the splay, resulting in complicated joints at the mullions. Slight adjustments to the sections will reduce the number of moulding operations and will simplify the joints.

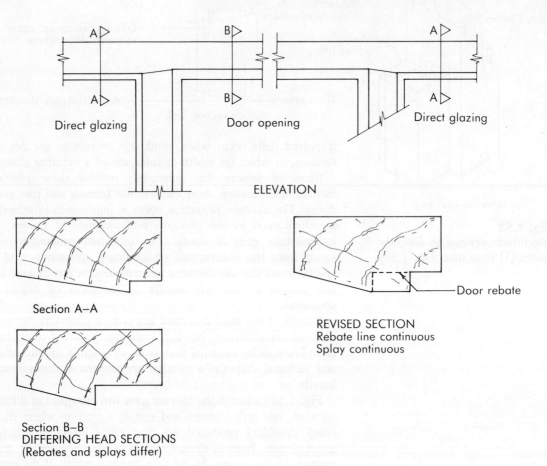

Direct glazing

Door opening

Direct glazing

ELEVATION

Section A–A

Section B–B
DIFFERING HEAD SECTIONS
(Rebates and splays differ)

REVISED SECTION
Rebate line continuous
Splay continuous

Door rebate

Fig. 1.54
Modified sections to simplify
joints (2)

Chapter 2
COMMUNICATIONS

Throughout the production of joinery, a large number of people of varying backgrounds, knowledge and skills, performing a wide range of functions, must be linked by a system of communication so that the contribution of each is beneficial to the whole process.

Communication concerns the passing of information from one person, department or organisation to another to inform, confirm or question so that each is sufficiently aware of the intentions or actions of the others to be able to perform his own work effectively.

The communication must be sufficiently full to give all the necessary information, without unnecessary 'padding' which may detract from the essential aims, cause confusion and waste time. It should be presented in such a way as to be usable and readily understood by those it is intended to inform. In some cases it will need to be conveyed by a method that enables it to be retained or stored for future use. By considering who the information is intended for, and its purpose, it will be possible to determine how much information is necessary and how it will be conveyed. In any organisation it is important to use routine methods and established lines of communication to ensure that the system works smoothly and effectively. In such a system, any individual should know the source of the information he receives, and expect it to be presented in the best way to suit his function, which he will then be able to carry out effectively. Effective communication is necessary to cooperation between those in contact.

EXTERNAL COMMUNICATION

Communications related to joinery manufacture concern firstly those made between the works and various contacts outside it; the range of these depends upon the size and nature of the joinery works itself. The organisation may exist and operate as an independent firm or company, in which case it will have its own management structure to deal with all external contacts.

Alternatively the works may be just one of several specialist departments, including building sites operating within a construction company, in which case most external contacts will be made by specialist departments at Head Office.

Whichever of these two alternatives applies, there will be a number of lines of communication leading to contacts outside the works, and these may be classified under three distinct headings, although they are of course interdependent.

External contacts may be classified as:

(a) Statutory, as demanded by law;
(b) Operational, and necessary for the well-being of the works itself;
(c) Working contacts, necessary for the production of the work in hand.

Under each heading there are a number of bodies with whom the joinery works makes contact, although they are not necessarily all involved in any one case of joinery manufacture.

Statutory Contacts demanded by law include those which must be maintained with the following:

- *The Factory Inspectorate* regarding the safety, health and welfare of people at work, where conditions provided must conform with the relevant Factory Regulations under the terms of The Health and Safety at Work, etc., Act, 1974.
- *The Inland Revenue* on matters related to Income Tax.
- *HM Customs and Excise* on matters concerning Value Added Tax.
- *The Department of Health and Social Security* regarding National Insurance
- *The Building Control Officer* regarding certain elements of construction and their conformity with the Building Regulations.

These examples are illustrated in Fig. 2.1

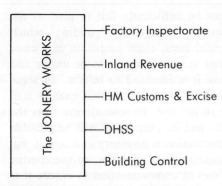

Fig. 2.1
Some statutory contacts

Operational Contacts concerned with the functioning of the joinery works itself arise occasionally with the following:

- *The Local Joint Council for the Building Industry* on matters concerning the agreed working conditions for the workforce, as set out in the Working Rule Agreement.
- *The Local Joint Apprenticeship Committee* on matters concerned with Craft Apprenticeships.
- *Traders/Employers Associations* on matters of common concern with other member companies.
- *Trade unions* as organised bodies representing their membership with a view to maintaining good relationships between the employer and the workforce.

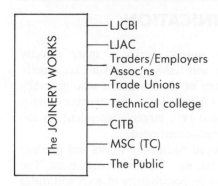

Fig. 2.2
Some operational contacts

- *The Construction Industry Training Board* on matters related to recruitment and training.
- *The technical college* on subjects of vocational education and training related to crafts and various aspects of general building, surveying and management.
- *The Manpower Services (Training) Commission*, on matters related to recruitment and training.
- *The general public* who may on occasion need to be kept informed on matters concerning 'goodwill', safety and nuisance.

These contacts are shown in Fig. 2.2

Working Contacts   concerned principally with the work being produced occur commonly between the joinery works and the following:

- *The Customer*, who in contract terms is known as the Employer. Probably the biggest communications problem here is as a result of the difference between the customer and the joinery producer in technical knowledge, so that particular care is necessary to ensure that adequate understanding exists on both sides. The contact may exist at the design stage or later at the fixing stage and particular problems may arise at either.
- *The Architect* (or designer) from whom the joinery producer will receive descriptions and detailed instructions for estimating and production purposes. Communications will continue throughout production to completion and approval.
- *The Quantity Surveyor* who, on behalf of the architect, may produce descriptions and measured quantities of the proposed work and be concerned with their valuation.
- *Materials suppliers* concerned with timbers and associated materials and with whom communications will be made for quotations and supply. Suppliers are sometimes 'nominated' by the architect, otherwise chosen at the discretion of the joinery producer.
- *Allied trades and sites* where full communication is necessary to ensure that component parts produced by different trades and at different locations come together as designed and in the proper manner.

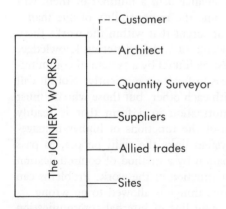

Fig. 2.3
Some working contacts

Fig. 2.3 shows these contacts.

All the examples listed as external contacts have something in common in that they are not under the control of the joinery producer, so particular care must be taken to achieve the understanding and cooperation sought. For reasons of recognition, clarity and routine, where these communications are on paper, they will generally be on standard forms, designed to ensure that the subject is covered adequately, in as direct a way as possible.

INTERNAL COMMUNICATION

Communication within the joinery works is more directly concerned with manufacture and links people who are closely involved with the technicalities of the work and who generally work for the same employer. Obviously the effectiveness of what occurs in the workshop is also very largely dependent on the external communications already mentioned.

The range of people employed within the works and needing to communicate depends on the way the firm is organised. The job description and breadth of responsibilities of each will differ from one works to another, but the functions carried out over the whole process must be broadly the same wherever joinery is produced.

The principal functions directly involved in purpose-made joinery manufacture, and probably all under the control of the joinery manager, may be listed as Estimating, Buying, Costing, Setting-out, Marking-out, Machining, Benchwork or Joinery, Finishing and Fixing. There must also be a number of subsidiary or support functions, less directly involved with manufacture but necessary to the overall process and these include storing and issuing materials, handling materials and joinery, cleaning and maintenance to premises and equipment and the upkeep of staff safety and welfare facilities.

In the larger firm it is likely that each specialist function will be carried out by an individual who is concerned with that function alone, whereas in the smaller firm a number of them will be grouped together to become the responsibility of one man.

From the list, it will be apparent that within the works there is likely to be a range of people of widely differing knowledge, skills and abilities, who must be linked by a system of communication that allows the process to function efficiently. Not all will come into direct contact with each other, but those who do must communicate necessary information in a form that is readily understood. It will be one of the functions of higher management to ensure that the system links the right people, to pass enough of the right information by a method of communication appropriate to that stage or function of the work. Problems can arise when any of these three things is allowed to go wrong.

Fig. 2.4 shows that the main line of internal communication is dictated by the work flow. It also shows that, in order to coordinate the whole process, the joinery manager will be in contact with each specialist function through its own supervisor or foreman. There will be some direct connections that do not conform to the diagram, where communication is necessary between those not shown to be in contact. Examples of these are between the setter-out and marker-out and between the marker-out and joiners at the bench, and the established system

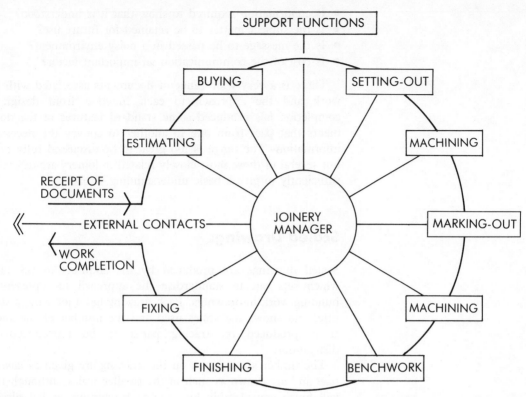

Fig. 2.4
Internal communications

will encourage such contacts. The diagram also shows that the subsidiary functions referred to earlier will form links of communication with the various specialised functions through the joinery manager.

As in most industries, common methods of communication used in connection with joinery manufacture include direct conversation, indirect conversation (telephone, audio equipment, etc.), physical expression or signs, written (including typewritten or printed) forms, formal drawing, sketching, photographs, patterns and samples. The use of computerised equipment as a means of communication is increasing in this, as in most other industries. In deciding which is the most appropriate method to be used in passing a particular piece of information, the following points should be considered, after which perhaps more than one method will be adopted so as to confirm or reaffirm the message:

- Who needs to be informed?
- What is the degree of urgency?
- What distance is involved between those concerned?
- Does the message include complex technical details?
- Is the recipient's understanding likely to be limited?
- How extensive and how detailed need the information be?

- Is confirmation required to show that it is understood?
- Is the subject matter to be retained for future use?
- Is the message to be passed in a noisy environment?
- Is cost of the communication an important factor?

There is a very wide range of documents associated with the work and the approach to each function from design to completion has produced some standard features in the documents that pass from one to another to convey the necessary information. The range is too great to be discussed fully here, but several of those most closely related to joinery are described sufficiently to give a basic understanding of each.

Scaled Drawings

Scaled drawings are produced by the architect to BS 1192, which sets out to standardise the approach to representing building work in drawings. Each drawing has a job title, a sheet title, and shows the scales used and the number of the sheet. It is produced on tracing paper to be reproduced for distribution.

The timber sizes shown on the drawing are given as *nominal sizes* and are drawn as such in the smaller scales, although they will finish considerably less due to machining, as has already been described. Some distortion can arise where features such as rebates and mouldings are drawn to exact finished dimensions but overall sizes are drawn as nominal. It is of considerable advantage in detail drawing to draw all dimensions as finished and this is quite feasible where the scale is 1:2 or larger.

Assembly drawings and detail drawings (see below) may, for small quantity work, appear together and carry a worded description or specification on the same drawing sheet.

For joinery, the types of drawing generally provided are as follows.

Small-scale Drawings

Small-scale drawings coordinate the work of the various trades and give the general impression of each, together with main dimensions. From these drawings the joiner can extract the number of items required, materials, quantities, handing, and a general concept of work involved. The scales used are likely to be 1:100, 1:50 or 1:20 and the selected scale will be as large as the paper size will allow. Fig. 2.5 represents part of a small-scale building drawing from which the setter-out (and, earlier, the estimator) will extract as much information as possible. It shows the elevation, vertical section and plan of a pair of doors and frame situated between a brick partition and a block parti-

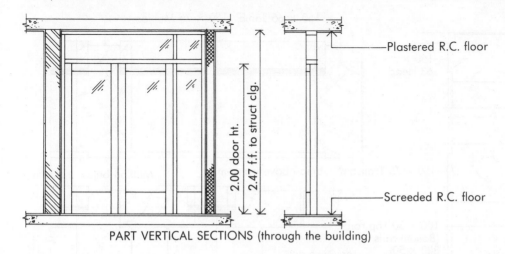

PART VERTICAL SECTIONS (through the building)

—Plastered R.C. floor

—Screeded R.C. floor

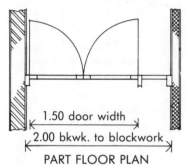

1.50 door width

2.00 bkwk. to blockwork

PART FLOOR PLAN

Fig. 2.5
Small-scale drawing

tion and between concrete floors. The general arrangement is clear: so far as we can see, there is a pair of single-action fully glazed doors within a glazed frame that is 'handed'. The main dimensions are shown, but it will be necessary to confirm with the site that these are measured 'brickwork to blockwork' and 'finished floor to structural, soffit' and that the figures are correct. The complete drawing would show how many such frames are required, together with their 'hand'. We cannot see the detailed features such as plaster thickness, rebates, mouldings, and glazing details, and it would be as futile to attempt to extract such information as it would for the draughtsman to attempt to show them in drawings to this scale.

Assembly Drawings

Items of joinery are sometimes shown separately from the small-scale building drawings, to a scale large enough to include the smaller features and so give a more realistic impression of what is to be produced. These are called assembly drawings and drawn to a scale of 1:20, 1:10 or 1:5, and are justified where the diagrams representing the work as a whole are to a considerably smaller scale.

Detail Drawings

Detail drawings are generally cross-sections of members showing in precise detail the features to be worked on each, and drawn to scales of 1:5, 1:25, 1:2 or full-size. Such drawings must of course be related to the small-scale representation already discussed. Fig. 2.6 shows examples of such details, related to the same item of joinery as before. Not all members are shown, and this is quite acceptable where a feature obviously passes from one member to another. It is unlikely that details of joints (in framed joinery) will be included in the given details.

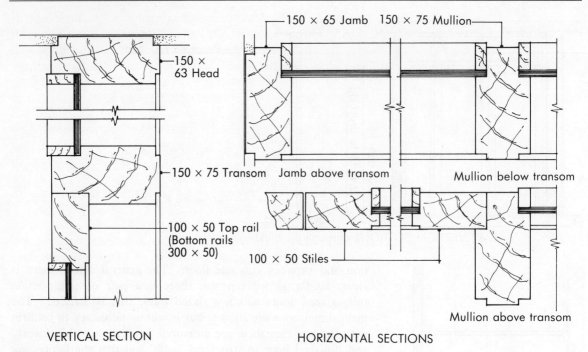

150 × 63 Head

150 × 75 Transom

100 × 50 Top rail
(Bottom rails
300 × 50)

VERTICAL SECTION

150 × 65 Jamb   150 × 75 Mullion

Jamb above transom

Mullion below transom

100 × 50 Stiles

Mullion above transom

HORIZONTAL SECTIONS

Fig. 2.6
Joinery detail drawings

The Specification

The need for a worded description will be obvious if the example already shown is considered further. It is possible, from the given drawings, to derive enough information to visualise the completed work, but there is still a good deal of vital information missing. The drawings do not show, and could not very easily show, information regarding type and quality of material, standard of workmanship, particular procedures, limits on dimensional tolerances, special treatments, finishes and any special instructions, and it is these things that the specification describes.

There are some crafts, notably painting and decorating and a few aspects of carpentry and joinery, that may be sufficiently described in a specification without a drawing, but for joinery work almost without exception there is a need for drawings with a specification.

The specification is best written by the designer of the work, who will consider the descriptions as he commits the drawings to paper, and it is important that it sets realistic standards that are capable of being met, otherwise it will be of little value. The specification may refer to suppliers or to their catalogue numbers for particular items to be used, and to British Standard Specifications for certain aspects of the work.

The British Standards Institution produces British Standards to give specific guidance on items to be manufactured and on procedures to be followed in carrying out certain operations. The architect may specify that an item to be used must have been manufactured to B.S. . . ., or that a working procedure must be carried out according to Code of Practice, B.S. . . . in the knowledge that considerable research has been carried out to determine its details. Certain items may be more confidently accepted by the customer and more readily approved in any form of statutory control where they are known to conform to a British Standard Specification.

An example of a Specification to accompany the drawings in Figs 2.5 and 2.6 is shown in Table 2.1.

In a larger contract, where there are a number of joinery items to be produced, the craft specification may commence with a preamble describing those aspects that are common to all; each separate item may then be effectively described more briefly and repetition avoided.

To summarise, the joinery specification, together with drawings, is used firstly by the estimator and then by the setter-out. During production these documents will also serve as aids to communication and discussion, and to relate the work to that of other trades. Inspection and approval is also measured against these documents. At the estimating stage it will be necessary to 'take off' quantities from the drawings to calculate the work and materials content.

Table 2.1
SPECIFICATION: Pair Glazed Doors and Frames

The timber to be of unsorted Swedish Upper Gulf Redwood, selected according to BS 1186 Part 1 and seasoned to 12–14% moisture content at the time of manufacture. 3 mm reduction in scantling sizes will be allowed in the finished work for each prepared face.

The work to be properly framed together in accordance with best current craft practice, with tight joints, flat and true, ready for a gloss painted finish.

Glazing beads to be fitted and prepared for brass cups and screws in readiness for site glazing with 6 mm clear Georgian wired glass bedded on mastic.

Knots to be sealed with knotting to BS 1336 and one coat priming to BS 2523 to be applied before the work leaves the workshop (see separate specification for painting and decorating).

The frame to be properly plugged and screwed to the walls before plastering and secured to the floor with two galvanised iron dowels per jamb. The doors to be hung on $1\frac{1}{2}$ pairs 100 mm cast iron butts per leaf (other ironmongery described elsewhere).

All is to be in accordance with the drawings provided.

The Bill of Quantities

The specification is inadequate where the contract is a large one, since each competing estimator will be faced with the task of meticulously measuring the scaled drawings and relating them to the descriptions to arrive at the labour and materials content. This is a costly and exhaustive operation which is eliminated where a Bill of Quantities is provided.

The Bill of Quantities is produced by the quantity surveyor and takes the place of the specification because it describes each item of work to be produced. In addition it states the measured quantity of work in each item described and gives these in standard units of measurement. Generally separated into trade headings, the items are described and measured according to the 'Standard Method of Measurement of Building Works' as agreed between the Royal Institute of Chartered Surveyors and the National Federation of Building Trades Employers.

The estimator is required to consider the item described and anticipate all costs that will be incurred in producing it, and, since the quantity is shown in standard units, costing can be simplified. Data concerning labour, machinery and material costs in a standard unit can be stored for repetitive use so that the costing operating for any particular item is already partially carried out.

The standard units to be used depend upon the item concerned, and may be 'enumerated' (number required), or given in linear metres, square metres or cubic metres. For example,

- *Floor boarding* is described and its thickness and methods of jointing and fixing are stated. Measured in square metres.
- *Skirtings* are described together with labours in fitting and fixing. Measured in linear metres.
- *Doors* are described stating their dimensions and details of construction. (Hanging is deemed to be included.) These are enumerated.
- *Composite items* such as joinery items assembled off site are described in the form in which they will be delivered. Reference will be made to drawings. Items of hardware included in the description are deemed to be fixed. Fixing to the building fabric is deemed to be included. Cover fillets and scribing fillets described elsewhere. Composite items of joinery are enumerated.

The bill of quantities also serves as an aid to communication throughout the work and will be a constant source of reference for inspection and approval purposes.

The Workshop Rod

The workshop rod is a full-size drawing produced by the setter-out from his understanding of the contract documents already described. Produced on thin boards of solid timber, plywood, whitened hardboard or lining paper, the workshop rod will be a means of communication throughout production between most of those involved in the work. The materials used for the rods are re-used where possible, by resurfacing through the thicknesser planer in case of solid timber, or applying a coat of white emulsion paint to plywood or hardboard. Paper has the disadvantage of shrinking or expanding with humidity changes.

The rod generally shows cross-sections, accurately representing the finished work. In the case of doors, windows and frames which are in the 'single plane', vertical and horizontal sections are all that are required. Cupboard fitments or any box-like structures demand sections through the three dimensions and each of these cases is shown in the following diagrams. Fig. 2.7 shows a workshop rod for a simple framed, ledged and braced door and frame.

It will be seen that:

(a) The rod is identifiable by the rod number (or job number) and a brief title to the work represented;
(b) It accurately represents the width and height of the work;
(c) Both sections are drawn on the same side to avoid turning over;
(d) Timber sizes and all features are exactly 'as finished';
(e) Critical dimensions are inserted to avoid mistakes. It is less likely for a mistake to be made in a figured dimension than in a drawn one. It is most unlikely that a mistake will be made in both at the same time;

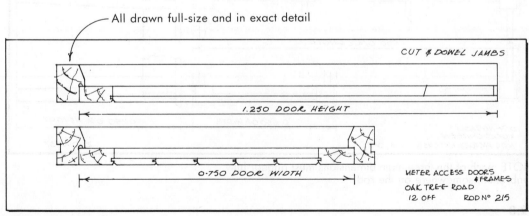

Fig. 2.7
A simple workshop rod

(f) No attempt has been made to show on the rod the mortice and tenon joints in the door or frame, but in some workshops it is the practice to do so.

Fig. 2.8 illustrates the workshop rod for an item with three framed dimensions, in this case a dining table. It is this type of rod that confuses the newcomer to joinery in that an item of work of three considerable dimensions is represented on a narrow board. This example is of course relatively simple as compared with rods for cupboard fitments, show cases, counters and the like, with all their usual associated features.

Where the elevation or plan of an item of joinery involves the geometrical development of shapes or decorative features, straightforward sections are not sufficient. In such a case it is necessary to draw the elevation or plan 'as seen'. Examples are glazed doors with decorative glazing bars, flush doors with circular apertures, door frames with 'shaped' fanlights, bullseye windows and stair winders. Fig. 2.9 shows a bullseye window as developed on a workshop rod, where the entire elevation is drawn. The necessary section is in this case superimposed, as is the normal practice. Had this been a door frame with a shaped fanlight, separate rods would have been necessary for sections and part elevation. In Fig. 2.9 it is seen that the critical dimensions are the overall diameter and the sight widths of glazing, which must be equal on the centre-line. The heading joints in the curved members are positioned to enable stock-sized timbers to be used, and to minimise short grain. The two windows required here are to be 'handed' or paired and the rod reminds the joiner of this.

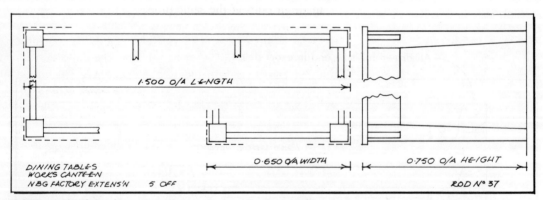

NOTE: each of the three main dimensions must appear fully (unbroken) somewhere on the rod.

Fig. 2.8
Rod for three-dimensional item of joinery

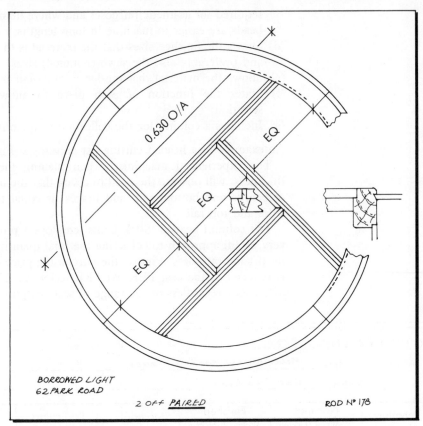

Fig. 2.9
Rod showing shaped elevation

Cutting Lists

The setter-out, having studied the contract documents, noted all the specified features and produced the workshop rods, now prepares a cutting list. This will accompany the rod throughout manufacture and will ultimately enable the collection of quantities of materials actually used in the work. It will be used firstly by the sawyer, who will withdraw the timber from the rack and cut it to the nominal sizes indicated. It is important that the cutting list:

(a) Is identifiable against the rod and the contract it is required for;

(b) Shows the precise lengths to be cut, including any necessary addition for manufacturing purposes, and so ensure that the sawyer does not think it necessary to add further waste;

(c) Generally should not show cumulative lengths, but should list the separate pieces required otherwise 'short ends' will never be used (longer pieces should be listed before shorter ones): exceptions to this are where continuity of grain is required for aesthetic purposes and where items like glazing beads are easier to machine in long lengths;

(d) Shows the finished sizes that the material is to be planed to, and preferably also the sawn (nominal) sizes;

(e) Shows the material that the list is to be cut from;

(f) States the function of each piece to allow appropriate selection;

(g) Includes a column for the collection of quantities.

An example of a headed cutting list appears in Fig. 2.10.

The experienced machinist, when planing the material to thickness, will observe the need to check that the total thickness of boards and bottom rail (and braces) is equal to that of the stiles and top rail.

The column headed 'Stick Units' employs a process that is a very useful approach to collecting the total quantity of timbers, for pricing purposes. Firstly, the purchasing price of the timber is reduced to the cost PER METRE RUN AT 25 MM (1 IN) SQUARE, regardless of the range of sections purchased. It will

CUTTING LIST for Rod No _215_   Date _____

Job _Meter access doors & frames_

Contract _Oak Tree Road_

No.	Length	Nominal Width	Nominal Thickness	Finished Width	Finished Thickness	Material	Particulars	Stick units
24	1.350	100	63	96	59	U/s Redwood	Jambs	
12	1.950	100	63	96	59	"	Heads	
24	1.300	100	50	96	44	"	Stiles	
12	0.760	100	50	96	44	"	Top rails	
12	0.760	200	32	196	29	"	Btm. rails	
12	0.800	100	32	96	29	"	Braces	
48	1.200	125	19	120	15	"	T&G boards	
12	1.200	150	19	132	15	"	" "	

Net total	
Waste at %	
Gross units	

Fig. 2.10
A typical cutting list

No.	Length	Nominal						Stick units
		Width	Thickness					
24	1.350	100	63	=32.40 x 4 x 2.5				324.00
12	1.950	100	63	= 23.40 x 4 x 2.5				234.00
24	1.300	100	50	= 31.20 x 4 x 2				249.60
12	0.760	100	50	= 9.12 x 4 x 2				72.96
12	0.760	200	32	= 9.12 x 8 x 1.25				91.20
12	0.800	100	32	= 9.60 x 4 x 1.25				48.00
48	1.200	125	19	=57.60 x 5 x 0.75				216.00
12	1.200	150	19	=14.40 x 6 x 0.75				64.80
							Net total	1300.56
							Waste at 20 %	260.11
							Gross units	1560.67

Fig. 2.11
Calculation of 'stick units'

be seen that there are 40×40 stick units in one cubic metre, or if the timber is purchased in, say, 225×75 sections there are 9×3 stick units in each metre run so it is simple to arrive at the purchasing price per stick unit.

Items on the cutting list are extended as stick units by simple multiplication, referring of course of the nominal sizes. If we had, for example, six pieces 3.000 long $\times 100 \times 50$, the calculation would be

$$6 \times 3 \times 4 \times 2 = 144 \text{ stick units}$$

The cutting list already shown is reproduced in Fig. 2.11 sufficiently to show the calculation carried out by clerical staff after the work is complete. The percentage addition for waste is variable, and should follow consultation with the joinery manager.

Labour Costs

In addition to the costs of materials, it will be necessary to collect the costs of labour in producing the work. The majority of people concerned will be hourly-paid operatives, mostly wood machinists and joiners and, to a lesser extent, labourers. The costs of such labour are collected by carefully recording time spent on the work, to be charged to the job on an hourly basis. It is important to realise that *the hourly cost per man* is far in excess of his hourly wage rate and *is the full cost of employing the man*. The current cost of employing a man is a figure approaching twice his wage rate, and this does not include overheads or profit.

Each firm has its own system for recording hours spent by operatives on specific items of work, but all will have the same main objective of computing the actual overall cost of hourly-paid workers in producing the job of work. (Other functions of the information collected will be concerned with comparing actual costs with estimated costs, financial incentive schemes, and compiling labour output rates for future use.)

Method of collecting times include:

(a) Records kept by the chargehand or foreman;
(b) Timesheets kept by the operative and validated by the foreman; and
(c) Clockcards for each job onto which each operative's time is 'clocked'.

This latter method operates generally in firms where operatives are required to use clockcards to register their attendance and punctuality, and for this additional function a similar card is allocated to each job. Such a card would be handled by the supervisor who allocates the work, rather than by the operative himself, and only the starting and finishing times of each operative are recorded, so it is necessary for the clerical staff to check that the named operative has attended fully between those two times recorded.

Machinery costs will also be charged to the work on a time basis, related to the *cost per hour of owning and running the machine*. Such costs can be calculated for each machine, to be charged individually, or for the smaller works they may be expressed as an average cost per machine hour. The recorded machinist hours will readily lead to the cost of machinery employed in the same work.

A number of people employed within the joinery works are not hourly paid, but the costs of employing them must be retrieved from the work produced. These costs, together with a number of others cannot easily be associated with any particular items of work produced and they are therefore treated as overheads. The indirect costs of overheads are added as a percentage to each collection of the direct costs of materials, labour and machinery in a job of work.

Typically, those whose costs are retrieved in this way include staff concerned with administration and supervision, and senior technical staff who, depending on the size of the organisation, may include the setter-out, mill foreman, joinery foreman and marker-out.

Patterns

Marking-out is the process of marking the timber itself for the operations to be carried out on it, and is done following the preparation or planing of its surfaces. It will entail some reference to the contract documents, but mostly depends on information extracted from the workshop rod and cutting list. Depending on the size of the workshop and the volume of work it handles, setting-out and marking-out may be done by the same man or they may be treated as separate responsibilities to be carried out by different people. From this point on, the timber that has been marked out becomes a means of communication in itself throughout the machining and joinery assembly operations, and this is particularly true of the *pattern*.

Wherever there is more than one of any component in joinery, the first marked out becomes the pattern for those that are to be identical to or paired with it. Having applied the face mark, pencilled and gauged lines to the pattern, and having checked its accuracy against the workshop rod, the marker-out will write instructions on the pattern itself as to how many, or how many pairs are to be prepared to it. The pattern is also marked with the rod or job number to identify it against the workshop rod.

The following diagrams show examples of patterns related to the workshop rod and cutting list in Figs 2.7 and 2.10. Fig. 2.12

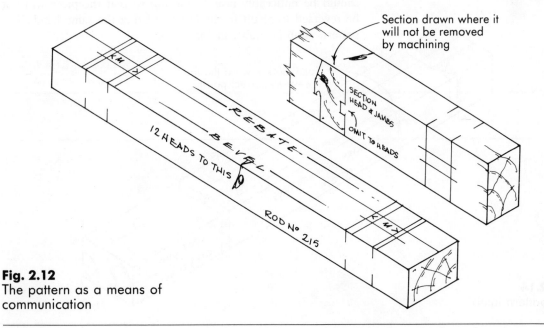

Fig. 2.12
The pattern as a means of communication

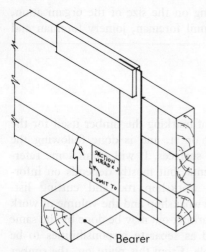

Bearer

Fig. 2.13
Squaring over from the pattern

shows the pattern for the head of the frame. Note that the face side is chosen to be the moulded side of the frame, because scribed shoulders are best carried out by the bottom scribing block on the tenon machine. The mortice is positioned in line with the rebate and its thickness comes within the flat member left by the bevel. The mortice has been set back to allow for the mortar groove. The section of the jambs and heads is shown on the reverse side, where it will not be lost due to machining.

It is normal practice to mark out all of the items having only mortices because to set up a mortice machine to work to stops is too involved to be justified except for large quantities. The other eleven heads in this case will therefore have mortice lines transferred from the pattern, and this is usually done by squaring the required lines over from the pattern as shown in Fig. 2.13.

Accuracy depends on the material being dead straight, and if there is any doubt about this a more precise method is to cramp several at a time between *two* patterns lying flat on bearers and transferring the lines with a straight-edge instead of a square.

In the case of the jambs, these are not 'squared over' since the tenon machine works very easily to stops. The pattern is marked out as before, by measuring and marking the critical dimensions then using the rod as a check; to simply transfer the dimensions from the rod could be to transfer a mistake. For the other pieces, the most important task will be in the application of face marks. The marker-out will observe any knots or faults which may be machined out in rebates, or best left at the back, and the face mark will control this. He will also ensure that the jambs are in pairs and it is for this reason that the face mark should be noticeably near to the top so that the piece will not be reversed to result in the last two being the same hand. The pattern jamb is shown in Fig. 2.14.

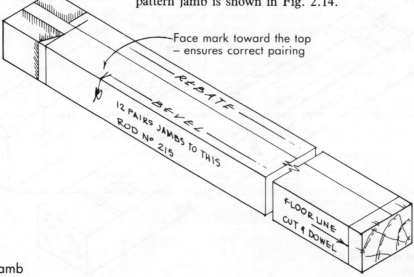

Face mark toward the top
– ensures correct pairing

Fig. 2.14
The pattern jamb

Three patterns are required for the doors, these being for the stiles, top rails and bottom rails. The boards will be machined to section (or drawn from stock) and the minimal amount of fitting left to the joiners. This applies also to the braces. For the doors, it is the stiles that will need to be squared over from the pattern which is illustrated in Fig. 2.15. Note here the instruction to stop the groove and chamfer, and that the mortices are haunched so as to leave the tenon width as only half the rail width. The position of the mortice within the material thickness is controlled by the bottom rail thickness, and the gauge is set to ensure that this is correct. The same setting is used for the top rail joints.

The same figure also shows the patterns for top and bottom rails. A convenient place to show sections of all door members, and it is normal practice to show sections unless machinists have access to workshop rods, is on the inner face of the bottom rail. If the match-boarding is to be specially machined, this is the place to develop its exact width, and this is also shown in the figure.

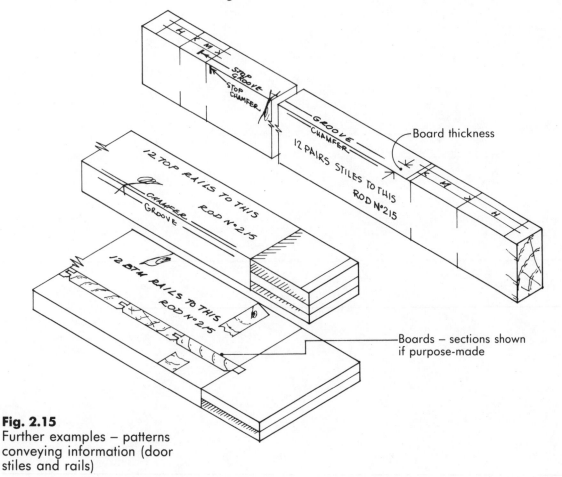

Fig. 2.15
Further examples – patterns conveying information (door stiles and rails)

Finally, the subject of communication in the field of joinery could not be covered without some reference to *sketching*. In joinery, and this may be true of other crafts also, sketching is used to a great extent as an aid to instruction or discussion and most craftsmen develop some degree of skill in the art of illustrating technical points on scraps of timber or the backs of sheets of glasspaper. A sketch is not necessarily produced freehand. Some drawings produced by architects and draftsmen are referred to as sketches when they are obviously drawn with the aid of instruments. A sketch should be in good proportion but is not intended to be scaled or measured. There is a trend towards the use of sketching instead of scaled drawing in many of the building courses at colleges of further education, and this is mainly because of the time saved in presenting and recording information in sketch form. It also recognises the fact that the skill has a good deal of value in industry.

Chapter 3

WORKSHOP GEOMETRY

Geometry is closely associated with joinery in its design, in setting-out and in manufacture. The joiner must appreciate the design in order to carry out its intentions properly, but he is mostly concerned with geometry as applied to the workshop processes and must have a sound knowledge of both Plane and Solid Geometry.

An essential aspect of geometry is precision, and this applies at the setting-out stage, in marking-out and in production. It is as much an attitude of mind as an ability to use and maintain the tools and equipment effectively. Precision is a shorter route to the successful completion of a job than a careless approach that is likely to create work in rectifying errors that arise as a result.

Geometry is an extensive subject, and this chapter is devoted only to topics that have direct applications to purpose-made joinery. Some items, applied to particular examples of joinery appear in succeeding chapters mostly in Joinery Projects. Where they are considered to be more effectively dealt with, they have been omitted, or less fully covered in this chapter. Examples of this are:

	Chapter
Surface developments in windows	4
Roof geometry	4
Spiral glazing bars	4
Elliptical windows	4
Conic sections and surface development	4
Louvre developments	5
Pivot-hung sash geometry	5
Raking mouldings	6
Seat frame at mitred angle	7
Stairs and handrailing	8

Also omitted from the chapter are the most basic items of geometry that are likely to be familiar to the reader through studies at Ordinary Craft Level.

Sheet 1 recalls some of the practical methods of setting-out or checking the accuracy of angles, when there are reasons for not relying entirely on the use of geometrical instruments.

At (a) the ratio of 3:4:5 in the sides of a triangle ensures that the figure contains a right-angle, and this is mostly employed when large dimensions are involved, such as in the measuring of a room for joinery, or in the setting-out of a large-scale right-angle in joinery.

Triangulation is a positive means of fixing exactly the magnitude of any angle, often used when three dimensions taken on site and later drawn to scale will determine the exact shape of the area of which the triangle is a part.

Diagonal checks for the accuracy of square or rectangular spaces in framed joinery are common practice because the use of such a relatively small instrument as a try square is impractical, when the exact straightness of frame members is uncertain.

Diagram (b) shows how a right-angle may be drawn from first principles by bisecting a straight line at the appropriate point, and this too has its application in large-scale work.

The testing of a try square for accuracy is shown at (c) where it is seen that by reversing the instrument against a known straight edge any inaccuracy is effectively doubled and is easily seen. The straight edge could have been checked in a similar manner, by reversal to double any discrepancy.

The setting-out of a 45° angle, particularly of large dimension, is most accurately achieved by drawing the diagonal to a square, as shown at (d), and a 60° angle is accurately produced as part of an equilateral triangle as shown at (e). In all cases, the use of large dimensions will produce more accurate results than smaller ones.

Sheet 2 is also concerned with the setting-out of angles, where firstly it is shown that in a right-angled triangle the other angles may be determined by knowledge of the lengths of two of the sides. Commonly applied to stairs, it is more usual to refer to the pitch as a ratio of two of the sides (Rise and Going) than by degrees in the angle of pitch.

In a pitched roof the degree of pitch may be given, but an alternative is to work to stated dimensions. In the example given, pitch is expressed in fractional form, where the Rise is related to the Span.

The setting-out of angles other than 45°, 60° and 90° can be achieved when the length of chord (of the sector) is combined with the radius or length of the other two sides. A SCALE OF CHORDS can be produced as shown, to any convenient dimensions, but preferably as large as is practicable. On the baseline AB, and the perpendicular BC, the quadrant is drawn. The circumference is divided into nine equal parts to be rotated down to the extended baseline AD. It will be seen that the nine spaces at the baseline A to D are progressively smaller.

Any angle up to a right-angle may now be constructed by drawing firstly its baseline TO THE DIMENSION AB, striking the arc radius AB to be cut by the arc having its radius taken from the scale as required.

The 'Bisection of Angles and Intersecting Mouldings' is the subject of *Sheet 3*. The need to bisect any angle occurs commonly in joinery and most often concerns a mitre at the intersection of moulded members. The mitre may occur between members that are not at right-angles to each other, involving either acute or obtuse angles, then the common 45° mitre will not apply.

There are of course other objectives in bisecting angles, as in solving geometrical problems at the drawing board or the setting-out rod. Sheet 3 shows firstly the bisection of acute and obtuse angles by the use of compasses as is commonly practised in geometry. In practical joinery, the use of parallel lines drawn equally from the edges, at each side of the angle, will bisect the angle just as effectively.

In producing a mitre, the bisection of an angle ensures that the moulded details of two identical pieces will intersect properly, so as to continue from one side of the joint to the other.

When the members are of differing widths as shown at the bottom of the sheet, then the mitre will not be a bisection of the angle, but an intersection of the differing widths. This fact can be employed to determine the moulding details of one member from another, so that if one of the members had been shown in detail with its moulding features, then the joint line will indicate where these must occur on the adjoining piece so as to come together properly. In the example shown there are two different widths of moulding that could have been developed in this way, from one given moulding.

Sheet 4 illustrates the construction of Regular Polygons, which by definition have more than four sides, all of equal length, and all containing equal angles.

The first diagram shows the construction of a Regular Hexagon, given the length of side. Starting from the measured base, the remainder of the figure is drawn by the use of a 60° set square and transferring the dimension by the use of compasses and the set square. Measuring is kept to a minimum, because this is where inaccuracies are likely to occur. A number of checks for symmetry are made during the contruction, as shown by the broken lines.

The second example shows a Hexagon produced from the given diameter of the circumscribing circle, and here the method uses the fact that the sides of the figure are equal to the radius of the circle. That dimension, stepped off around the circle, produces the points required.

An Octagon within a given square is then shown, where the diagonal lines allow the compasses to produce the points required on the square.

If the dimension of the side of the Octagon is given, then by the use of the 45° set square and compasses to transfer the dimension the figure is produced. Measuring, as before, is kept to a minimum, and symmetry checks ensure accuracy.

A practical method of constructing any other Regular Polygon, given its length of side, is to find its circumscribing circle so that its sides can be stepped off around it. The method is shown progressively by illustrating firstly how the centre for a four-sided figure may be found. The centre for a six-sided figure is then produced to allow that for a five-sided to be found by bisection. Equal distances, stepped off, give centres for other figures. The method is then shown in the construction of a Regular Pentagon.

The Circle and some properties that have applications to joinery are the subject of *Sheet 5*, where the first two diagrams show some of the relevant parts of the circle.

A very common need is to determine lines that are normal to the circular curve, and the third diagram shows a very useful property that is used for this purpose; this is that the line that bisects a chord will pass through the centre of the circle. It follows that if this exercise is repeated elsewhere on the circumference then the second bisecting line will cut the first at the centre of the circle. In practice this geometry does not have to be carried out every time a normal is required, since *the centre square*, which is based on that geometry, can be used against a circular curve of any radius. Made by the joiner from 9 mm plywood, the essential features of the tool are that two projecting dowels, which will rest against the curved member, are equidistant from its straight edge, and are on a line that is at right-angles to it.

Another common need in setting-out is to draw a circular arc, or segmental curve, to pass through three given points. The centre needed to construct the curve is found by bisecting the line between two adjacent points, then repeating this between the other pair of points, and the bisecting lines will cross at the centre required. If, as in a segmental arch, a centre-line exists, then it is only necessary to produce one bisecting line to cut the centre-line at the centre required.

In some cases the centre is too far away to be of practical value, and the curve must be drawn without it. A useful property is illustrated, showing that in a segmental curve, contained angles anywhere within the curve will all be alike. This angle can be predetermined from the three given points to produce a template as shown in the lower diagram, to slide against nails at the two outer points to produce the curve required.

It will be appreciated that the template must be considerably longer than the overall dimension of the curve, so as to maintain contact with the two nails. For economy of material in making the template, the curve can be produced half at a time, as shown in the final diagram.

Sheet 6 is concerned with the subject of Tangents to Circles, or straight lines in tangential contact with circles. The subject is a necessary part of the setting-out of work involving circular curves and of mouldings that include parts of circles. The work of this sheet is closely related to that of Sheet 5 (Normals) and Sheet 7 (Circles in Contact).

Firstly Sheet 6 shows a number of Roman mouldings which include circular curves in their sectional shapes, and the broken lines indicate the centres from which the curves are drawn. The geometrical principles of normals, tangents and circles in contact can be related to a number of the mouldings shown.

At (a) a line is to be drawn from point P, so as to be tangential to the given circle. The bisection of the line from the centre of the circle to point P allows the semicircle to be drawn. *Contained angles within a semicircle, at any point on the circumference, are right-angles.*

The semicircle cuts the circumference of the given circle at the 'point of contact', where the normal and tangent meet at right-angles.

At (b) a straight line is to be drawn so as to make tangential contact with two dissimilar circles. Referred to as an 'external' tangent, this means that the tangential line does not pass between the circles.

The radius of the smaller circle is deducted from the larger one, leaving a small 'remaining circle', within it. A tangent is now drawn, as in the first example, to this remaining circle, from the centre to the small circle.

The second normal is parallel to the first.
The required tangent is parallel to the first.

In (c) an 'internal' tangent is to be drawn between the two dissimilar circles. Here the radius of the smaller circle is added to the larger one, then a tangent is drawn to that largest circle from the centre of the smallest, as in the first example.

The second normal is parallel to the first.
The required tangent is parallel to the first.

Mouldings and curved joinery may also require dissimilar circles to make contact with each other, and *Sheet 7* illustrates some of the related principles.

In the first diagram two dissimilar circles are in external contact, illustrating that they *meet at one point only, share a common normal,* and *share a common tangent.* When setting-out shapes involving circles in contact in this way it is important to ensure that those conditions exist, as in the second diagram where the two curves of differing radii meet end to end and flow smoothly without any sudden change of direction.

The third diagram shows two dissimilar circles making internal contact, and the same conditions emerge. The circles meet at one point only, share a common normal and a common tangent. The last diagram shows an application of this where the curves, meeting end to end, show no sudden change of direction.

A common application of these principles is in the Approximate Ellipse that is used in arches of brickwork, and therefore in associated joinery. The setting-out of the arch is shown later in Sheet 9, but here it is seen that the circular curves of differing radii meet end to end at a common normal. The diagram also confirms that where normals are required elsewhere in the arch, they will radiate from the appropriate centres of circles.

Sheet 8 concerns the Ellipse, a number of associated geometrical properties, and some methods of construction. Firstly, diagrams illustrate that the ellipse is:

(a) The shape of the cut surface produced by an inclined plane that passes through opposite sides of a cone;
(b) The shape of the cut surface produced by a inclined plane passing through a cylinder;
(c) The path followed by a point which moves so that the sum of its distances from two fixed points is always the same.

An elliptical curve is a line that is constantly changing and as part of any geometrical design is generally considered to be more graceful and elegant than a circular curve. The geometry is complicated by the fact that there is no centre, as there is in a circle, and that a normal is unique to each point around the ellipse.

The ellipse has many applications to purpose-made joinery, but such shapes do create practical problems as a result of the ever-changing curve, and for reasons of economy various forms of approximate ellipse employing circular curves are sometimes used. These shapes do not offer the same visual appeal as the true ellipse.

The first method of construction illustrated employs a trammel which may be of wood, card or paper, depending on the nature and scale of the work. Dimensions of an ellipse are given for the lengths of the major axis and the minor axis. The trammel is marked as shown with the lengths of half of each axis, then by sliding the trammel so that the marks follow the axes, the end of the trammel traces the outline of the ellipse. This method has practical applications and is in common use.

The 'Concentric Circle Method' is favoured for drawing board work and is equally applicable to setting-out on the rod. The diameter of the inner circle is equal to the minor axis, and the larger circle is equal to the major axis. Any number of radiating lines are inserted, at any angle. For each radiating line, a horizontal line from the inner circle is made to meet a vertical line from the outer circle to give a point on the ellipse. In the diagram some points have been left undeveloped for clarity.

If a line parallel to the ellipse is required, this must not be constructed as a separate ellipse, but must be marked off parallel to the first.

The use of pins and string in constructing an ellipse employs the principles described in diagram (c) which are perfectly good principles that are unlikely to produce accurate results due to the varying tautness of the string.

Sheet 9 is devoted mainly to normals to the ellipse and is of value because elliptical members in joinery will often require parts to be joined together to make up the ellipse, and joints between parts must be normal to the curve for aesthetic and practical reasons.

It has been shown that in circular work the use of the 'centre square' is a quick means of finding a normal to the curve. In elliptical work there is no quick solution except at the four points where the normal is an extension of the major or minor axes.

To construct a normal at any other point, the first need is to locate the two focal points. (These are the two fixed points referred to in the definition, and are where the nails would be positioned in the 'pin and string method'.) After drawing the major and minor axes, the focal points are found by taking half the major axis, with compasses, then from one end of the minor axis, cutting the major axis at focal points f1 and f2 as shown in the first diagram.

The normal at any point P is found by projecting lines from both focal points, through P to produce an angle outside the ellipse. The line that bisects this angle is the normal required. This operation must be repeated for any other normal, other than those at the ends of axes, but it is possible in some cases after finding one normal, to determine another that must be 'handed' to it, by symmetrical measurement. Joinery Project III shows an application of the geometry described.

A tangent to an ellipse, as with a circle, is at right angles to the normal at the same point of contact.

Complexities related to normals to the ellipse make some work uneconomic. A true elliptical arch in brickwork is an example, because every brick would be a different shape from the next and every joint between bricks would need to be individually developed as described.

An approximate ellipse, made up of circular curves, may be produced from three centres and constructed as shown in the third diagram. The span AB and the rise CD will be given, and the diagonal CA is produced as shown.

With compasses set to radius AD (half span) and from centre D, the centre-line above is cut at E. With radius CE, the diagonal is cut at F. The remainder of the diagonal AF is now bisected, and where this line cuts AB is centre 1. Centre 2 is where the same line cuts the centre-line. Centre 3 is symmetrical to centre 1 and is transferred with compasses.

Arcs produced from the three centres together describe the approximate ellipse, and the differing curves come together at common normals as shown earlier in Sheet 1. Within each curve the simpler geometry of circular curves applies, often with considerable economies in production. Economies resulting in brickwork using geometry of this kind will be reflected also in the shaped joinery associated with it.

Sheet 10 illustrates another interesting detail in joinery, involving the intersection of curved and straight moulded members. End to end joints present no geometrical problems, but in the example shown, two joints result from straight members being normal to the curve and the other from a straight member that is tangential to a curve. In order that the details of the moulding intersect accurately, the mitre in each case must be curved and the need is more noticeable in wider mouldings than in narrower ones.

The given examples show shaped mouldings that are fixed to the face of a panel, and the considerable width of the members illustrates clearly the need for curved mitres. To develop the shapes of the cuts the outline shapes of the moulding are shown in elevation, and the given section is added at a convenient place for details to be projected from it. Prominent or salient points in the section are numbered and projected accurately so as to continue around the shaped elevation. It is important that the sequence of numbers is continuous, so that the number at the outer edge, for example, continues as such. This need would have been more apparent if the moulding section had not been symmetrical about its centre-line.

It will be found that as a result of the spacing of lines being exactly alike in all members, they will meet at the intersections in a curved line that is now added by joining the intersecting points.

It may be necessary, where there is a wide gap between lines, as when there is a wide curved feature, to insert additional points so as to make it easier to insert the curved mitre line. Such a point was added in the given example, at the centre of the half-round feature.

Sheet 11 illustrates the most common method of presentation of three-dimensional objects as scaled drawings used in the construction industry.

British Standard Orthographic Projection shows three or more views of the solid, each projected from the others in a standard layout and drawn to recommended scales. Each drawing is a true representation of a particular view of the object and is capable of being measured or 'scaled'. Collectively, the drawings convey the three-dimensional features of the subject to the reader who is capable of seeing in the several separate drawings the one object they represent.

Buildings and their component parts are shown by drawings of this kind, often supported by additional, more detailed drawings in the form of large-scale sections.

In the example given, there are two elevations and one plan as is most often the case, although two additional elevations could have been added if it had been considered that information was lacking.

The side elevation was drawn first in this example, to determine the sloping lines before other drawings could be completed.

Each drawing has information projected from the other two, without remeasuring. Projections between the plan and side elevation were by the use of 45° lines which are evident in the drawing. The use of compasses to rotate the salient points through 90° would have achieved the same result.

In this form of projected drawings, each view, as seen from a particular standpoint, is projected through the object and is shown beyond it. Viewing directions related to each drawing are given here for information, but would not normally be shown. In normal practice, a drawing of this kind would include all notation necessary to convey technical information, but here the interest is limited to geometry.

Scaled Pictorial Drawing which is the subject of *Sheet 12* is not commonly used as a means of passing technical information, or as working drawings used within the industry, but more often to convey in one picture an immediate impression without demanding the skills needed to read other forms of formal drawing.

There are several different kinds of Pictorial Projection, each offering a particular advantage over the others. Some present a true undistorted plan, or a true elevation which may be measured and are particularly useful in selected cases. None offer the realism of perspective drawing, and are not 'artist's impressions' since they are measured and drawn with the use of instruments.

Sheet 12 illustrates Isometric Projection which is the most commonly used, probably because it comes closest of all to presenting the object with some pictorial realism. Many of the illustrations in the following chapters are presented in this way for that reason.

It must be realised that in Isometric Projection each of the three faces presents a distorted shape which has limited value as a working drawing.

The sheet shows firstly that measurements must only be made along the three axes. A horizontal line is drawn and measured along one of the two 30° axes, and a perpendicular line along the perpendicular axis.

Angles cannot be produced by any means other than the measurement of horizontal and perpendicular dimensions. Curves must be produced by measurements along ordinates, which must run in the direction of either of the three axes. The ordinates are placed firstly on the true drawing, then transferred to the pictorial drawing so that the curve can be completed freehand.

The example given is the same as was produced in the previous sheet, and dimensions have been taken directly from it. The drawing demanded the use of all of the principles discussed here, and involved some construction lines that have been removed for clarity.

The curved line resting on a sloping surface required ordinates to be placed on both drawings so that vertical dimensions could be measured as on the curved surface.

Sheet 13 employs the same example again, but here it is a described example of joinery and concerns the development of surface shapes related to the cylinder.

A cylindrical ventilation shaft exists in a room where there are two steps between differing floor levels, and a joinery fitment is to be constructed around the shaft as part of the development of the room into a lounge bar.

A rectangular base unit will be made to the profile of the steps, to be clad in vertical strip panelling, and will support a projecting shelf feature. The boxed shelf will be at two levels connected by a sloping portion to follow the stair pitch, and will be finished in plastic-faced plywood. The upper portion of the fitment will provide a direct cladding of vertical strip panelling to the cylindrical shaft.

The first problem covered by Sheet 13 is the development of the shape of the curved surface of the cylinder, and the procedure begins which the division of the circumference, on plan, into a number of equal parts. The length of the curved surface is produced by stepping off the numbered parts as shown, to determine the length of the circumference which, together with the straight upper edge, will show three edges of the surface.

To find the shape of the lower edge, the numbered divisions from the plan are projected upward, to the sloping surface, then horizontally to cut the vertical ordinates, indicating the curved line required.

The second problem is to develop the shapes of the two sloping surfaces. In Sheet 8, earlier, it was shown that an oblique cut surface to a cylinder has an elliptical outline, and these two shapes required conform to that outline.

It will be seen that the ellipse will have as its minor axis the diameter of the circle as seen on the plan, and it will have as its major axis the oblique line as seen in the elevation. The ellipse could have been constructed from this information.

The procedure followed here will combine the unchanged 'width' dimensions of the ellipse with the increased 'length' dimensions which result from contact with the oblique plane. Numbered points from the plan are projected horizontally across, the distances between them being the unchanged dimensions. The same points are taken up to the oblique line, then the resulting increased dimensions are projected downward, each cutting the horizontal line of the same number. The line that passes through these points produces the required ellipse. The two surfaces required are identical, their curved edges being part of the elliptical curve. Other edges are found by following the same procedure as for the curved edges.

The development of surfaces of the cylinder has many applications to joinery, so too does geometry related to the cone.

In *Sheet 14* the elevation and plan of a cone are shown, to illustrate the development of the shape of its curved surface. The oblique cut through the cone in the manner illustrated produces an elliptical cut surface and a shaped cut edge to the curved surface. Both surfaces are developed here.

The curved surface of the whole cone is developed first by drawing the curve having its centre at the apex or vertex of the cone and its radius equal to the sloping height. The distance around its lower edge is equal to the circumference of the circular base. By dividing the circumference on plan into a number of equal parts, those numbered divisions may be stepped off around the edge of the surface development to determine its length.

On both the plan and the developed surface, radiating lines dividing the area will be used in the following development, but here alternate lines have been omitted for clarity.

To determine the cut upper edge to the curved surface the radiating lines seen on plan are shown in the elevation, so as to meet the oblique cut line. These are squared across horizontally to the side of the cone, where the sloping height is a true one. By rotating these around the developed surface, to meet the correspondingly numbered radiating lines, the shape of the cut edge may be drawn freehand.

The plan of the cut surface is determined by finding its position on each radiating line on the plan. The point where each radiating line meets the inclined surface in elevation is taken down vertically to cut the appropriate radiating line on plan. In this manner each point will be on the curved outline to be produced freehand. The shape produced is not the true shape of the cut surface, because it is a sloping surface, and the only true dimensions are those that are perpendicular as viewed on the drawing board.

To develop the shape of the sloping cut surface, each point on a numbered ordinate on plan is squared across horizontally and the distances between these lines are true. Correspondingly numbered points on the cut surface are truly spaced as seen on the oblique line, and these are brought down as shown, each to cut the horizontal line of the same number. The elliptical line passes through these points and is drawn freehand.

An application of geometry related to the cone appears as part of the Joinery Project IV in Chapter 4, and concerns a hyperbolic curve that results from cutting a cone in a different manner from the above example.

Shapes that may be produced by cutting the cone are as follows:

Circle	Cut by a horizontal plane at any height
Ellipse	Cut by an oblique plane that passes through both sides of the cone
Isosceles Triangle	Cut by a vertical plane that passes through the apex or vortex
Parabola	Cut by an oblique plane that is parallel to the side of the cone, and passes through the base
Hyperbola	Cut by an oblique plane that forms an angle with the base, greater than the side of the cone forms with the base

The principles used in the development of surface shapes of simpler solids may be used in solving many kinds of geometrical problems in joinery.

Sheet 15 shows two examples of solids having sides that are not viewed directly in any of the given views and are therefore not seen true to shape.

In each view, some dimensions are true, some are not, and it is important to recognise which are which. By bringing together the true dimensions of a surface its true shape is revealed.

In the front elevation of the triangular prism, the true widths of the long faces are seen and, in the plan, their true lengths. (The hidden under-surface is true to shape).

To develop the shape of the upper surfaces, the true widths are hinged upward to the horizontal and projected down to combine with the lengths, where true shapes appear in the lowest drawing.

The oblique triangular end has a true height in the front elevation and a true base width on the plan. This end is hinged downward on the plan and the height transferred from the elevation.

The hexagonal pyramid has been cut by an oblique plane and no surface is seen in its true form.

The side identified as having af as its base is hinged downward. The true lengths of its two sides are seen in the elevation, where only the two outer 'hips' are true to length, and this dimension completes the true shape of the first side (before the solid was cut).

The six sides are all identically shaped, so the other five are added by striking part of a circle from the apex, to be cut into the base dimensions.

The six angles on plan are identified by the letters a to f, so too are those on the developed surface. The true length of each 'hip', after the solid is cut obliquely, must be taken from the elevation where, as shown, only those for a and d are true. These dimensions are transferred to the development. Lengths of other 'hips' on the elevation become true only after they are squared across to the outer edges. When all have been transferred to the development, the cut edge may be completed.

The cut surface is now shown on the plan, by projecting points downward from the elevation onto the appropriate 'hip' lines. The shape shown (hatched) is not a true shape, but its width dimensions, which are seen as perpendicular on the drawing board, are true. True dimensions on the sloping surface are brought down to combine with the other true dimensions to produce the true shape.

Sections of solids are used extensively in drawings for joinery, where plans or elevations are cut to reveal the details of the work. Such sections are usually drawn to a larger scale than is used in the elevations or plans and are referred to as Detail Drawings. It is important for the joiner to be able to relate the two kinds of drawing and to be able to differentiate between 'horizontal sections' and 'vertical sections' which are terms in very common usage.

Many examples of such sectional drawings occur throughout the book, and the subject is therefore not pursued further in this chapter.

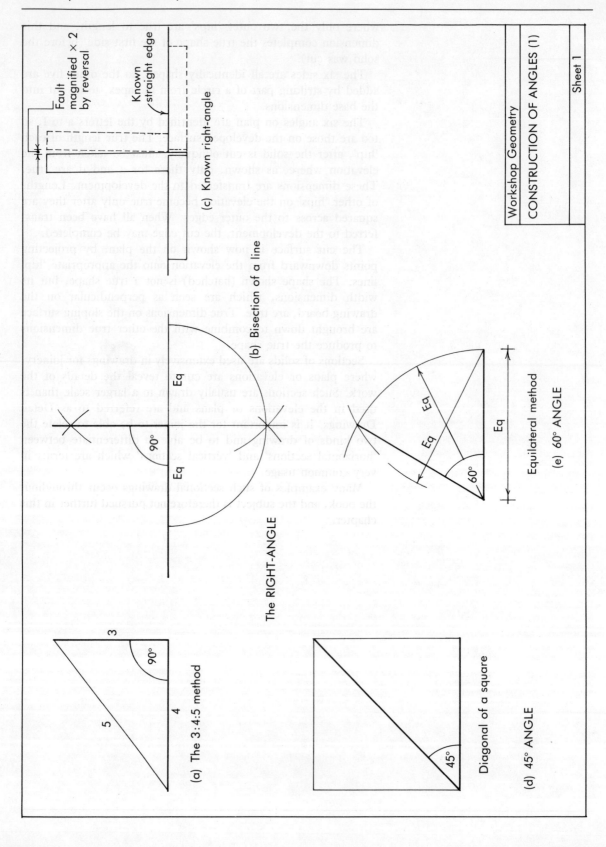

(a) The 3:4:5 method

Fault magnified × 2 by reversal

Known straight edge

(c) Known right-angle

(b) Bisection of a line

The RIGHT-ANGLE

Diagonal of a square

(d) 45° ANGLE

Equilateral method

(e) 60° ANGLE

Workshop Geometry

CONSTRUCTION OF ANGLES (1)

Sheet 1

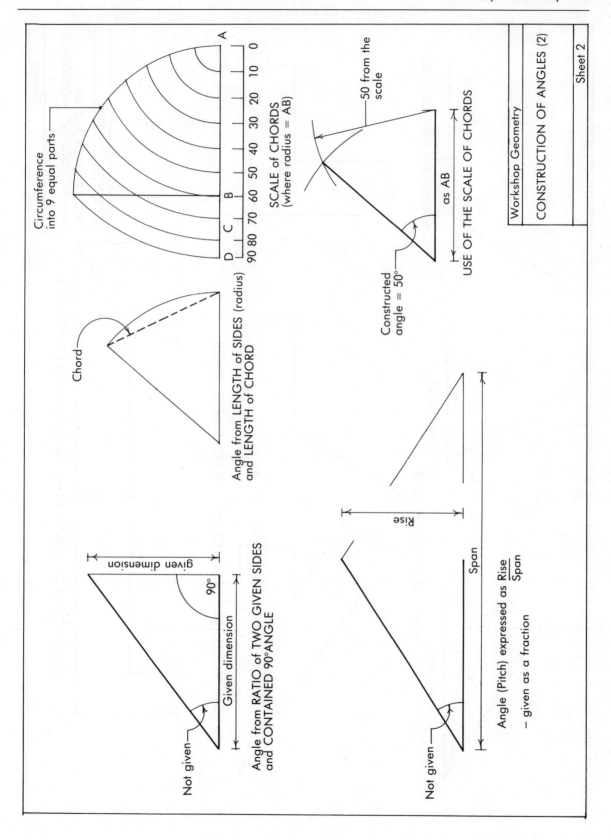

Circumference into 9 equal parts

SCALE of CHORDS (where radius = AB)

A 0 10 20 30 40 50 B 60 70 C 80 90 D

50 from the scale

as AB

Constructed angle = 50°

USE OF THE SCALE OF CHORDS

Chord

Angle from LENGTH of SIDES (radius) and LENGTH of CHORD

given dimension

90°

Given dimension

Not given

Angle from RATIO of TWO GIVEN SIDES and CONTAINED 90° ANGLE

Rise

Span

Not given

Angle (Pitch) expressed as Rise / Span
– given as a fraction

Workshop Geometry

CONSTRUCTION OF ANGLES (2)

Sheet 2

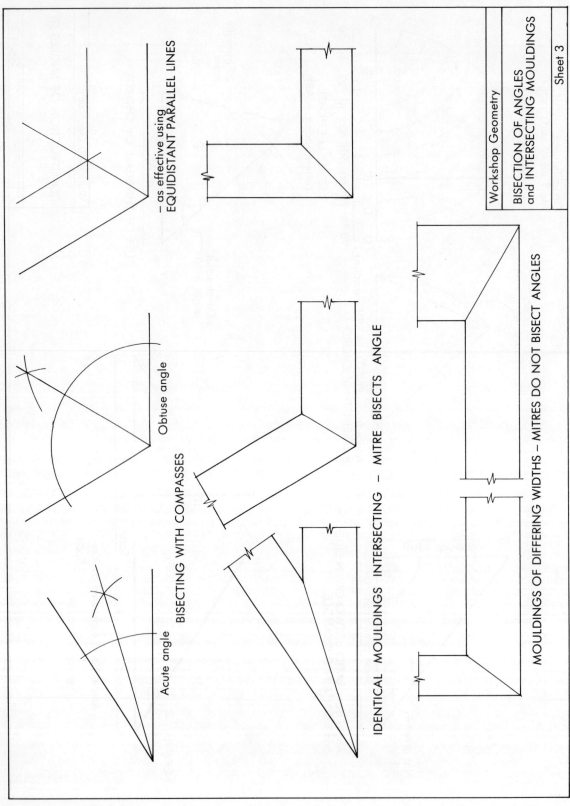

– as effective using
EQUIDISTANT PARALLEL LINES

Obtuse angle

BISECTING WITH COMPASSES

Acute angle

IDENTICAL MOULDINGS INTERSECTING – MITRE BISECTS ANGLE

MOULDINGS OF DIFFERING WIDTHS – MITRES DO NOT BISECT ANGLES

Workshop Geometry

BISECTION OF ANGLES
and INTERSECTING MOULDINGS

Sheet 3

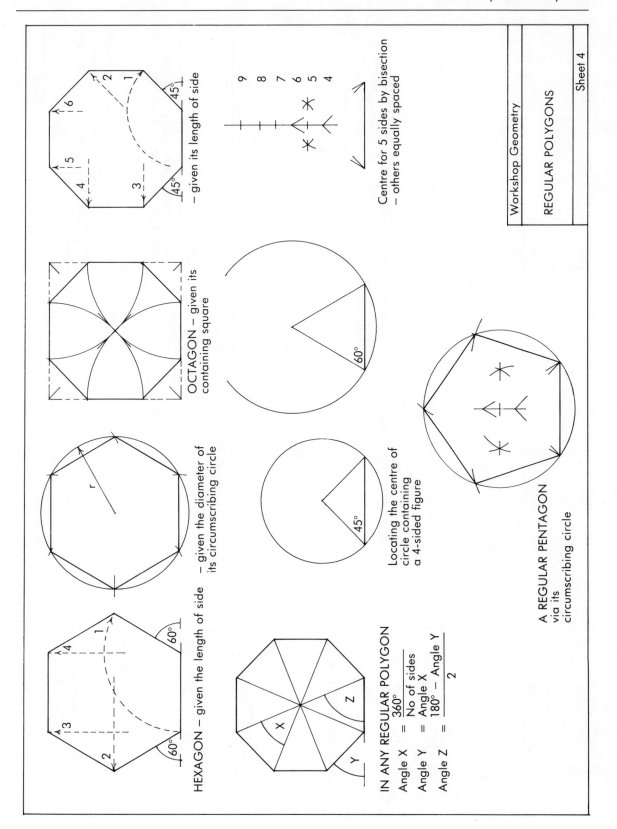

- given its length of side

Centre for 5 sides by bisection
– others equally spaced

9
8
7
6
5
4

Workshop Geometry

REGULAR POLYGONS

Sheet 4

OCTAGON – given its containing square

60°

Locating the centre of circle containing a 4-sided figure

45°

A REGULAR PENTAGON via its circumscribing circle

HEXAGON – given the length of side   – given the diameter of its circumscribing circle

r

60°

60°

60°

IN ANY REGULAR POLYGON

Angle X = $\dfrac{360°}{\text{No of sides}}$

Angle Y = Angle X

Angle Z = $\dfrac{180° - \text{Angle Y}}{2}$

X

Z

Y

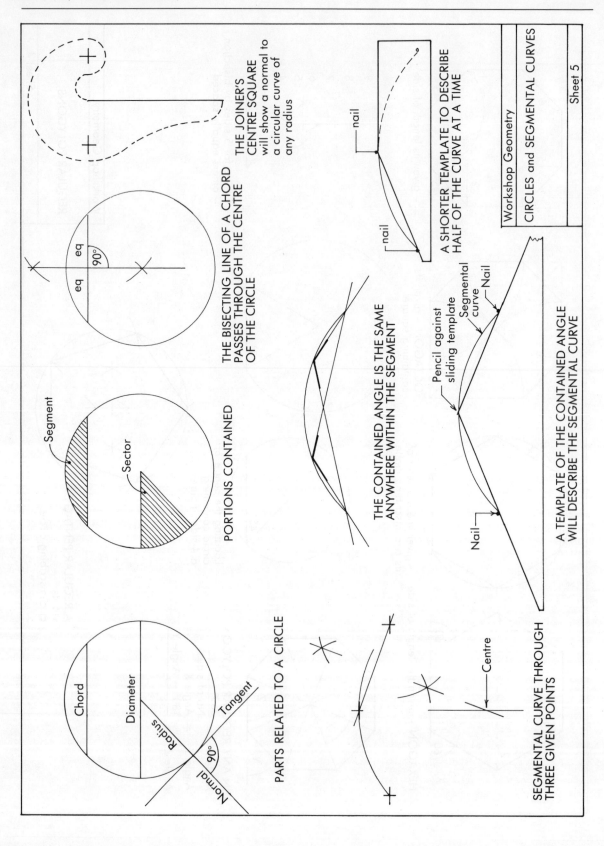

THE JOINER'S CENTRE SQUARE will show a normal to a circular curve of any radius

THE BISECTING LINE OF A CHORD PASSES THROUGH THE CENTRE OF THE CIRCLE

A SHORTER TEMPLATE TO DESCRIBE HALF OF THE CURVE AT A TIME

nail

Segment

Sector

PORTIONS CONTAINED

Pencil against sliding template

Segmental curve

Nail

THE CONTAINED ANGLE IS THE SAME ANYWHERE WITHIN THE SEGMENT

Nail

A TEMPLATE OF THE CONTAINED ANGLE WILL DESCRIBE THE SEGMENTAL CURVE

Chord

Diameter

Radius

Tangent

90°

Normal

PARTS RELATED TO A CIRCLE

Centre

SEGMENTAL CURVE THROUGH THREE GIVEN POINTS

eq   eq   90°

Workshop Geometry

CIRCLES and SEGMENTAL CURVES

Sheet 5

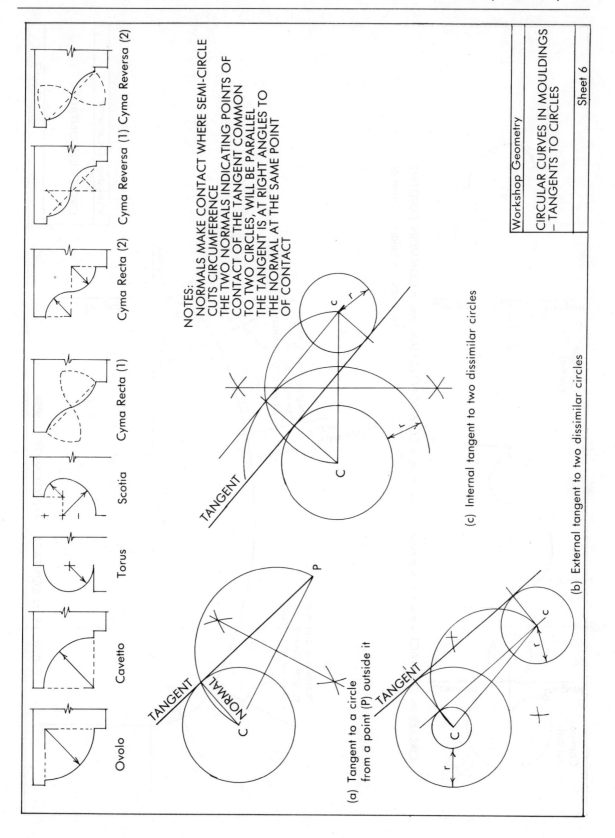

Ovolo Cavetto Torus Scotia Cyma Recta (1) Cyma Recta (2) Cyma Reversa (1) Cyma Reversa (2)

NOTES:
NORMALS MAKE CONTACT WHERE SEMI-CIRCLE
CUTS CIRCUMFERENCE
THE TWO NORMALS INDICATING POINTS OF
CONTACT OF THE TANGENT COMMON
TO TWO CIRCLES, WILL BE PARALLEL
THE TANGENT IS AT RIGHT ANGLES TO
THE NORMAL AT THE SAME POINT
OF CONTACT

(a) Tangent to a circle from a point (P) outside it

(b) External tangent to two dissimilar circles

(c) Internal tangent to two dissimilar circles

Workshop Geometry

CIRCULAR CURVES IN MOULDINGS – TANGENTS TO CIRCLES

Sheet 6

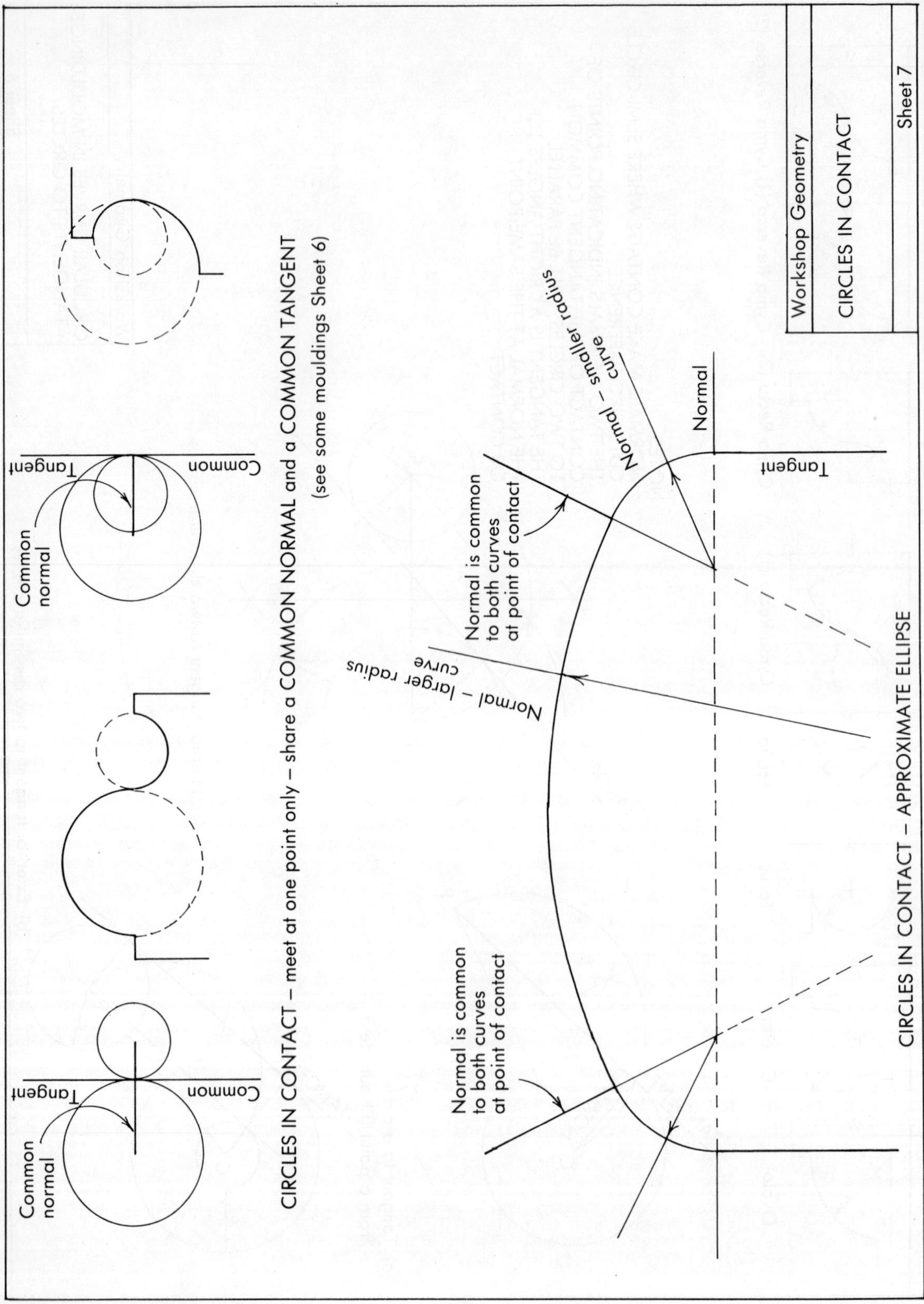

CIRCLES IN CONTACT – meet at one point only – share a COMMON NORMAL and a COMMON TANGENT
(see some mouldings Sheet 6)

Common
normal

Tangent

Common

Common
normal

Tangent

Common

CIRCLES IN CONTACT – APPROXIMATE ELLIPSE

Normal – smaller radius
curve

Normal

Tangent

Normal is common
to both curves
at point of contact

Normal – larger radius
curve

Normal is common
to both curves
at point of contact

Workshop Geometry

CIRCLES IN CONTACT

Sheet 7

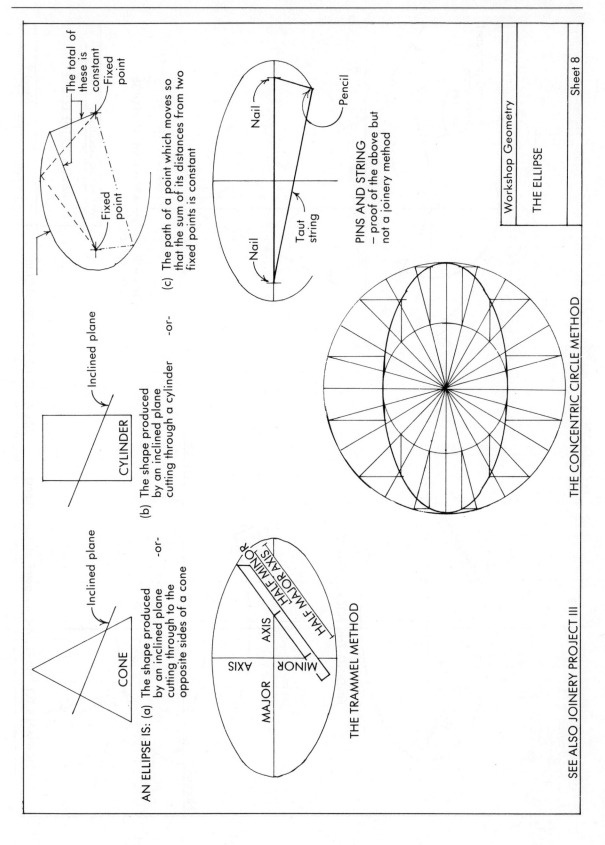

AN ELLIPSE IS: (a) The shape produced by an inclined plane cutting through to the opposite sides of a cone   -or-

CONE

Inclined plane

(b) The shape produced by an inclined plane cutting through a cylinder   -or-

CYLINDER

Inclined plane

(c) The path of a point which moves so that the sum of its distances from two fixed points is constant

The total of these is constant

Fixed point

Fixed point

PINS AND STRING
– proof of the above but not a joinery method

Nail

Nail

Taut string

Pencil

THE TRAMMEL METHOD

MAJOR AXIS

MINOR AXIS

HALF MINOR AXIS

HALF MAJOR AXIS

THE CONCENTRIC CIRCLE METHOD

SEE ALSO JOINERY PROJECT III

Workshop Geometry

THE ELLIPSE

Sheet 8

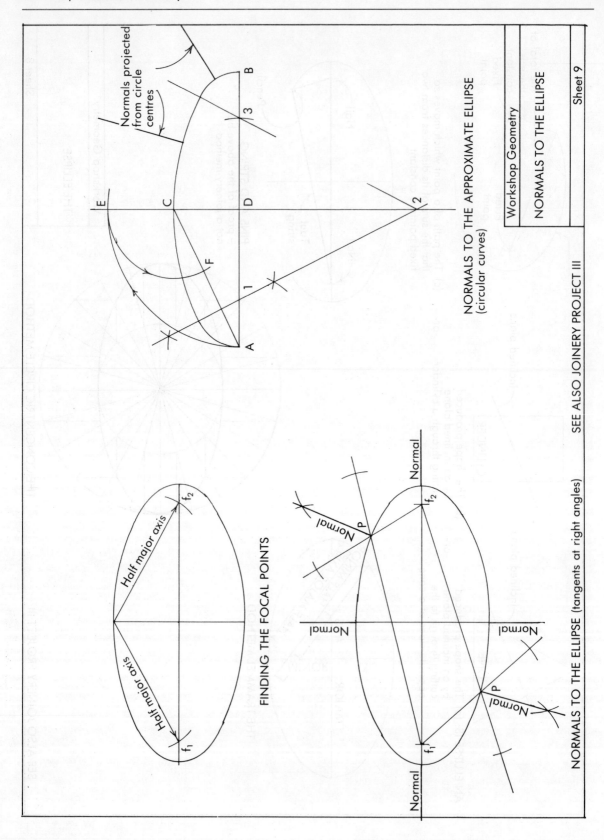

NORMALS TO THE APPROXIMATE ELLIPSE
(circular curves)

Normals projected from circle centres

FINDING THE FOCAL POINTS

Half major axis

NORMALS TO THE ELLIPSE (tangents at right angles)

Normal

SEE ALSO JOINERY PROJECT III

Workshop Geometry

NORMALS TO THE ELLIPSE

Sheet 9

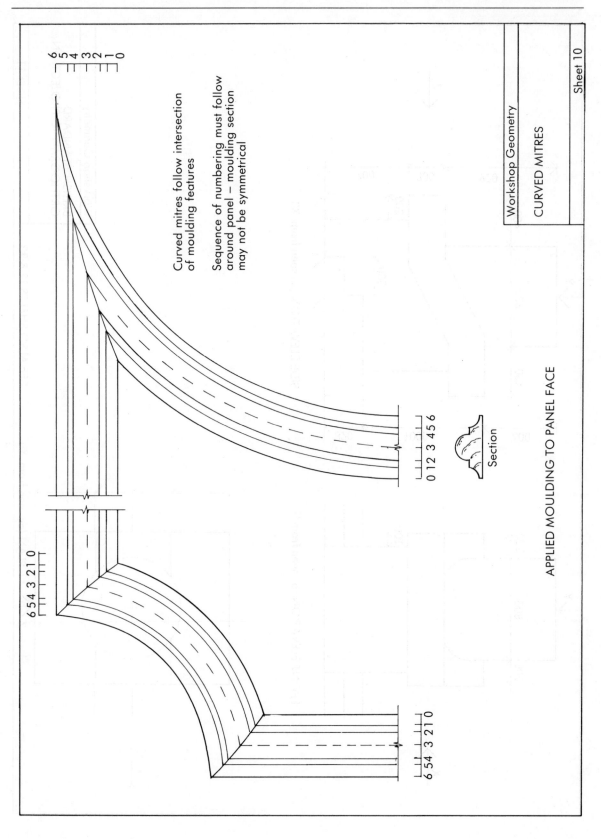

Curved mitres follow intersection of moulding features

Sequence of numbering must follow around panel – moulding section may not be symmetrical

Section

APPLIED MOULDING TO PANEL FACE

Workshop Geometry

CURVED MITRES

Sheet 10

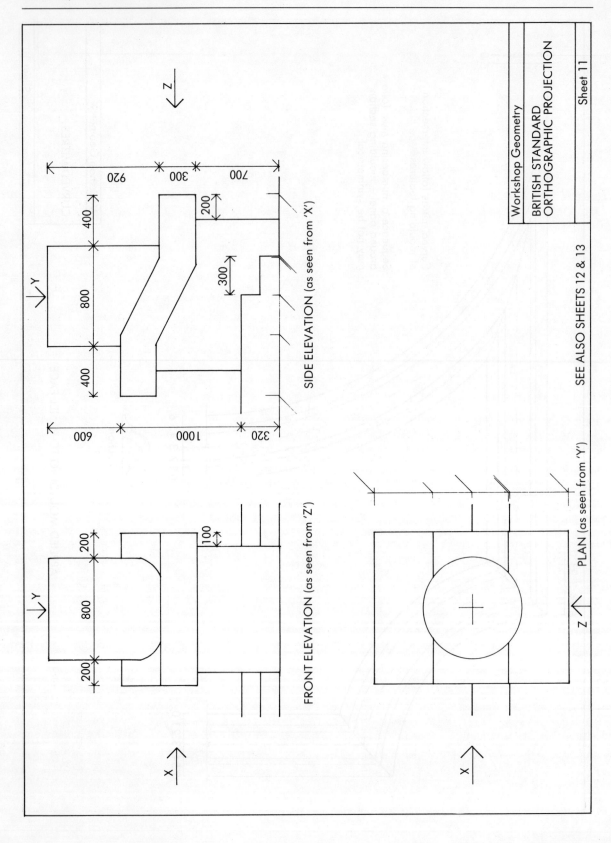

SIDE ELEVATION (as seen from 'X')

FRONT ELEVATION (as seen from 'Z')

PLAN (as seen from 'Y')

Workshop Geometry

BRITISH STANDARD
ORTHOGRAPHIC PROJECTION

Sheet 11

SEE ALSO SHEETS 12 & 13

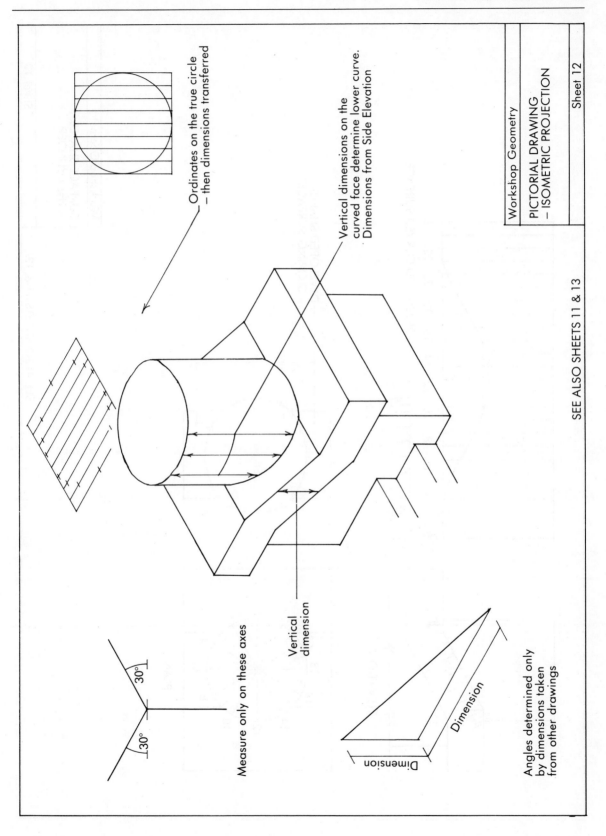

Ordinates on the true circle
– then dimensions transferred

Vertical dimensions on the
curved face determine lower curve.
Dimensions from Side Elevation

Vertical
dimension

Measure only on these axes

30°

30°

Dimension

Dimension

Angles determined only
by dimensions taken
from other drawings

Workshop Geometry

PICTORIAL DRAWING
– ISOMETRIC PROJECTION

Sheet 12

SEE ALSO SHEETS 11 & 13

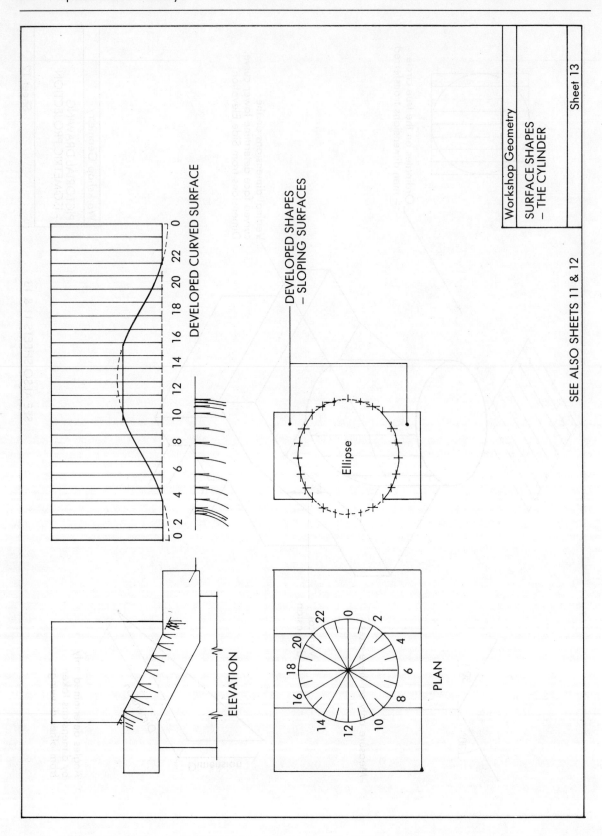

DEVELOPED CURVED SURFACE

0 2 4 6 8 10 12 14 16 18 20 22 0

DEVELOPED SHAPES
– SLOPING SURFACES

Ellipse

ELEVATION

PLAN

0 2 4 6 8 10 12 14 16 18 20 22

Workshop Geometry

SURFACE SHAPES
– THE CYLINDER

Sheet 13

SEE ALSO SHEETS 11 & 12

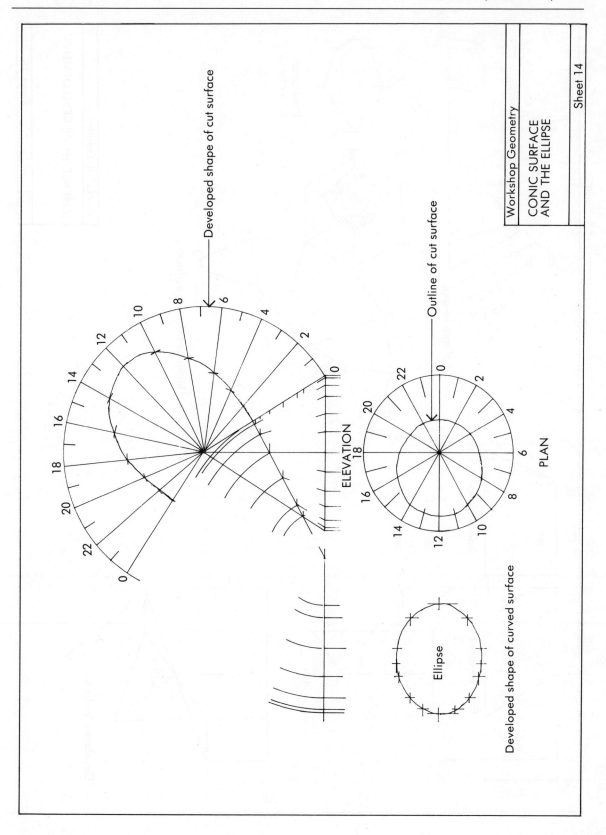

Developed shape of cut surface

Outline of cut surface

ELEVATION

PLAN

Ellipse

Developed shape of curved surface

Workshop Geometry

CONIC SURFACE
AND THE ELLIPSE

Sheet 14

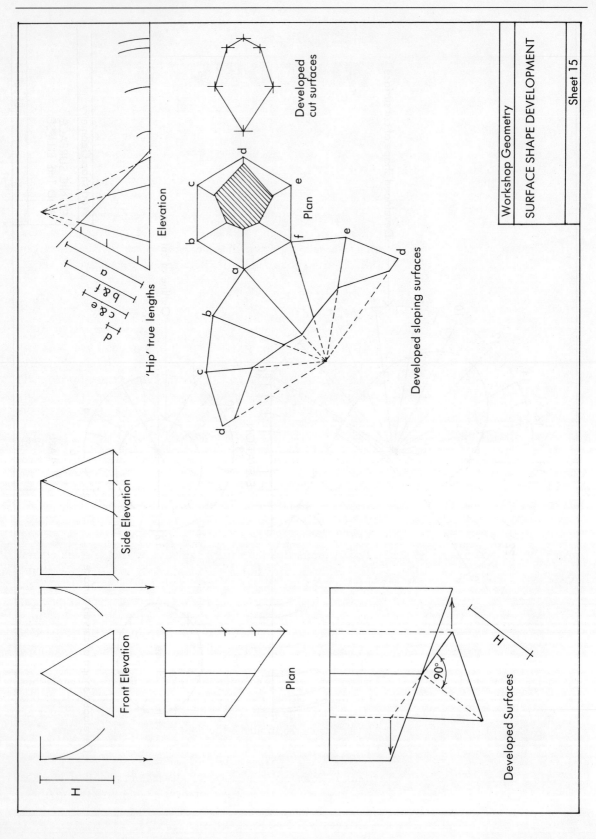

Elevation

Developed
cut surfaces

'Hip' true lengths

a
b & f
c & e
d

c

b

a

d

c

b

d

e

f

Plan

e

d

Developed sloping surfaces

Side Elevation

Front Elevation

H

Plan

90°

H

Developed Surfaces

Workshop Geometry

SURFACE SHAPE DEVELOPMENT

Sheet 15

Chapter 4
WINDOWS

To introduce this subject, it would be of some value to summarise the principal features of the basic types of purpose-made wood windows and the features of their construction which may equally apply to more advanced examples.

FUNCTIONS

A window will in most cases be built into an outer wall, but may in some cases be situated internally. It will be required to serve a number of functions and the order of importance of these will differ from one job to another.

Light Admission

This may determine the size of the glazed area, the arrangement and sizes of frame members and the type of glass to be used. It also depends upon the orientation of the window and the proximity of other buildings which may obstruct light. In some cases, direct entry of sunlight is to be avoided.

Ventilation

This will concern the part of the window that may be opened or is permanently open. Depending on the nature of the room's use, the air will need to be changed by ventilation for the comfort, health or safety of the occupants or the well-being of whatever is contained in the room. In some cases, statutory regulations will demand that the open area is of a specified minimum size and is in a suitable position. The most common example of this concerns windows serving a habitable room where, to satisfy the requirements of the Building Regulations, the total opening area of windows must be not less than one-twentieth of the floor area of the room and its highest point not lower than 1.75 m above the floor.

Draught Exclusion

This is necessary to reduce the discomfort and heat loss that results from the necessary clearances around opening windows.

Such clearances must be sufficient to allow for seasonal moisture movement, particularly swelling, which would otherwise restrict their function. Draught excluders may be fitted to seal such gaps without obstructing their movement. Some forms of double glazing will also effectively prevent draught.

Through Vision

This is most often concerned with outward vision but sometimes, as in display windows, is the reverse. In either case the need for clear vision may influence the design arrangement of the frame and its members. Some windows are made to project from a wall face to increase the field of vision. Glass will be chosen to provide clear vision, and in some cases to avoid distortion which results from its surfaces not being perfectly flat. Design details may also be concerned with the avoidance of condensation and of reflection, each of which may impair clear vision.

Obscurity

Where inward or outward vision is to be prevented or restricted, this is generally achieved by the selection of a type of obscure glass from the wide range of patterns available. Obscure glass is most commonly embossed with a pattern rolled into one face during manufacture, the degree of obscurity depending on the depth and closeness of the pattern. In external windows, such glass will normally be fixed 'smooth side out' to avoid the collection of grime from the atmosphere. Coloured glass, most often in small pieces arranged as a pattern and held together in lead strips or *cames* as 'leaded lights' also offers obscurity. Privacy may also be achieved by locating the window in a position where vision is difficult to achieve.

Ease of Operation

This concerns the design of the opening window, and the choice of ironmongery, which should be readily accessible, easily operated and require the minimum of maintenance.

Weather Resistance

External windows are subjected to extremes of weather conditions depending on the degree of exposure. The choice of timber and ironmongery, and the details of construction will all be in consideration of the effects of weather. The most extreme wet conditions are felt where external windows are surrounded by walls of non-absorbent materials that allow rainwater to collect and cascade down the face of the building in quantities not experienced where the walls are of brick. Particular care is necessary, for example, where a large area of the elevation of a building is of glass, as in curtain walling.

Security

A window is potentially a vulnerable part of a building for illegal entry because glass is easily broken and the fastenings are generally not very secure. Windows hidden from the public eye are most at risk, and small areas of glass are more attractive to the intruder than large ones. Possible measures to reduce risk of intrusion include the selection of toughened or wired glass, double glazing, more secure fastenings and the fixing of metal bars. The avoidance of locating a window in an unattended situation may also reduce the risk.

Thermal Insulation

Glass has the disadvantage of being a very good conductor of heat, and in windows we may be concerned with the outward transmission of heat which has been expensive to produce, or the inward transmission of heat which may cause damage or discomfort. Heat transmission of this kind may be reduced by having smaller expanses of glass, but this would detract from other properties required of the window. Double glazing is the most effective way of reducing heat transmission through the glazed area, but depending on its details may have no effect on transmission through frame members or on the draught allowed to pass between them. Closely associated with this is the problem of condensation, which will be considerably reduced by double glazing. Where the two panes of glass are sealed with no moisture between, and the window is of timber, the problem is virtually eliminated.

Sound Insulation

As with heat transmission, sound may penetrate windows through the glass, through the frame members and between any spaces that occur between members. As a frame material, timber is probably the best choice in reducing sound transmission. It may be further reduced by sealing the clearances around opening windows, possibly with draught-excluding strips, and by double glazing. The features of double glazing designed for sound insulation are different from those for thermal insulation, although either will have some beneficial effect with regard to the other.

Appearance

The visual effect of windows, both internally and externally, will always be of some importance. The subject of aesthetics has already been broadly discussed but there are features associated with windows, concerning the shape and proportions of openings and the geometry of frame members, that are particularly relevant because light coming through a window does command attention. The alignment of members and the continuity of sight lines are worthy of careful consideration.

Ease of Maintenance

The intention should be to reduce the need for attention as far as possible, and to make the necessary maintenance as easy as possible. By design features it may be possible to reduce or simplify window cleaning, lubricating and the application of decorative and protective finishes.

CONSTRUCTION

Some constructional details that result from these functional requirements, and which could be applied to the more advanced examples of purpose-made windows, are shown in the following notes and diagrams.

Putty and Glazing Beads

Fig. 4.1 shows typical glazing details to compare the use of face putty with that of glazing beads to secure the glass. Face putty should be used only where the work is to be painted, and not for stained or clear finished work. It is also essentially suitable only for external glazing (where the glass is inserted from outside). Rebates must be primed before glazing, and the glass is bedded on putty and secured with pins before the face putty is applied.

Glazing beads are used where the work is stained or clear finished, and for interior work or where work is internally glazed. Glazing beads exposed to the weather are likely to allow moisture penetration since they are not normally bedded in any way. (The glass itself is bedded to achieve good contact with the rebate.) Where glazing beads are fixed with pins, the fixings should be kept sufficiently clear of the mitre to allow the bead to be 'sprung' out. In better class work, beads will be fixed with non ferrous screws and matching cups which give a decorative effect and leave the screws exposed for easy removal. Fig. 4.1 also illustrates a glazing bead and two alternative forms of cup, one best used with raised head screws and the other with countersunk screws.

Where the bedding material is on the side exposed to the weather it may be of a mastic compound which, unlike putty, will retain its resilient property and therefore probably give longer service as a sealant against rainwater.

The figure also shows the clearance necessary around the glass to allow for thermal expansion which over the normal range of temperature change could be about 0.5 mm per metre of glass length. This movement in the glass will of course be felt as contraction with falling temperatures or expansion with increasing temperatures, while movement in the length of timber in the framing members will be negligible. This empha-

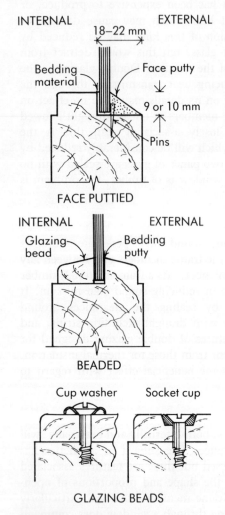

Fig. 4.1
Glazing details

sises the value of resiliency in the bedding material, and the inadequacy of putty particularly for the larger panes of glass.

Weather Resistance Features

Some basic details concerning the weather resistance of joinery were introduced in Figs 1.20–1.24, and the reader will probably already be familiar with the need for weatherings, sinkings, projections, drip grooves, anti-capillary grooves, check grooves and throatings. Fig. 4.2 illustrates examples of each of these.

A   shows the groove at the back of a jamb to accommodate a vertical damp-proof course (VDPC).

B   shows a throating which serves to check windblown rain.

C   indicates an anti-capillary groove situated where water, drawn into the narrow space by capillary attraction, is checked by the sudden increase in the width of the space.

D   shows the opening window set back slightly from the face of the frame, which gives considerable protection to the sash.

E   is a rebate designed to accommodate a mastic fillet, which may be used to seal the joint between the frame and the brickwork.

F   is the reveal formed by setting the frame back from the face of the brickwork; this gives considerable protection to the frame.

G   is the depth of the splayed rebate or weathered sinking, here the transom shown is 'twice sunk and weathered'.

H   is the slope to the upper surface and referred to as a 'weathering'.

J   is the drip groove to the lower surface, which prevents the clinging water from running back. The shape of the groove is not as important as its size, which should be sufficient to prevent water being blown across it by the wind.

K   shows the projection of the horizontal member, in this case the transom, which offers protection to the work beneath it.

Fixed and Opening Windows

In modern joinery it is most likely that the windows shown in Fig. 4.2 are opening ones. Traditionally, fixed and opening windows would be made to the same details, those to be fixed being fitted tight, primed and fixed. Opening windows, reduced to give the necessary clearances or joints to be hung would result in the continuous sight lines across fixed and opening windows referred to earlier. For economy reasons this consideration may be ignored, and the fixed areas 'direct glazed', where the glass is fixed to the frame itself. Fig. 4.3 shows the same frame members as in Fig. 4.2, but in this case direct glazed. Note that all of these could occur in the same frame, as in a four-light

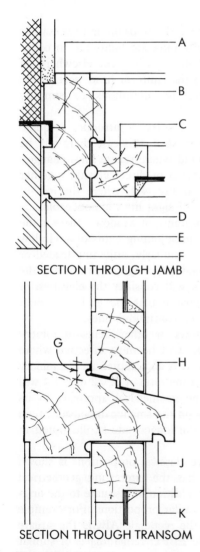

SECTION THROUGH JAMB

SECTION THROUGH TRANSOM

Fig. 4.2
Weathering details – windows

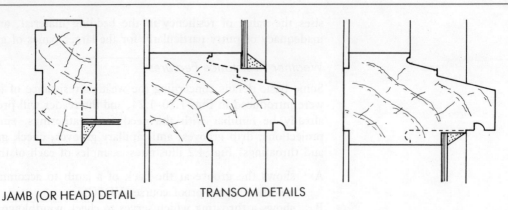

JAMB (OR HEAD) DETAIL   TRANSOM DETAILS

Fig. 4.3
Direct glazing

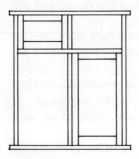

Fig. 4.4
Visual effect – part direct glazed

window having two fanlights above the transom and two sashes below, where only two diagonally opposite lights are to open. Broken lines show the sash rebates which occur elsewhere on the same members. Note that in the jamb (or head) section the face dimension of the rebates is continuous to simplify shoulders.

On the transom section it is necessary to introduce a square edge as a guide to the face putty, so in this case there will be some benchwork in fitting by hand where rebate lines change.

The visual effect on the elevation of direct glazing together with opening windows is seen in Fig. 4.4, where the loss of symmetry and loss of continuity of sight lines is noticeable.

Also on the subject of the appearance of windows, there is the need to ensure that glazing bars in adjoining lights of a window follow through in a straight line. Similarly, adjoining leaded or coppered lights should line through properly and to this end the glazier in setting out such work will consider the elevation of the frame in its entirety and ensure that the lead or copper cames in adjoining sashes produce continuous lines.

Rectangular shapes, in windows or other items of joinery where visual effect is important, will be most effective where they are of pleasing proportions. It is an accepted fact in joinery that the rectangle having sides in the ratio of $1:\sqrt{2}$ or $1:1.4$ will be of pleasing proportions. The geometrical approach to its construction is to draw a square on the smaller dimension, then to use its diagonal to produce the longer side as illustrated in Fig. 4.5(a).

A rectangle said to have more classical proportions is shown in Fig. 4.5(b). This rectangle has the interesting geometrical property that the subtraction or addition of a square to the original shape produces another of similar proportions. For example Fig. 4.5(c) shows that if from the rectangle ABCD the square AECF is removed, the rectangle EBFD remaining is of similar proportions to the first. Similarly, if the square GHFD is further removed, the proportional rectangle EBGH remains. If the

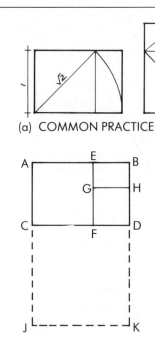

(a) COMMON PRACTICE

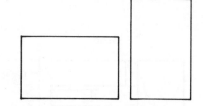

(b) MORE CLASSICAL PROPORTIONS

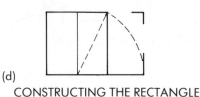

(d)

CONSTRUCTING THE RECTANGLE

Fig. 4.5
The golden section
(**a**) Common practice
(**b**) More classical proportions
(**c**) Proportional enlargement/
reduction
(**d**) Constructing the rectangle

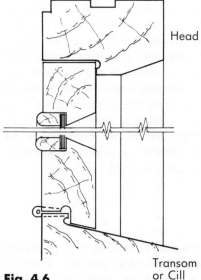

Fig. 4.6
Bottom-hung window

square CDJK is added to the original, the larger ABJK has similar proportions.

The construction of a rectangle to this proportion is illustrated in Fig. 4.5(d) where it will be seen that the diagonal of half the square gives the radius required to produce the longer side. Known as THE GOLDEN SECTION, a further application of its geometrical principles is shown later in Fig. 8.37.

Where a window is to open inward, there is a critical problem in preventing rainwater entering the opening. The most positive solution is where such a window is 'bottom hung'. Fig. 4.6 shows the detail where the bottom edge joins the cill or transom, also the associated head and jamb details. Note that the width of the butt hinges will dictate the width of the 'flat' left on the cill. The sash must be supported in its open position by resting on metal quadrants or being held in a special fanlight fastener.

Windows may also be pivot-hung where the upper edge opens inward and the lower edge outward as a very effective means of excluding rainwater when the window is open. The sash may be situated centrally in the frame thickness, with planted beads on both sides to locate its position by acting as 'stops', and for weathering purposes. The general arrangement of this is shown in Fig 4.7(a) and the beads indicated will be fixed in some cases to the sash itself and in others to the frame, and it is necessary to determine geometrically the precise details of this. On the vertical section of the workshop rod the sash, together with both beads, is shown in its most open position, then an allowance of, say, 5 mm is allowed for clearance to establish points A and B as shown in Fig. 4.7(b). By passing a line through points A and B then constructing the offsets at 90°, the bevel cuts of the beads and their positions are established.

Those portions of bead shown as on the opened sash are fixed to the sash, and the others to the frame. The pivot point, which

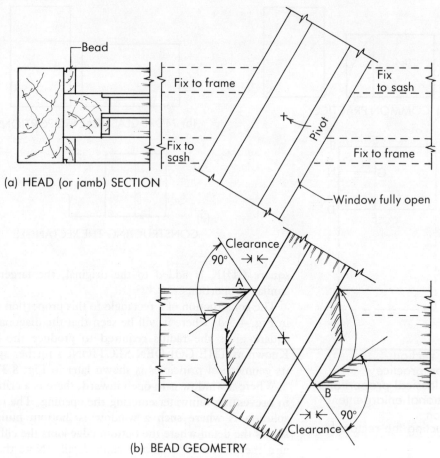

(a) HEAD (or jamb) SECTION

(b) BEAD GEOMETRY

Fig. 4.7
Pivot-hung sash
(**a**) Head (or jamb) section
(**b**) Bead geometry

must be established before all else, is slightly above centre to ensure that the sash will tend to close rather than open. The pivot fittings are not readily accessible once fitted and are ideally made from brass to avoid corrosion. Older patterns entail a good deal of labour in recessing into both the sash and the frame and it is for this reason as much as any that a more recent approach to pivot-hung sashes simply entails the fixing, on the outer face, of a backflap hinge. Fig. 4.8 illustrates this, where it will be seen that a fillet attached to the upper half of the frame and to the lower half of the sash has a weathered cut at or just above the centre line where the backflap hinge is fixed.

Louvres

Where there is a need for permanent ventilation with protection against rainwater, louvres offer a practical solution. They are satisfactory where there is no need for vision or daylight, although there is the possibility of making louvres from glass

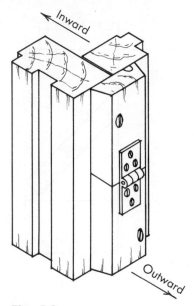

Fig. 4.8
Pivot-hung window – alternative approach

and some proprietary forms of these are capable of being closed. Timber louvres are horizontal slats, pitched to shed water outward, each offering protection to the one beneath and generally slightly overlapping to prevent through vision. For stability, the ends of the louvres are housed into a frame and their thickness will depend upon their length and the stiffness of the chosen material. Fig. 4.9 shows a typical section through a louvred frame where it may be seen that the louvres are pitched at 45° and this is most common mainly for the convenience of setting-out; they project on the outside (and this could be increased) and are flush on the inside, which is usual. The figure also shows that for reasons of neatness on the outer face the depth of the housing coincides with a bead worked on the frame, or as an alternative the housings may be stopped and the louvres shouldered. The shaped end to the face of the louvre is chiselled after assembly for decorative effect.

Louvred frames become more complicated when the louvre and the frame member are not at right-angles to each other and there is a need to develop, by geometry, the shapes of the end of the louvre and the housing required to accept it. Fig. 4.10 shows an example of this as seen in the outside elevation and vertical section of an irregular shaped frame, and these views would be shown, full-size, on the workshop rod. These views

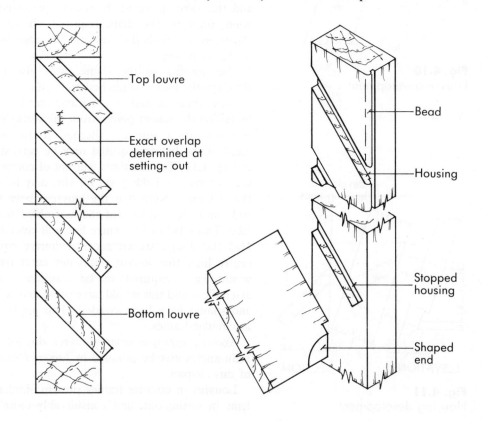

Fig. 4.9
Framed louvres

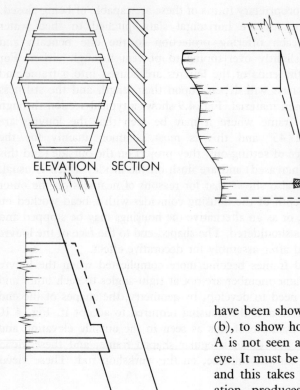

ELEVATION   SECTION

(b)

(c)

(a)

Fig. 4.10
Louvre development

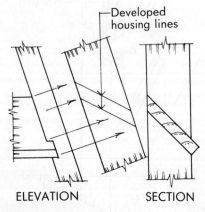

Developed
housing lines

ELEVATION   SECTION

Fig. 4.11
Housing development

have been shown, in part, to a larger scale in Figs 4.10 (a) and (b), to show how the louvre shape is developed. The louvre in A is not seen as a true shape since it is sloping away from the eye. It must be rotated to the vertical plane to see the true shape and this takes place in (b) which, projected back to the elevation, produces the shape required, shown separately here for clarity in (c). Both the face and the edge bevels are developed in the same way.

The housing to the frame must also be developed since although the louvre is pitched at 45° the housing will not appear as such when marked on the frame material. This can be found by taking the salient points from the workshop rod direct to the material with a 'square'. Alternatively the geometrical development of the bevels required may be carried out on the rod as in Fig. 4.11. The housings will not of course be cut square into the material, and the bevel for this may be taken directly from the elevation. Note that the louvres above the centre line will slide into the housings of the assembled frame from the outer face. Those below the centre line will enter from the inner face. Had the design shown a centre louvre equidistant about the centre line, that louvre could not enter from either face and would have required to be positioned as the frame was assembled, and this would have presented considerable difficulty and should have been avoided. This applies equally to louvres in circular frames.

Another example where louvres do not meet the frame at right-angles may be pursued in *Joinery Project No. V* at the end of this chapter.

Louvres in circular frames present similar geometrical problems in setting-out, and considerably more practical problems in manufacture. The shape of the louvre may be found in the same way as those already shown, by hingeing or rotating into the vertical position to see the true shape, but the difference here is that the end will be curved. Fig. 4.12 shows the elevation and vertical section of a louvred circular frame, and a part elevation to show the development of one louvre. Numbers 1, 2, 3 and 4 on the part elevation show points that may be at any spacing and in any number, to be transferred to the vertical section to be rotated into the vertical plane. When projected back to the elevation, they establish points through which the developed curved end is traced. The edge bevel may also be seen, but this will not be constant through the whole width of the louvre.

A second approach that may be used on the workshop rod is based on the fact that the shaped ends of each louvre are elliptical curves. This is because the circular frame is a cylinder, and the oblique plane of the louvre cuts the cylinder to form an ellipse, as illustrated in Fig. 4.13.

On the workshop rod, the *minor axis* of the ellipse is equal to the diameter of the frame, as measured over all the depth of the housings. The *major axis* is determined by the louvre pitch. By constructing the half ellipse beside the vertical section on the rod (only part is shown here), each louvre face may be projected across to find its position on the ellipse, and therefore its shape and length. Templates may be taken from the rod for both upper and lower surfaces, and if these are located accurately about the centre line (major axis) the length will be determined; so too will the twisted, bevelled cut at each end of each louvre.

The construction of the ellipse itself may be carried out by any one of a number of methods, as shown in Chapter 3. In this case, the concentric circle method is probably the most appropriate.

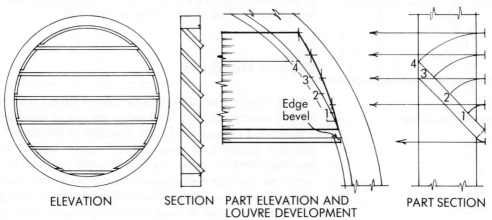

ELEVATION   SECTION   PART ELEVATION AND LOUVRE DEVELOPMENT   PART SECTION

Edge bevel

Fig. 4.12
Louvres to circular frame

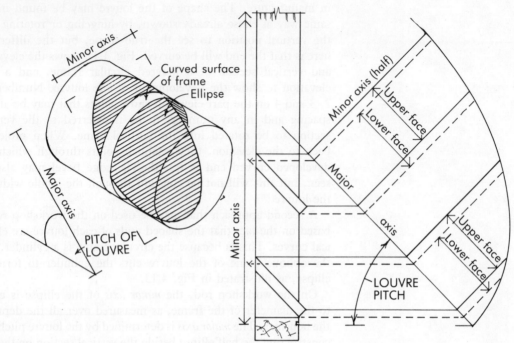

Fig. 4.13
Elliptical curves in louvres

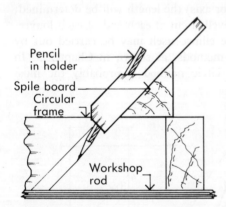

Fig. 4.14
Marking-out housings

The circular frame will have been assembled before marking-out the housings for louvres. The lines will of course have to be drawn on the inner, curved surface and this presents a practical problem. The four main points which locate the extremities of each housing may be taken direct from the workshop rod by laying the frame over the rod and 'squaring up'. The line connecting these may be applied with the aid of a triangular board (spile board) having the same pitch as the louvre (usually 45°) and this will serve as a guide to the marking tool which for flatness may be a long paring chisel, or a pencil held in a straight holder or 'spile' of wood as seen in Fig. 4.14.

Curved Members

Curved members in purpose-made framed joinery may be made up in a number of ways from pieces cut out of solid material.

Bent *glued laminated work* can generally be discounted for the principal members of stout section, unless there is sufficient repetitive work to justify the considerable preparation, equipment and time that this approach demands. A later chapter will deal with the principles of 'Glu-Lam' work, but for the purpose of this topic it may be said that it is probably only the more slender curved members such as glazing bars that might economically be of glued-laminated construction.

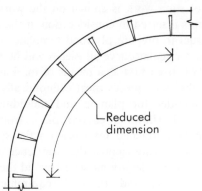

Fig. 4.15
Saw-kerfing

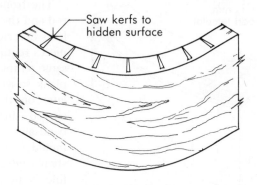

Saw kerfs to
hidden surface

Saw kerfing as a method of producing curved members is also unsuitable for framed joinery. This method entails the making of a number of sawn cross-cuts almost through the thickness of the material so as to allow the shortening of the inner face of the curve as the saw-cuts close. A reasonably smooth curve can be achieved on one face but there is an unsightly effect on the kerfed or inner face and a considerable loss of strength. Saw kerfing is suitable only where all-round appearance and strength are not important, so the method may be used for coffin making, and joinery items like skirtings and fascias fixed to convex curves. The saw cuts are best made by machine to achieve constant depths. Fig. 4.15 illustrates the principle of saw kerfing, and it will be appreciated that the number of saw cuts necessary will depend upon the thickness of each cut and the difference in dimensions between the outer and inner circumferences of the intended curve. In practice the effect will not be as smooth as illustrated, since it will be a series of 'flats' although the outer face will be improved by cleaning-up and sanding.

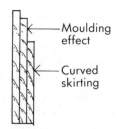

Moulding
effect

Curved
skirting

Fig. 4.16
Dry-laminating

Fig. 4.16 shows a practical alternative for skirtings or fascias where a better effect can usually be achieved by *dry-laminating* where, for example, three laminates of 6 mm individually fixed are used to make up 18 mm. Where appropriate a 'moulding' can be produced to conceal the joints.

Curved work in joinery also demands mention of 'staved work', which will be referred to in a later chapter where it will be applied to more appropriate work; it is unsuitable for members in the general range of framed joinery.

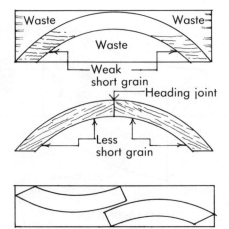

Waste   Waste

Waste

Weak
short grain

Heading joint

Less
short grain

Less wastage

Fig. 4.17
Solid curved members

Curved members in purpose-made framed joinery are most likely to be cut from solid material and joined together as necessary. The two most vital defects that come from this approach are that there is likely to be considerable waste and with the resultant short grain there is likely to be loss of strength. Fig. 4.17 illustrates how such weakness and waste occurs, and how both of these problems are reduced by the introduction of a heading joint.

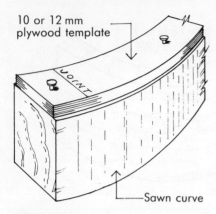

Fig. 4.18
Part-prepared curved member

The front elevation of such work is shown on the workshop rod and the heading joints inserted in consideration of the problems described. It is usual to prepare plywood templates of the pieces required, and for a circular curve all pieces will be to the same template. This aid is used first as a means of marking the plank so as to provide the sawn pieces most economically, and later on the spindle moulder for planing and moulding the curved surfaces. Fig. 4.18 shows a curved piece from the bandsaw, with the template attached for work on the spindle moulder. The template will locate against the ring fence and it should be noted that the surplus length allowed beyond the joint line is necessary as a 'run-on' and 'run-off' requirement in machining.

The curved pieces to be joined together end-to-end should be brought as near as possible to their finished sections before assembly, as any further working afterwards will be difficult, due to the change in grain direction at either side of the heading joint, and some tearing-out is likely.

There are several ways of joining the curved pieces together to make up the frame members, some becoming less popular because of the degree of hand skill demanded in their execution. One such is the *hammer-headed key* joint where the key is made from hardwood, recessed into the hidden face to about two-thirds of the material depth, glued and wedged into place, so cramping and securing the joint. Shown in Fig. 4.19, the joint includes two tongues of plywood which prevent rotation. The diagram shows the work as seen before the wedges are driven home and all is cleaned off flush.

A more recent approach to the same problem is the use of a *handrail bolt* and *dowels*, which together will effectively cramp

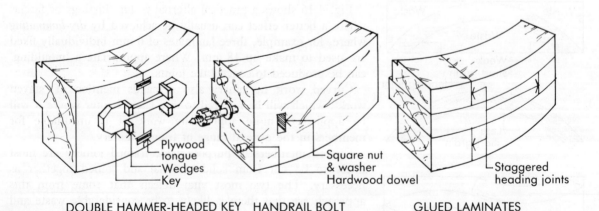

DOUBLE HAMMER-HEADED KEY   HANDRAIL BOLT   GLUED LAMINATES

Fig. 4.19
Alternative joints in curved members

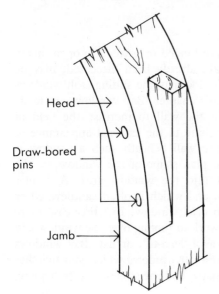

Fig. 4.20
Jamb-to-head joint

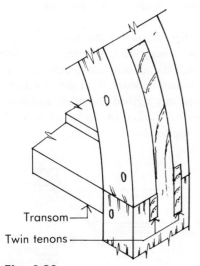

Fig. 4.21
Joint with transom

and secure the joints, and prevent rotation. This joint and a third alternative are also shown in Fig. 4.19.

The third alternative, which obviates the need for complicated heading joints, is where the member is built up of several thicknesses with staggered heading joints which themselves are simply butted together. Preferably not less than three laminates should be used, and the joints should if possible be made to coincide with rebates or moulding lines so as to conceal them. The effect can be likened to brick bonding and the pieces are generally screwed together as a means of cramping the glued laminates together. The screws may be concealed by being counter-bored and pelleted unless they are to be covered by some form of cover moulding. The Figure illustrates the method and shows a moulded section which dictates the joint positions. Note also that from this approach comes the possibility of forming a rebate by machining the pieces to their finished width before assembly, so avoiding the machining of a curved rebate.

A curved member is sometimes required to join end to end with a straight member, as in a semi-circular headed window or door frame. The simplest way to do this is to form a long tenon on the top of the jamb, to enter an open mortice in the curved head. Cramping is best achieved by draw-boring and pinning with hardwood dowel as shown in Fig. 4.20, where the tenon is shown before cleaning off flush. Note that the inner edge of the tenon is kept clear of the inner face of the frame, which is generally rebated and moulded.

If the job shown is in clear finished hardwood, the pins will be counter-bored and pelleted over. Care should be taken here to avoid contact between the underside of the pellet and the end of the pin, otherwise as the frame material shrinks the pellet will become proud of the surface.

The joint is often further complicated by a transom, so that three pieces will join together at the same point. Fig. 4.21 shows the usual means of solving this problem, where twin tenons on the transom fork around the long tenon on the jamb. The intricate details such as tenon widths and shoulder treatment will be dictated by moulding and rebate details.

Curved work in windows can be further complicated by the geometrical arrangement of glazing bars, one example of which is shown in Fig. 4.22, and a further example appears as *Joinery Project No. II*. Curves in windows do not only occur in elevations, but may appear in plan shapes so that horizontal members such as heads, transoms and cills will need to be shaped on plan. The principles already described can generally be applied to these situations and an example appears as *Joinery Project No. IV* which concerns a Bow Window.

Non-circular curves sometimes occur in windows, and one example of this is in *Joinery Project No. III*, concerning the making of an Elliptical Borrowed Light.

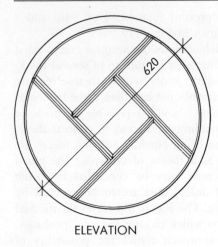

ELEVATION

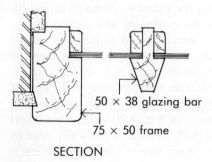

50 × 38 glazing bar

75 × 50 frame

SECTION

Fig. 4.22
Bullseye window (as a
borrowed light)

Bay Windows

Casement windows, which are hinged or pivoted to open, many of the features of which have already been discussed, may be made up as bay windows. So too may the sliding sash windows which will appear later in this chapter. Bay windows are made to project from the face of the wall to increase the field of outward vision and to contribute to the external appearance of the building. The supporting wall beneath such a window is shaped to coincide with the plan shape of the window, so the floor will generally extend into the window area. A similar window to an upper storey, and which is often cantilevered or supported on brackets is an oriel window. In either case there will generally be associated work in roofing over the window and this may be either pitched as a 'lean-to', or flat. Bay windows are in most cases two or more flat windows which join together at angles to form the plan shape, and the angles may be 'square' or obtuse as seen Fig 4.23.

Work in forming an angle to a bay window will be concerned with forming a corner post, and the mitring together of the head and cill. In Fig 4.24 it will be seen that most of the features that appear on the mullion section occur also on the corner post, except that the moulding cannot be made to match those on both sides of it so a compromise is made or the arris may be left plain.

Tenons on the corner post line through with others on the frame and become a box tenon, where the two outer faces may be worked by two passes through the tenoner using only the top block. Inner faces on the tenon may be worked on the morticer, or by hand. It will be noted that any scribed shoulder, and here there is one at the cill, cannot be worked in the usual way on the tenoner, and will be left long for hand scribing.

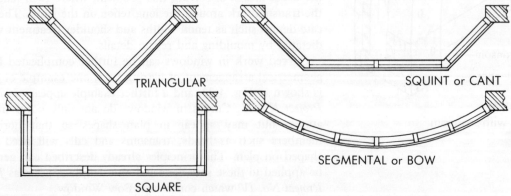

TRIANGULAR

SQUINT or CANT

SEGMENTAL or BOW

SQUARE

Fig. 4.23
Bay windows – plan
arrangements

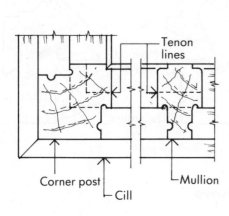

Fig. 4.24
Square corner post

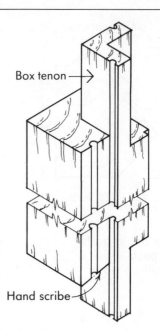

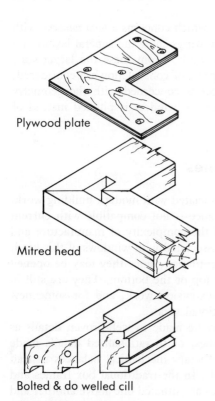

Plywood plate

Mitred head

Bolted & do welled cill

Fig. 4.25
Head and cill joints

The mitred cill, which in most cases is of hardwood, is best secured with a handrail bolt and dowels in a similar way to that in Fig. 4.19, while the head, which is under less stress, is often nailed together. A plywood plate screwed to the upper surface of the head, where it will be concealed by the roof members, is an effective way of securing the head joint, as will be seen in Fig. 4.25.

Difficulties in producing a corner post from one piece of solid material lie mostly in the working of box tenons and their shoulders, and in those for obtuse angles, in the special settings and waste in bringing them to the required section. Fig. 4.26 illustrates a corner post for an obtuse angle. In (a) these problems are apparent. In (b) the two parts have produced less waste, and machine settings are mostly as for other members in the frame. The section shown in (c) has a decorative fillet inserted to give a more interesting appearance and to allow smaller section material to be used. Note that for external work the surfaces coming together will be primed, and possibly treated with fungicide before assembly.

A square post may be made up in a similar way to gain the advantages described, as shown in Fig. 4.27, where casings have been employed to complete the built-up post.

An example of an item of joinery which incorporates many of the features discussed may be seen in *Joinery Project No. I*, which involves a *splay-fronted bay window*. As a result of its design the window presents a number of useful and interesting geometrical and workshop problems in the window itself and in the pitched roof above it, and these may be pursued in the several drawings presented as parts of the Project.

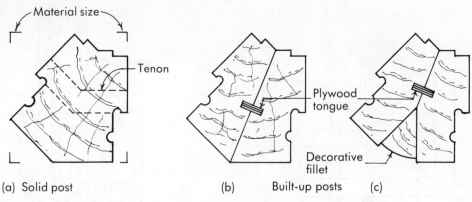

Fig. 4.26
Alternative angle posts
(**a**) Solid posts
(**b**), (**c**) Built-up posts

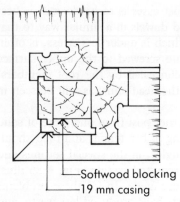

Fig. 4.27
Built-up square post

Bow Windows

A bow window is segmental on plan and will involve some curved members, particularly the head and cill. To simplify its construction and to avoid the need for curved glass, the horizontal or 'lay' bars are in short straight lengths fitted between the vertical bars. Glazing rebates in the curved head and cill will be machined as curves then straightened between bar mortices before assembly.

In *Joinery Project No. IV*, which concerns a *bow window* with a flat roof, the small-scale drawings show the general layout and principal dimensions of the work. From these the larger-scale details are produced and aspects of construction are considered. A second part of the Project is concerned with the geometry involved when the roof over the window is pitched instead of flat.

Vertical Sliding Sashes

These are not commonly associated with modern building work, partly because their appearance is not compatible with current design, but also because of the complexity of manufacture and the maintenance problems associated with windows of this kind. Sliding sashes offer good ventilation, since they may be opened to any chosen extent at the top or the bottom. They are still in demand for restoration or extension work, and for some new buildings designed in traditional styles.

This type of window may be made to well-proven details as box frames and sliding sashes, or to rationalised details made possible by employing proprietary mechanical balances instead of balance weights and cords. In the traditional box frames and sliding sashes, the two sashes are situated one above another and suspended on cords (and sometimes chains) which pass over pulleys to weights housed within the box frame. Each sash has

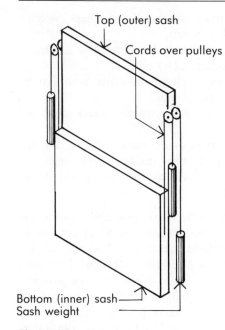

Top (outer) sash
Cords over pulleys
Bottom (inner) sash
Sash weight

Fig. 4.28
Sliding sash principle

two weights which together equal the weight of the sash so that it may be left stationary at any point within its vertical travel (Fig. 4.28).

The design details of the window are very much concerned with the need to house the weights and to give access to them and the cords for maintenance purposes. Fig. 4.29 shows a vertical section through a typical box frame and sashes where it will be seen that the head is of box construction (to match the jambs) and, because of its bulky appearance, is largely concealed behind brickwork. The cill is of solid hardwood and, as is normal practice, does not project from the face of the jambs, which is so that the outer lining may pass across and be nailed to it. The sashes are contained within the frame by removable beads which allow easy access for renewal of sashcords.

The figure also shows a horizontal section through the window, as seen below the level of the meeting rails and this should be related to the previous figure. The parts indicated are listed below together with typical finished sizes.

A   *Outside lining.* Width sufficient to accommodate weights. Thickness 15 mm.

B   *Pulley stile.* Width depends on sash thickness, with clearance. Thickness 28 mm.

C   *Sash weight.* Generally of cast iron. Diameter 35–45 mm depending on weight.

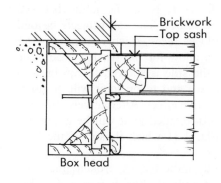

Brickwork
Top sash
Box head

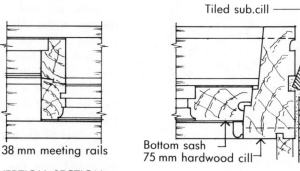

38 mm meeting rails

VERTICAL SECTION

Tiled sub.cill
Bottom sash
75 mm hardwood cill

Fig. 4.29
Box frame and sliding sashes

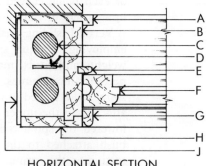

A
B
C
D
E
F
G
H
J

HORIZONTAL SECTION

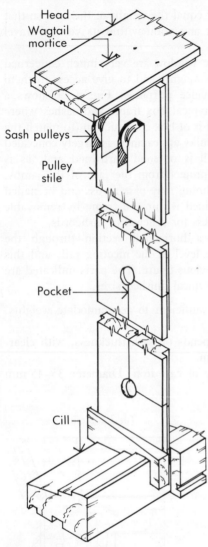

Fig. 4.30
Frame assembly

D   *Wagtail*. Suspended from the head and keeps weights separated. Sawn to 40 × 6 mm.

E   *Parting bead*. Separates sashes and is removable for access to the top sash and pocket; 22×9 mm.

F   *Sash stile*. Grooved at the back for the nailed cord. Thickness 42 or 47 mm. Width 47 mm.

G   *Staff bead*. Removed for access to the lower sash and pocket; 22 × 15 mm.

H   *Inside lining*. Is narrower than the outside lining, but the same thickness. Exposed to view inside the building.

J   *Back lining*. Closes the back of the box jamb; 4 mm plywood or hardboard.

Fig. 4.30 shows the box frame partly assembled, when the pulley stiles and head are joined together in a similar way to door linings. Glued wedges hold the stiles to the cill. At this stage the pulleys are already fitted and the pocket cuts have been made. Note that the holes, 18–25 mm diameter bored part-way through the pulley stile, are to facilitate the cross-cutting of the pocket. On the other side, the parting bead groove will serve the same purpose. The next stage will be to 'square' the frame, flat on the bench, and fit the outside linings followed by the inside linings. The pocket will be knocked out (splitting the short grain) just before the inside linings are fitted.

Another feature of the work, which is rather complicated and may add considerably to the cost, is in the joints between meeting rails and stiles of the sashes. The rail projects beyond the face of the stile and should be recessed where it passes over it. It will also be cut back to allow for the parting bead. The simplest joint here is where the stile is allowed to run on as a 'joggle', in which case a mortice and tenon joint will be used. The joggle is shaped for decorative effect. Alternatively, the stile may be cut off flush, when a dovetailed joint will be necessary. Each of these is shown in Fig. 4.31 which illustrates the joint as applied to the bottom sash.

The grooves for sash cord, indicated as broken lines, are machined after the sash is assembled. Box frames and sashes may be further complicated in design by having shaped heads or even being curved on plan. The sash bars may be arranged in a variety of ways and the windows may be designed as bays.

Vertical sliding sashes may be simplified considerably by employing 'Unique spiral sash balances' instead of the sash weights and cords, mainly because there will no longer be the need for box frames. The Unique sash balance consists of a spiral rod attached to the sash, and a helical spring within a tube attached to the upper end of the jamb. As the sash is raised or lowered the spiral rod passes in or out of the tube, turning a bush attached to the spring, so increasing or decreasing the torsion on the spring. The spiral rod has a varying pitch so that

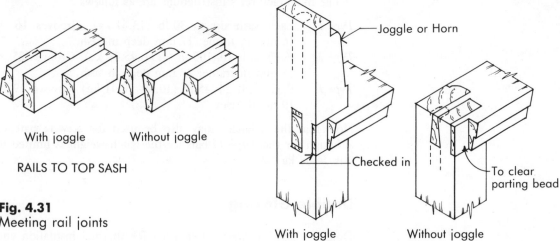

With joggle   Without joggle

RAILS TO TOP SASH

Fig. 4.31
Meeting rail joints

Joggle or Horn

Checked in

To clear
parting bead

With joggle   Without joggle

JOINTS TO BOTTOM SASH

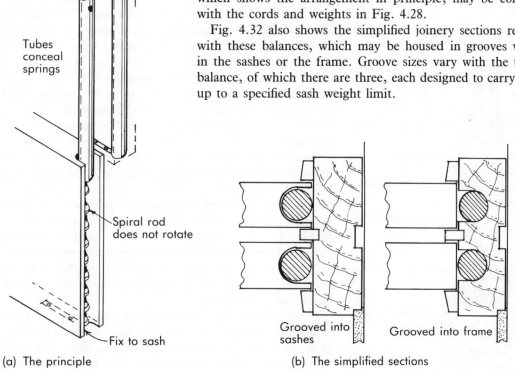

Fix to frame

Tubes
conceal
springs

Spiral rod
does not rotate

Fix to sash

(a) The principle

Grooved into
sashes

Grooved into frame

(b) The simplified sections

Fig. 4.32
Unique sash balances

as its steepness increases, demanding more effort to move it through the bush, so the torsion on the spring decreases, maintaining a state of balance at any point in its travel. Fig. 4.32, which shows the arrangement in principle, may be compared with the cords and weights in Fig. 4.28.

Fig. 4.32 also shows the simplified joinery sections required with these balances, which may be housed in grooves worked in the sashes or the frame. Groove sizes vary with the type of balance, of which there are three, each designed to carry sashes up to a specified sash weight limit.

The manufacturer's instructions are as follows:

Type D   Each sash up to 30 lb (13.61 kg). Grooves 16 × 16 mm in frame; 17 mm deep in sash.

Type M   Each sash 10–100 lb (4.54–45.36 kg). Grooves 25 × 25 mm in frame; 27 mm deep in sash.

Type F   Each sash 24–45 lb (10.89–20.41 kg). Groove 19 × 19 in all cases.

Note that the balances may also be used for serving hatches although for the Type D balance the hatch weight is limited to 9 lb (4.08 kg).

Double Glazing

Double glazing is most often used for thermal insulation and sometimes for sound insulation and in certain cases with the intention of achieving improvements in both respects.

For thermal insulation, the principle is that of containing still air between two panes of glass, which may be spaced as little as 4 mm apart. Ideally, the contained air is dry, or dehydrated, to avoid condensation between the glass and the only way to achieve this is in controlled conditions in a factory where the glass is made up as hermetically sealed units. Such units employ glass of various types and thicknesses, spaced from 4 to 12 mm apart and resulting in overall thicknesses from 13 to 35 mm.

Rebate sizes will be greater than for single glazing and because mastic glazing compounds are recommended in most cases (and these cannot be 'struck off' as face putty) internal glazing beads are usually employed. In Fig. 4.33(a) a joinery detail for a sealed unit is shown. The rebate depth will be at least 12 mm and, depending on the area of glass, up to 25 mm may be recommended by the manufacturer. The rebate width must be sufficient to accommodate the sealed unit and the screwed glazing bead. Note that before applying the mastic compound the timber must be sealed to prevent absorption in the same way as, before applying putty, it is necessary to prime the timber. In Fig. 4.33(b) a detail is shown for a stepped unit which is manufactured to allow rebates of normal dimensions to be used, and here it will be seen that putty is suitable. This unit is unsuitable for internal glazing beads since the stepped unit should not be reversed.

Double or coupled sashes are an alternative to the use of sealed units, since in these a single pane of glass is used in each of the two sashes which are connected together. The additional sash may be screwed to the inner or outer face of the first as seen in Fig. 4.34 but there will be a need to gain access occasionally for cleaning the inner faces. There is a probability also of condensation occurring between the panes of glass, and while

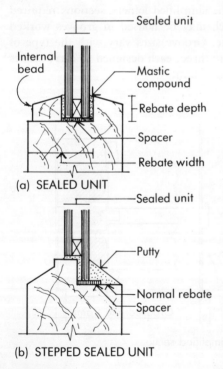

(a) SEALED UNIT

(b) STEPPED SEALED UNIT

Fig. 4.33
Sealed units

air vents are sometimes incorporated, these diminish the insulating value of the window.

A popular alternative to either of those already shown is in the use of a separate internal window or secondary frame which may be opened independently of the other, and this offers three advantages. Firstly it may be made to cover the whole window area, so reducing heat loss through the frame itself and more noticeably through the clearance joints around opening windows. Secondly, by independent opening of the main window, access is gained for cleaning purposes. The internal or additional window may be hinged, or more commonly may slide to open. Thirdly, since the space between the glass is likely to be greater there could be an improvement in sound insulation.

An example employing this approach to double glazing is also shown in Fig. 4.34 where instead of a secondary frame, a fibre track is employed for the sliding glass. This track is shown in a groove worked in the window frame, but in improving existing windows this would be mounted on the surface.

Double glazing intended primarily to reduce sound transmission will have different features from that designed for thermal insulation. The following details should be considered when a window is designed for this purpose and they concern not only the glazed area itself but also the window frame, and could apply as much to an internal borrowed light or vision panel as to an external window. It is unlikely that all the listed features will be worth including in any window unless the fabric surrounding it has been given similar attention.

(a) The frame, which will normally be of slender sections, and so will exclude the use of the principle of mass in sound insulation, will give best results when it is of absorbent material. Wood will be more effective than metals.

(b) Two separate frames within the wall thickness and, having no mechanical connection between them, will give better results than a single frame.

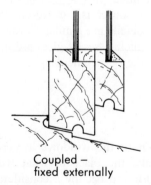

Coupled –
fixed externally

Coupled –
fixed internally

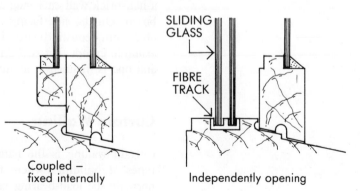

SLIDING GLASS

FIBRE TRACK

Independently opening

Fig. 4.34
Secondary double glazing

(c) Joints or clearances around opening windows, and any other similar sound paths, should be effectively sealed.

(d) Thicker (heavier) glass is more effective than thinner glass.

(e) Glass should be on a resilient bedding material.

(f) The space between panes in double glazing should be 100–200 mm.

(g) The frame surface between the panes should be of absorbent material.

(h) Two panes of differing thickness will produce less 'sympathetic resonance' and therefore give better results.

(i) Improved results will be gained from the panes being inclined at about 5° to each other.

Fig. 4.35(a) shows a window to serve as a vision panel in a partition wall between an office and a factory workshop. The wall is only of half-brick thickness and will not give very effective sound insulation although it is improved slightly by the plaster finish on the office side and glue-on fibre insulation board on the workshop side. The window is double glazed with the two panes bedded on resilient material and enclosing a 100 mm space. There would be little value in elaborating further on the joinery details in this case as the partition wall offers so little resistance.

The second example (Fig. 4.35(b)) has a wall one brick thick and the factory side has insulation board glued to softwood grounds. The window here is of two separate frames with a packing of medium hardboard between them. Similar material separates the brickwork from the frames. Between the two panes of glass the frame is lined with medium hardboard both for its absorbency and to serve as a resilient bed for the glass. The space between the glass here is in excess of 150 mm and the effect overall would be considerably better than in the first example.

Finally, Fig. 4.35(c) shows a situation where sound insulation is more important, and the wall comprises a one-brick wall and a half-brick wall enclosing a cavity filled with 50 mm insulation board. On the side facing the noise source is a glued-on finish of 25 mm acoustic board. Joinery details are similar to the last example except that two different thicknesses of glass are used, and one is inclined at about 5° to the perpendicular.

Curtain Walling

Curtain walling is the name given to the windows in certain types of building, where they take the place of what would normally be load-bearing brickwork and occupy a considerable part of the elevation. Curtain walling occurs when the wall is non-structural, as in framed construction and cross-wall

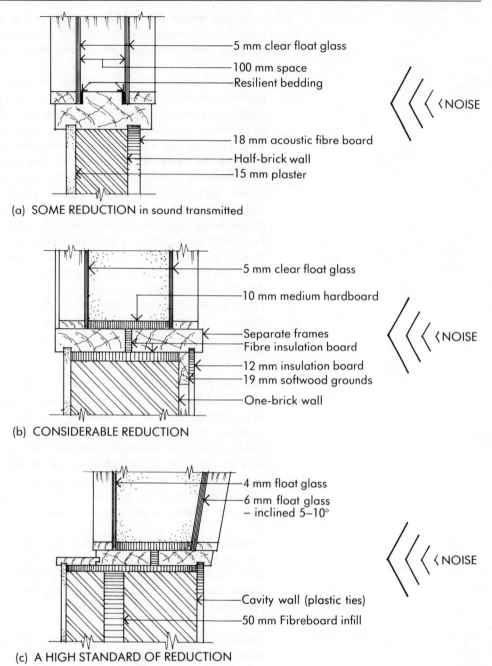

(a) SOME REDUCTION in sound transmitted

- 5 mm clear float glass
- 100 mm space
- Resilient bedding
- 18 mm acoustic fibre board
- Half-brick wall
- 15 mm plaster

(b) CONSIDERABLE REDUCTION

- 5 mm clear float glass
- 10 mm medium hardboard
- Separate frames
- Fibre insulation board
- 12 mm insulation board
- 19 mm softwood grounds
- One-brick wall

(c) A HIGH STANDARD OF REDUCTION

- 4 mm float glass
- 6 mm float glass – inclined 5–10°
- Cavity wall (plastic ties)
- 50 mm Fibreboard infill

Fig. 4.35
Double glazing – sound
insulation

construction, where it is possible to design most or all of the wall as a window. These large expanses of window offer some advantages over brickwork, principally in their lightness, the greater admission of daylight and the fact that they are prefabricated. Many examples of curtain walling are proprietary systems made from steel or aluminium, but timber is often employed for the work and where this is the case there are a number of points related to construction that will need more careful consideration than for normal windows made from wood, as follows.

Weather Resistance. As a result of the large expanse of non-absorbent material, mainly glass, there is a much greater concentration of water passing over the work. Also, due to the degree of exposure, particularly in the higher buildings, the effects of wind pressure can add to penetration problems; so too can the fact that the water will in some cases flow upward. From these considerations comes the need for the most durable materials, deeper rebates, more positive weather checks, steeper slopes, and greater projections to transoms and cills. Joints between the prefabricated units need particular attention, particularly the horizontal ones, where it may be necessary to introduce water bars of metal or plastic and possibly drainage tubes.

Of the timbers that could be selected for this work the most durable are Afrormosia, Agba, Iroko, European Oak, Teak, Doussie, Western Red Cedar and Pitch Pine. Less durable are Sapele, African Mahogany and Brazilian Mahogany. European Redwood or Whitewood, and Canadian Hemlock would need fungicide treatment.

Strength Requirement. The frames are likely to be of large sections of hardwood made up into units of considerable dimensions limited only by the lengths of timber available and by transport problems. The weight of such units demands care in handling to avoid excessive stress on joints; even so the design of joints will be in consideration of handling stresses. After fixing there will be a need to resist wind pressure, and for this reason most members will be of considerable depth to resist bending. Fixings to the structure must also be adequate.

Moisture Movement. Changes in frame dimensions are likely as a result of the considerable lengths of timber involved, and the accumulated widths of members crossing them at right angles. Connections to the structural framing or fabric should make allowance for differential movement.

Spandrel Panels. At each floor level, and up to the normal window cill height, it is usual to include an obscure panel for safety and privacy. This panel may be faced externally in a variety of materials including weatherboards of timber or plastic, laminated plastic or metal-faced plywood and hung tiles. Behind this facing will be materials selected to give thermal insulation and fire resistance together with features to prevent the occurrence of condensation within the panel. Frequently a wall of bricks or blocks is erected as a backing to the spandrel panel as in the example shown in Fig. 4.36.

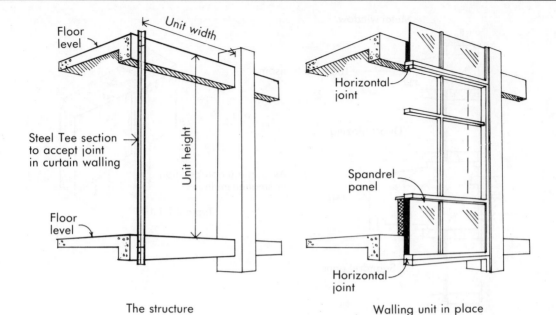

Fig. 4.36
Curtain walling – pictorial view

As shown in the sketch, a typical prefabricated unit will occur between the two floor levels indicated, giving a typical height of 3.50 to 3.75 m. The width in the region of 3.00 m is convenient for transporting and for the resulting vertical joints, mild-steel T sections are fixed to the structure to be enclosed between the two members to be bolted together as seen more clearly in Fig. 4.37.

Note that the direct glazing, shown here and in Fig. 4.38 entails external beads which should be glued with a suitable adhesive and pinned. The inner beads should be cupped and screwed. The spandrel panel in this case is treated the same as

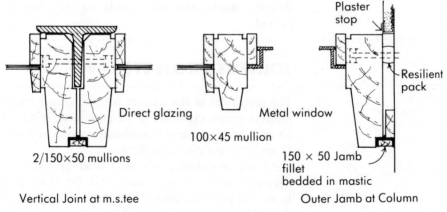

Fig. 4.37
Horizontal section – curtain walling

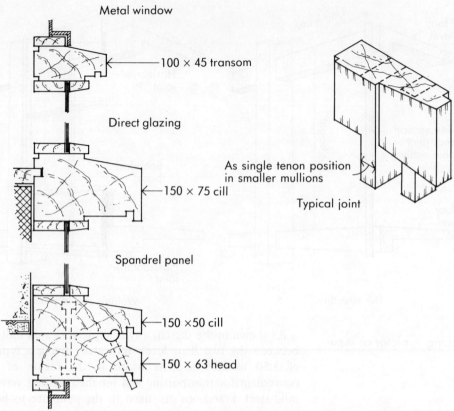

Metal window

100 × 45 transom

Direct glazing

150 × 75 cill

As single tenon position
in smaller mullions

Typical joint

Spandrel panel

150 × 50 cill

150 × 63 head

Fig. 4.38
Vertical section – curtain walling

direct glazing, but using coloured glass. Vertical joints are shown as sealed with a hardwood fillet bedded in mastic. In the horizontal joint, a 10 mm plastic tube is inserted for drainage.

The joints used to frame the work together must cope with the stresses already mentioned and allow for the fact that the horns will be cut off flush. In members 150 mm wide it is likely that the marker-out will decide on twin tenons, glued and pinned.

JOINERY PROJECTS I–V

The remainder of the chapter is devoted to a number of joinery projects giving examples of purpose-made windows which may be used both as *practical workshop exercises* and as opportunities to apply *related classroom activities*.

All are described firstly in a brief Specification, leading to drawing board exercises necessary in the design of the work and in related problem solving that may be necessary in the workshop. Drawings are presented in a way that could be used to a larger scale as student drawing board exercises to be produced as classroom Technology. They are intended to encourage the pursuit of geometry and other aspects of technology related to applied examples that may be produced in the workshop.

List of joinery projects on windows is as follows:

No.	Item	Drawings
I	Splayed bay window under a tiled, hipped roof	I.1, I.2, I.3, I.4, I.5
II	Bullseye window with alternative geometrical arrangements of glazing bars	II.1
III	Elliptical borrowed light with surrounding simulated stonework	III.1
IV	Bow window with flat or pitched roof	IV.1, IV.2
V	Louvred frame with sloping head and boarded central panel	V.1

Project No. I
Splayed Bay Window to the Front Elevation of a Restaurant within a shopping precinct

Brief Specification

Forward splaying square bay window under a hipped tiled roof, and supported on shaped and framed wood brackets. All is to be as shown in the accompanying sketch (Fig. 4.39) properly framed together in softwood and brought to a high standard of finish ready for painting.

The windows are to be internally glazed in 'small squares', framed up as fixed sashes within the main framing.

The roof is to be of prepared timbers, pitched at 40°, sprocketed, clad in plain tiles and with shaped timbers exposed at the eaves.

The supporting brackets to be adequately tied back to carry the display stallboard through the brickwork so as to project internally.

Interpretation

The work may be dealt with in three separate parts, these being the window framing itself, the roof structure and the supporting brackets. Due to its considerable weight, and a tendency to fall

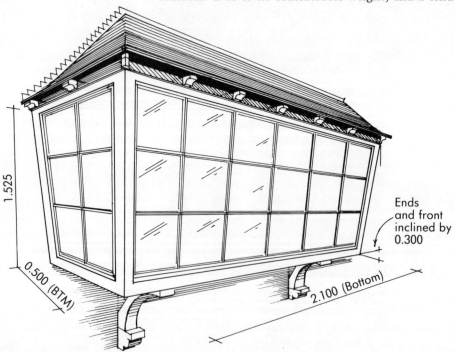

1.525

0.500 (BTM)

2.100 (Bottom)

Ends and front inclined by 0.300

Fig. 4.39
Splay-fronted bay window with tiled hipped roof and resting on wood brackets

forward away from the brickwork as a result of its design, not only must fixings be substantial, but also the roof ties (ceiling joists) and the heads of supporting brackets must be well secured to the wall. Although the architect would normally provide Joinery Details in the form of large-scale sections to convey to the setter-out exactly what is required, joinery courses do require the student to develop an ability to produce such details himself. This, together with a number of related geometrical problems are pursued in the following drawing sheets.

Drawing I.1   Window Details

This drawing shows firstly the front and end elevations. These are drawn as far as is possible from the sketch information given, and can only be completed after the large-scale details have been determined. It should be noted that these elevations do not show the true shape of the frames themselves because they are not viewed squarely from their face. The true shapes must be determined geometrically as on following drawing sheets, and in practice would be developed full-size on the workshop rod.

In the larger-scale sections the details shown are based on a stout main framing, comprising a mitred head and cill, two wall jambs and (nominally) square corner posts. These members are rebated internally to accept the separately framed sashes.

In the horizontal section it will be seen that the sashes to the ends of the window are of 38 mm material, designed to be inserted prior to the placing of the 50 mm front sash. This is a practical solution to the preparation of the corner post to accept both sashes effectively. The vertical section is broken in height only to allow the large-scale details to be developed, and when drawn later on the workshop rod would appear in its full and true height. Note that the inner face of the head, to avoid an acute angle with the ceiling, is shown as being from wider material. Adjoining portions of the roof timbers show the ceiling joists allowed to run through to be exposed at the eaves. This differs from usual roof details where the rafters would notch around and pass beyond the supporting framework. The detail shown is appropriate to this particular job where the roofing is to be of prepared timber and as far as possible will be framed together as joinery in the workshop.

Note that:

(a) The 12 mm plywood fascia will be of separate pieces between joists and will be housed into them for support;

(b) The 25 mm stallboard is to pass through the brickwork together with the heads of the supporting brackets. This plywood will contribute to the connecting together of the mitred cill, if securely fixed to it.

Drawing I.2   Geometry in Surface Shapes
       Geometry in Framed Bracket (setting-out)
       Geometry in Isometric Projection

The principles of the surface development of solids were shown earlier, in Chapter 3, and the student should continue to develop an ability to solve such problems through drawing board exercises, as well as in workshop practice. In this project, the true shapes of the framing and sashes must be derived from the given elevations in order to determine true lengths, spacings and shoulder bevels in the setting-out of members. Drawing I.2 shows the development of part of the front of the window by bringing together true dimensions taken from different parts of the given elevations. The drawing shows the principle of super-imposing the required shape over the given elevations, as is likely on a workshop rod in order to save space. On the full-size workshop development the precise details of all features would be included, so that the marking-out of each member from the rod is then possible. The aesthetic effect of geometry in setting-out mouldings and other examples of shaped work was also discussed earlier. In this project the main dimensions, timber sizes and outline shape of the bracket would probably have been provided by the architect. The drawing shows the setting-out of the bracket, where curved lines meet adjoining straight lines in the correct manner, in this case the straight lines being normal to the curve. Note that the mortice and tenon joints would be draw-bored and pinned. Under load, the upper shoulder of the brace will tend to slide along the head of the brace, and this could have been treated in a similar manner to the rafter feet shown elsewhere, but it is considered here that the joint shown would be adequate.

Isometric Projection, as a form of pictorial drawing, is probably the most commonly used means of illustrating a solid pictorially. It is also a very good basis for pictorial sketching and some practice is therefore beneficial. The methods of representing given angles and curves in isometric have already been discussed in Chapter 3, (Workshop Geometry sheets 12 and 13) and this example is included here as an interesting application of the techniques involved.

Drawing   I.3 Roofing Geometry
The roofing work in this project is treated as a joinery exercise, and it is appropriate that it should be of prepared timber throughout. The lower part of the drawing sheet is devoted to a vertical section with part plans of the roof at ceiling joist level and at rafter level. As stated earlier, the ceiling joist or ties are allowed to pass beyond the rafter feet to be exposed at the eaves. To achieve the same effect at the hip rafters an additional feature has been introduced in the form of a dragon-tie. Under load the

feet of hip rafters and common rafter will tend to slide, so their connections to the supporting timbers are designed to resist this as indicated in the section. It follows that in order to function properly, the ties must be well secured to the wall. It will be noted that the projecting ends of the ties are shaped for decorative effect, and to add further interest to the eaves detail, sprockets are fixed over the rafter feet, producing a curvature to the tiled surface. The *common rafter plumb cut* (A) and *seat cut* (B) together with the true length of the rafter are seen in the roof section. Those bevels apply also to the *jack rafters*. The Surface Development of the roof shows the *jack rafter side cut* (C).

The *hip rafter* development is also shown on the drawing where, from its plan, the rafter is laid flat to reveal its *plumb cut* (D) and *seat cut* (E), where (H) is the vertical height of the rafter taken from the section. Note that the head of this rafter rests against a common rafter positioned against the wall, and the resulting adjustment to the length of the hip rafter is also shown on this development at (D). The *side cut* to the hip rafter is finally developed at (F).

A further aspect of geometry in the roof occurs on the next drawing sheet, numbered I.4.

Drawing I.4 Roofing Geometry (cont'd)
Hip Rafter Dihedral Angle

The upper surface of a hip rafter should strictly be twice bevelled to provide a proper seating for the tile battens, or in some cases boarding, fixed to it. Without this preparation, the battens or boards will rest only on the arrises of the hip and this will be more noticeable where the roof pitch is steeper. The problem is usually ignored on the most common pitches, below 45° but with steeper pitches it becomes more necessary to apply such bevels to the hip rafter. On drawing I.4 the geometry is shown firstly as applied to a square pyramid. The first diagram shows the pyramid with a portion cut away in a manner that would reveal the true angle between the surfaces. The plane of the cut surface is at right-angles to the fall of the hip. The true shape of this cut surface and its upper angle would be seen when viewed at right angles to it.

The procedure is shown at Stage 1, where the 'hip' has been laid flat, in the horizontal plane. The line of the undercut surface is drawn at right-angles to the hip, at any point along its length.

At Stage 2, the base line of the cut surface is drawn across the pyramid at the base end of the undercut line, this base line being at right-angles to the plan of the hip.

Finally, the length of the undercut line is rotated to meet the hip, to give the apex of the triangular cut surface. The angle at the apex is the angle required, and is known as the *Dihedral angle* or *backing angle*.

The drawing also shows the geometry applied to this Project where (A) is the derived Backing Angle for the hip rafter, and (B) the angle for the upper edge of the sprocket.

Referring back to Drawing I.1, the section of the corner post shown is as seen in a horizontal section, and not as seen as a true cross-section of the material itself. To find the true shape of the corner post involves the same geometry as the backing angle for the hip rafter. The outer surfaces of the window are similar to those of the roof, except that the window is an inverted 'pyramid'. Fig. 4.40 should be read after Drawing I.4. The 'Inverted Plan' is looking upward at a corner of the window, and the view is similar to the plan of a hip of a roof. As before, the 'rafter' is laid flat, and the undercut line drawn at 90° to it. The triangular cut surface is completed as before to reveal the dihedral angle at 'x'. The true section of the corner post is within a *rhombus*, (not a square) and is completed by drawing the rebate lines parallel to those forming the dihedral angle, as shown in Fig. 4.40.

Drawing I.5   Some Joints in Roof Members
As stated earlier with regard to Drawing I.3, a dragon-tie has been introduced at each outer corner of the roof, firstly to give the desired visual effect of a projecting roof timber at the eaves, and secondly to provide an adequate seating for the hip rafter.

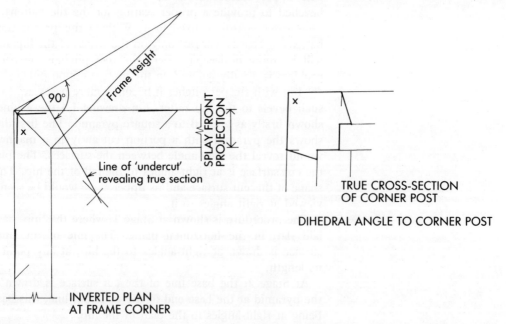

Fig. 4.40
Dihedral angle to corner post

The first diagram in drawing I.5 shows pictorially the arrangement of timbers connected with the dragon-tie. The tie itself has its projecting end shaped so as to align with the other projecting ties along both faces of the window. The decorative shape would need to be developed, since the member is placed at 45° and the curve would therefore be elliptical. The 'vee' effect within the curve would diminish to nothing as the curve comes to its highest point.

The diagonal piece to which the dragon-tie is connected lies flat on the head of the window frame and must be well fixed to it. This member will be subjected to a bending stress under load, and the greatest dimension of its section resists that. The joint between these two members is not a full halving since less than half of the thickness is removed in the housing.

Also on the first diagram, the 'backing' of the hip rafter and its sprocket will be noted.

The second diagram shows the two joints in the dragon-tie, one already described and the other where the hip rafter is notched into the tie to resist the sliding effect. This diagram shows the joint where the rafter is 'bridled' over an upstanding piece left in the centre. To reduce the work involved in the joint, a simplified notch is more likely to be employed, and this is shown in the lower diagram.

The geometry of this joint, designed for structural effectiveness, is shown at the bottom left of the drawing sheet. Under load, the potential movement will be in the direction shown, and the member is given a bearing surface at right-angles to that direction of thrust. The depth is such as to give a reasonable resistance to movement, without too much loss of material from the tie. The geometry in this joint applies also to doors or gates, where braces are notched into ledges or rails.

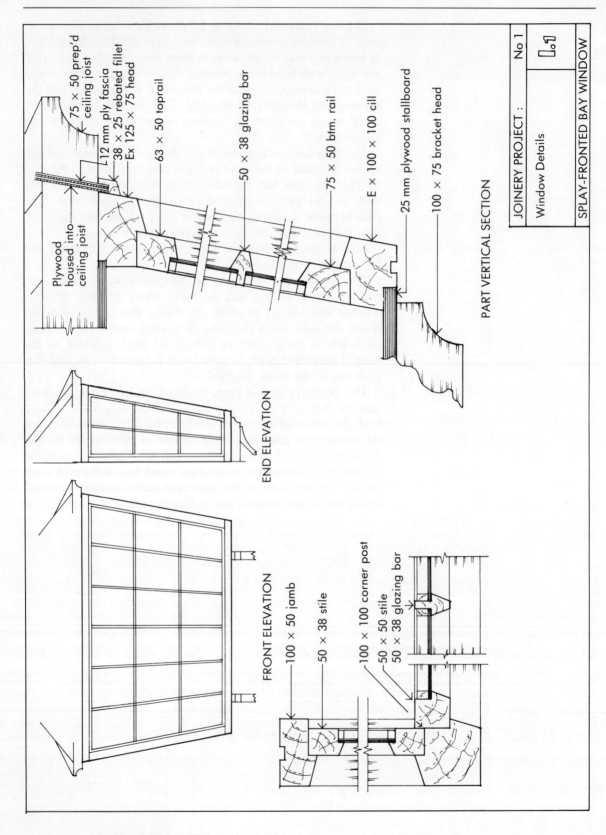

PART VERTICAL SECTION

75 × 50 prep'd ceiling joist

12 mm ply fascia

38 × 25 rebated fillet

Ex 125 × 75 head

63 × 50 toprail

50 × 38 glazing bar

75 × 50 btm. rail

E × 100 × 100 cill

25 mm plywood stallboard

100 × 75 bracket head

Plywood housed into ceiling joist

END ELEVATION

FRONT ELEVATION

100 × 50 jamb

50 × 38 stile

100 × 100 corner post

50 × 50 stile

50 × 38 glazing bar

JOINERY PROJECT :   No 1

Window Details

SPLAY-FRONTED BAY WINDOW

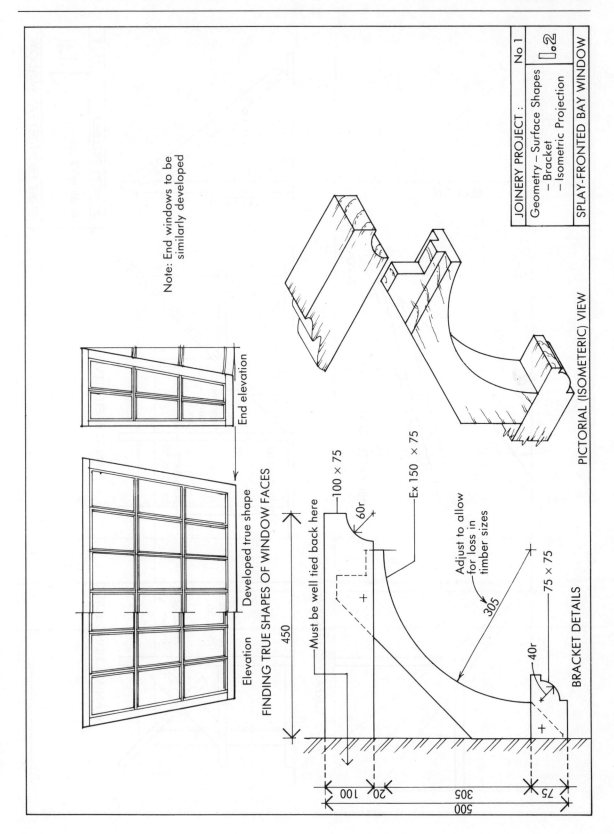

Note: End windows to be similarly developed

End elevation

Developed true shape

Elevation

FINDING TRUE SHAPES OF WINDOW FACES

450

Must be well tied back here

100 × 75

60r

Ex 150 × 75

Adjust to allow for loss in timber sizes

305

75 × 75

40r

BRACKET DETAILS

100

20

305

75

500

PICTORIAL (ISOMETERIC) VIEW

JOINERY PROJECT :   No 1

Geometry – Surface Shapes
  – Bracket
  – Isometric Projection

1.2

SPLAY-FRONTED BAY WINDOW

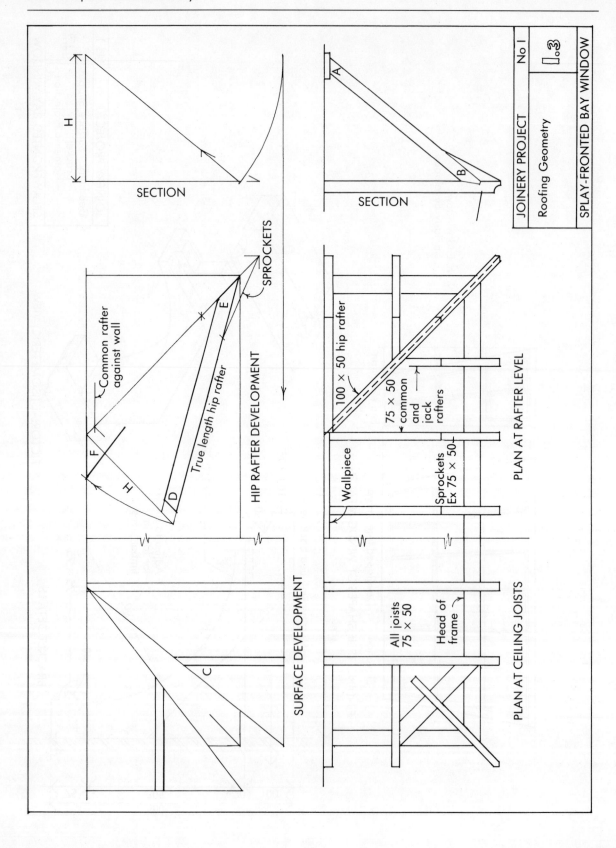

SECTION

SECTION

H

T

A

B

HIP RAFTER DEVELOPMENT

Common rafter against wall

True length hip rafter

SPROCKETS

E

F

H

D

SURFACE DEVELOPMENT

C

PLAN AT RAFTER LEVEL

100 × 50 hip rafter

75 × 50 common and jack rafters

Wallpiece

Sprockets Ex 75 × 50

PLAN AT CEILING JOISTS

All joists 75 × 50

Head of frame

JOINERY PROJECT   No 1

Roofing Geometry

SPLAY-FRONTED BAY WINDOW

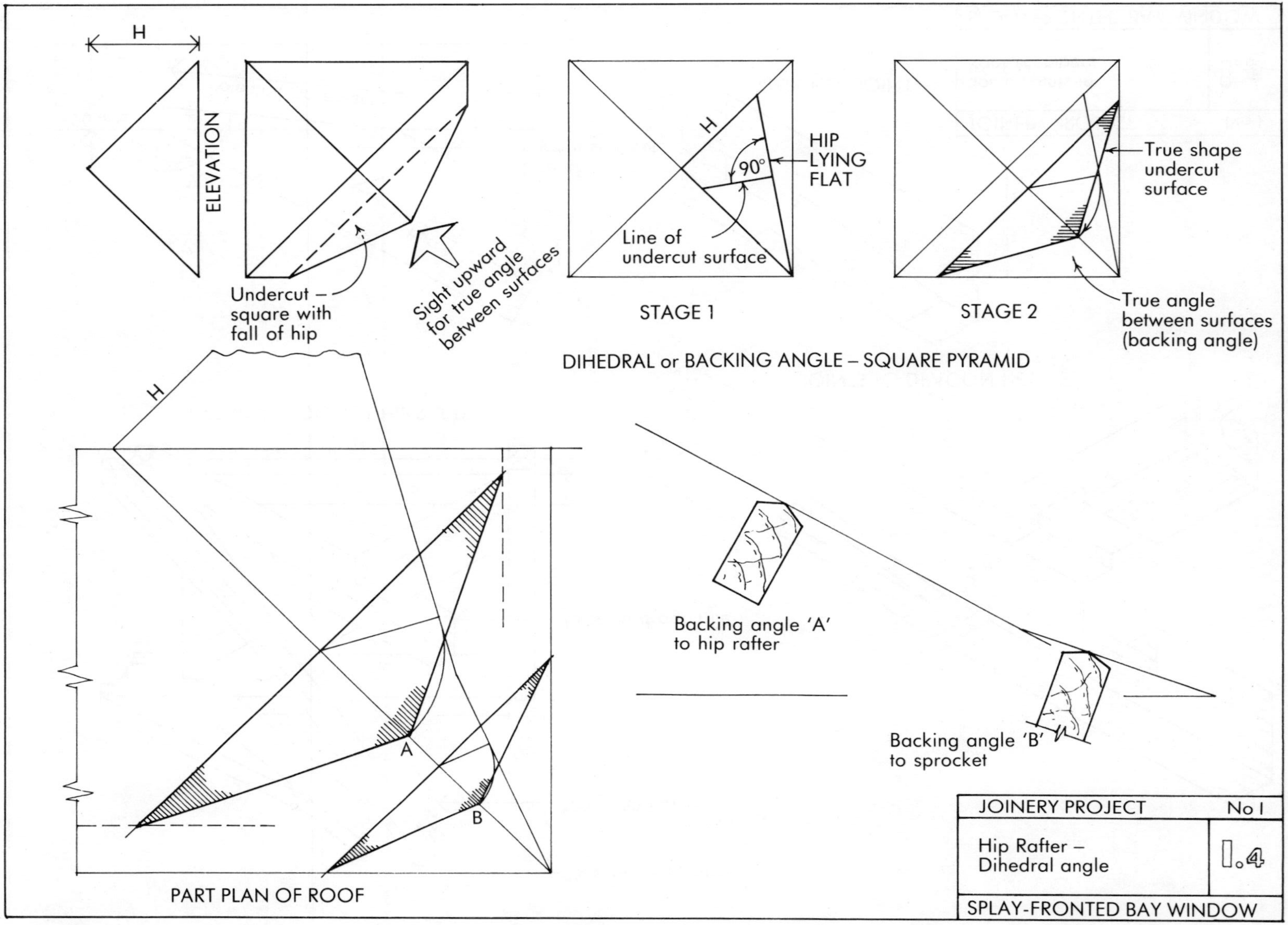

True shape undercut surface

True angle between surfaces (backing angle)

STAGE 2

HIP LYING FLAT

90°

H

Line of undercut surface

STAGE 1

DIHEDRAL or BACKING ANGLE – SQUARE PYRAMID

Sight upward for true angle between surfaces

Undercut – square with fall of hip

ELEVATION

H

Backing angle 'B' to sprocket

Backing angle 'A' to hip rafter

H

A

B

PART PLAN OF ROOF

JOINERY PROJECT   No I

Hip Rafter – Dihedral angle

SPLAY-FRONTED BAY WINDOW

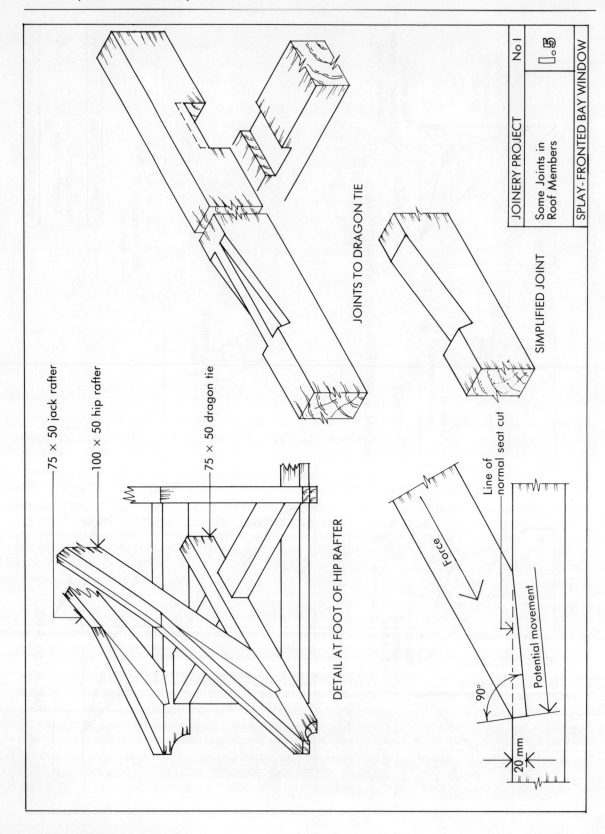

JOINTS TO DRAGON TIE

SIMPLIFIED JOINT

75 × 50 jack rafter

100 × 50 hip rafter

75 × 50 dragon tie

DETAIL AT FOOT OF HIP RAFTER

Line of normal seat cut

Force

Potential movement

90°

20 mm

JOINERY PROJECT   No 1

Some Joints in
Roof Members

SPLAY-FRONTED BAY WINDOW

Project No. II
2 No. Bullseye Windows with Spirally Radiating Glazing bars in softwood to be painted.

Note: This project provides an alternative geometrical design to that illustrated earlier in Fig. 4.22 which would have been less demanding both in geometry and in construction than this example.

Specification

Two bullseye windows (paired) 750 mm diameter overall, and with spirally radiating glazing bars connected to a 100 mm diameter turned central boss. The windows are to be externally glazed and the circular frames are to comprise five solid shaped segments with each heading joint twice hardwood dowelled and glued.

The glazing bars are to be bent, glued laminated and properly joined to the frame and turned central boss, and all in accordance with Drawing No. II.1.

The work is to be of selected clear European Redwood, properly framed with close-fitting glued joints, and brought to a good standard of finish, ready for painting.

Interpretation

The circular frames, from solid timber in segments as shown, will come easily from 150 × 75 mm material. The curved pieces, with some surplus length determined by a plywood template can be machined to the finished shape and section ready for bench-work in cutting and fitting the heading joints. To facilitate cramping, projections can be left on the outer surfaces, to be removed after assembly.

A workshop rod, showing the elevation in detail will allow the geometrical development of joint positions and bar shapes. It will also serve later as an aid to the fitting together of machined parts.

The geometry of the circular frame and its joints can usefully employ the principles of the setting-out of a Regular Pentagon, as shown in Chapter 3.

The geometry in the spiral centre lines of the bars is also shown on Drawing II.1 where each bar occupies a sector (one fifth) of the circle. On the inner circumference the sector is divided into any number of equal parts, in this case six. The available part of the radius is then also divided into the same number of equal parts. The intersecting points between these two sets of divisions determine the spiral centre line of the bar.

The width of the bar must be measured equidistant either side of the centre line, so finding the curved faces of the bar and the shape of cramping pieces to be used in gluing the laminates together.

The bars will be stub-tenoned to the frame and to the boss, and should be so fitted as to be assembled over the workshop rod with the minimum of cramping.

Glass will be cut to shape, by the glazier, to conform to information provided by the joiner. This could be a template of plywood or hardboard for five identical pieces of glass, but if the glass is to be 'obscure' with any decorative pattern to be continuous across the whole window, then a drawing (or the workshop rod) showing the whole job will be required.

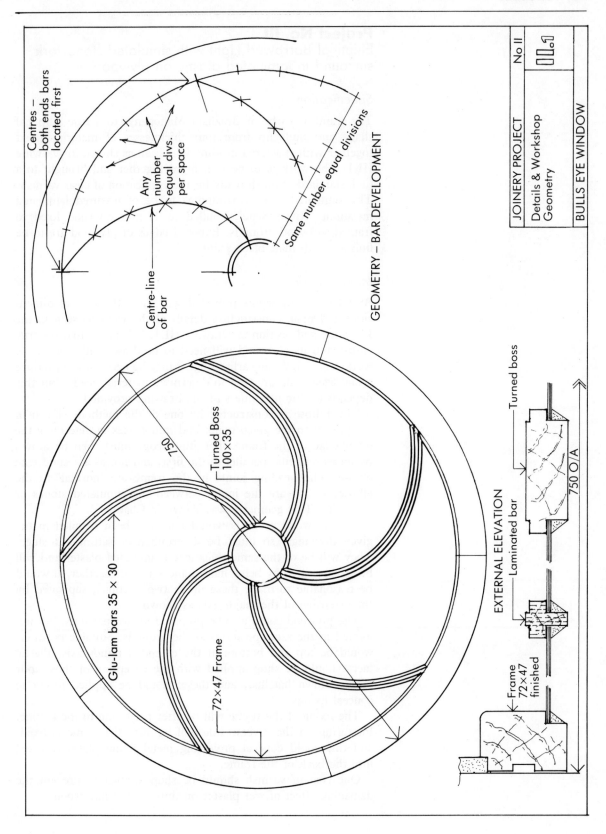

Centres – both ends bars located first

Any number equal divs. per space

Centre-line of bar

Same number equal divisions

GEOMETRY – BAR DEVELOPMENT

Turned Boss 100×35

Glu-lam bars 35 × 30

72×47 Frame

750

Turned Boss

EXTERNAL ELEVATION

Laminated bar

Turned boss

750 O/A

Frame 72×47 finished

JOINERY PROJECT   No II

Details & Workshop Geometry

BULLS EYE WINDOW

Project No. III
Elliptical Borrowed Light with simulated stonework surround in laminated plastic on plywood.

Specification

The frame is to be of Brazilian Mahogany, to a true elliptical shape and built up from four thicknesses of material glued together with staggered heading joints, all as shown in Drawing III.1. The work is to be well fitted together and brought to a high standard of finish ready for the application of clear varnish. The simulated stone surround is to be of textured laminated melamine 'Riven Slate', bonded to 12 mm plywood fixed to framed softwood grounds. Exposed edges of plywood are to be finished with matt black paint.

Interpretation

Architectural drawings provided will show the critical dimensions and main construction details of the work as seen in the Elevation and Section in Drawing III.1. It is noted that the true ellipse and its surround will need to be drawn full size on the workshop rod. At an earlier stage it may be necessary to produce a fair-sized scale drawing to determine material needs, but this depends on the usefulness of the drawing provided.

The Ellipse is constructed by one of the methods shown in Chapter 3, to the given major and minor axes to determine the outer edge of the frame. The inner edge must then be drawn by measurements, parallel to the first, and not as a second true ellipse. The heading joints in the frame are 'normal' to the ellipse, so too are the joints between the simulated stones or voussoirs. This geometry was shown in Chapter 3.

The softwood grounds would not have been detailed in the given drawings, so must be determined at setting-out stage. They will be of the same thickness as intended plaster and will be prefabricated by being halved and screwed together. It would be reasonable to make these up in two portions, separated by the extension of the major axis as shown.

The plywood could also be prepared in two portions, but not jointed in the same positions as the grounds. Suitable positions would be top and bottom at the extended minor axis. Plastic faces should be shop applied with the exception of those four pieces shown hatched, and these should be applied *in-situ* to conceal fixings.

The fixing of the frame will be after plastering to the lounge. Plastering on the reverse side will be after the frame is fixed, and this could conceal projecting metal fixing plates recessed into the back of the frame.

One coat of varnish should be shop applied to prevent the damaging effect of wet plaster on unprotected hardwood.

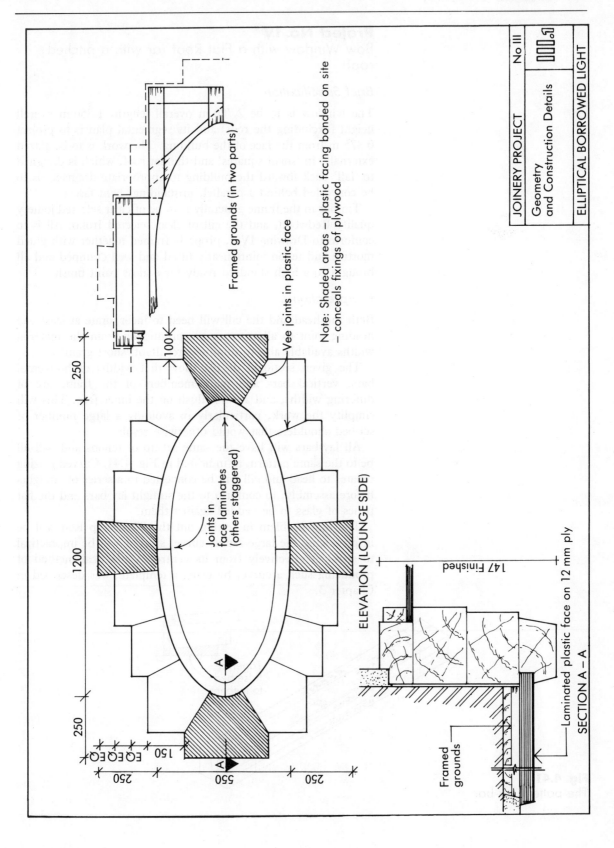

Project No. IV
Bow Window with a Flat Roof (or with a pitched roof)

Brief Specification

The window is to be 2.700 m overall length, 1.350 m overall height (excluding the roof) and its segmental plan is to project 0.375 m from the face of the building. The work is to be glazed externally in 'small squares' and the flat roof, which is designed to 'fall' back toward the building to appropriate drainage, is to be concealed behind a parallel, upstanding, bent fascia.

Timber in the frame generally is to be of clear selected joinery quality Redwood, and the cill of clear selected Iroko. All is to conform to Drawing IV.1, properly framed together with glued mortice and tenon joints neatly fitted and well cramped and all brought to a high standard ready for a gloss paint finish.

Interpretation

Both the head and the cill will need to incorporate at least one heading joint to allow economic production from the material widths available also to minimise resultant 'short grain'.

The given sectional details show that widths of horizontal bars, vertical bars and main members of the frame are of differing widths, and are not flush on the inner face. This will simplify the work, particularly in avoiding a large number of scribed shoulders that would otherwise result.

All lay-bars will have the same set-up of tenons and will all be to the same pattern, as indicated in Fig. 4.41. Curved glazing rebates to head and cill will be converted to a series of straights before assembly, to conform to the straight lay-bars and the flat panes of glass to be bedded against them.

The first problem in setting out the Workshop Rod will be in producing the large radius curve, since it will be impractical to strike it effectively from its centre. A practical method of producing such a curve, by using a template, was described in Chapter 3.

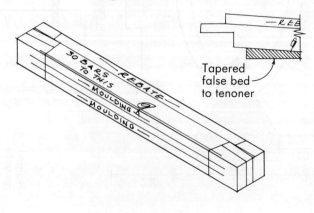

Tapered
false bed
to tenoner

Fig. 4.41
The pattern lay-bar

Inner faces of jambs and vertical bars should strictly be normal to the curve and their sections therefore not parallel in thickness. In this case the effect would be too small to be noticeable, so this may be ignored in the sectional shapes which may be as shown in the drawing. Very careful setting-out of the positions of vertical bars will be essential, to ensure that the lay-bars may all be identical.

After assembly, temporary stretchers of timber should be fixed across the chord of the frame to ensure that during transit, excessive stress on cill and head joints is avoided.

The site work in the flat roof structure will best be carried out in prepared or 'regularised' timbers for accuracy, and the fascia will be of three laminates for ease of bending. The roof will include both a vapour barrier just above the ceiling, and a 100 mm thermal insulating quilt placed between the joists.

Drawing IV.2 following, and the related notes illustrate the geometry involved in the roof, if it had been pitched.

Pitched Roof to Bow Window

As an alternative to the flat roof already discussed, the window could have had a pitched roof which would probably have been clad in plain tiles.

The construction of the roof would have been similar to any other lean-to-roof, except for the geometrical aspects resulting from the curved support at the eaves. Construction details are not pursued here except to say that the rafters, on plan, will be placed normal to the curve and will be spaced at 400 mm centres at their widest. (Tile battens will need to be fixed to a curved line to suit the gauge of tiles).

Associated geometry is developed in Drawing IV.2 where it is firstly important to appreciate that the roof is a solid shape cut from a cone by a vertical plane.

The plan of the roof is produced first, as part of the circle which passes through the three points determined by the width of the window, and its projection from the building. On the arc produced, the rafter positions are marked at 400 mm centres starting from the centre-line, and are then drawn so as to radiate from the centre of the circle. This plan of the roof is a part plan of the cone from which it is cut.

The side elevation is projected upward from the plan, and with the roof pitch of 50° the outline elevation of the cone is determined. Rafter positions, as seen in the side elevations are also projected from the plan and drawn so as to radiate from the apex of the cone.

From these two views, the front elevation is produced by projection. Firstly the baseline and the position of the rafter feet are transferred from the plan. The upper end of each rafter is found by projection from both drawings, and the curved line which shows the abutment of the roof with the wall of the building is drawn through the upper ends of rafters. This is a hyperbolic curve, and is the upper edge of the wallpiece to which the heads of rafters will be fixed.

The true shape of the curved surface of the roof is part of the curved surface of the cone, and will be developed so as to show both the true length and the side cut of each rafter. It will be noted that plumb and seat cuts are as for any common rafter, and are seen here in the central rafter in the side elevation of the roof.

As with the surface development of the complete cone, the circumference is drawn first, with its centre at the apex of the cone, and the radius being equal to its slanting height. The distance around the circumference is the same as that seen on the plan, and is best measured here by transferring the rafter spacings. Rafters are identified on the drawing by numbering outward from the centre, this simplifies identification later. On the surface development, the direction of rafters is shown so as to radiate from the apex of the cone.

The final stage of the development is to determine the true lengths of the rafters, then their upper ends will enable the upper curve to be drawn. THE ONLY RAFTER SEEN IN ITS TRUE LENGTH AT THIS STAGE IS THE CENTRE RAFTER as seen in the side elevation. To see any other rafter in its true length would require the cone to be rotated until that rafter is seen in true side elevation. This is done on the drawing by transferring the upper end of each rafter, as seen in the side elevation, horizontally to the outer edge of the cone. This information is now 'rotated' with the compasses, to cut the appropriate two rafters identified by numbers, to length. The curved line which passes through these points shows the upper curved edge of the surface, and shows also the bevel required as a 'side cut' to each pair of rafters.

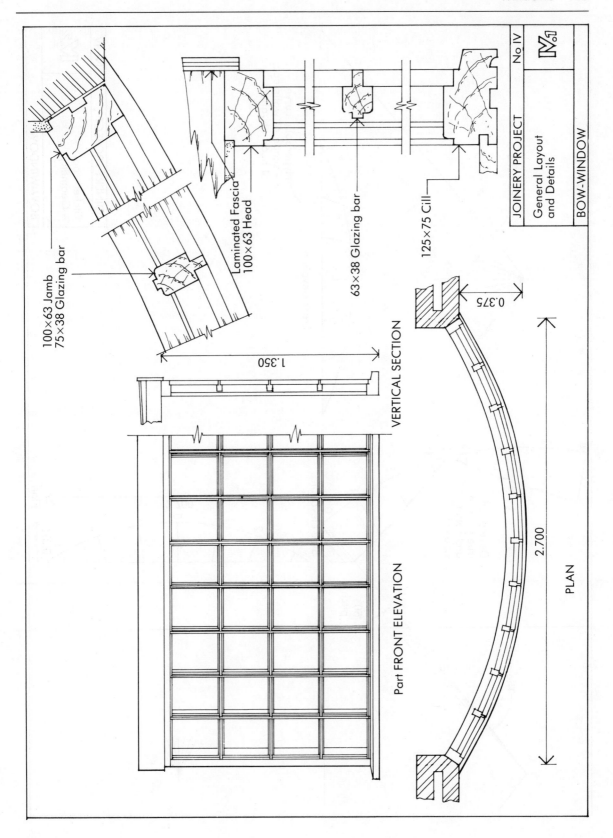

100×63 Jamb
75×38 Glazing bar

Laminated Fascia
100×63 Head

63×38 Glazing bar

125×75 Cill

1.350

VERTICAL SECTION

Part FRONT ELEVATION

0.375

2.700

PLAN

JOINERY PROJECT

No IV

№1

General Layout
and Details

BOW-WINDOW

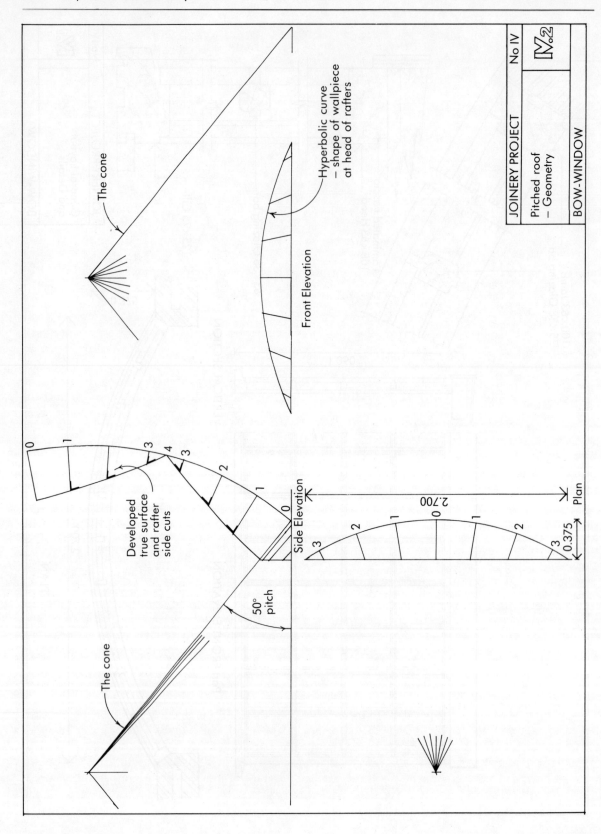

The cone

Hyperbolic curve
– shape of wallpiece
at head of rafters

Front Elevation

0
1
3
4
3
2
1
0

Developed
true surface
and rafter
side cuts

The cone

50°
pitch

Side Elevation

Plan

2.700

0.375

3
2
1
0
1
2
3

JOINERY PROJECT   No IV
N⍥2

Pitched roof
– Geometry

BOW-WINDOW

Project No. V
Louvred Frames to Warehouse Brief Specification

4 no. (2 pairs) louvred frames in hardwood, to be situated in the gable walls to a single storey warehouse, and with upper edges to run parallel with the $22\frac{1}{2}°$ roof pitch. Each frame is to comprise three spaces, the centre one infilled with shiplap boarding over a subframe and the two outer spaces louvred, all as shown in Drawing V.1.

The frames are to be morticed and tenoned together, glued and hardwood pinned. Louvres are to be properly housed to the frame and the shiplap boarding fixed with rust-proofed nails to the subframe.

All is to be of African Iroko, well fitted and cramped together and brought to a good standard of finish ready for the application of non-gloss water repellant stain finish.

Interpretation

The sloping head is designed to conform to the pitch of the roof, which is $22\frac{1}{2}°$, and the inside width of the frame or louvre length must be determined so that the louvres will intersect effectively with the upper corners of the frame. Louvres in the two separate spaces must align properly with each other over the length of the frame. To satisfy these requirements, the joinery details will have been designed before the frame dimensions were determined.

In the workshop the setter-out will need to be aware of these problems in order to produce the work satisfactorily, and Drawing V.1 shows the details and geometrical work that he will be concerned with.

The first Vertical Section shows how the height of the frame results from the 95 mm finished thickness of the frame and the 45° pitch of the louvres. By spacing the louvres as shown, the inner height of the frame will be in 95 mm multiples, plus the additional dimension 'X' which results from the detail of the lowest louvre.

The second Vertical Section shows details of the centre panel where the sections of the boards are made to align with the louvres. The lowest board is specially moulded to avoid an impractical narrow strip at the bottom. An important feature is the clear ventilated space at the vertical and lowest edge of the boards to avoid the collection of water that would result from closer fitting joints.

In the Elevation, the widths of openings are shown to be such that at points 'A' the upper rear edges of louvres meet the upper frame angles, and at points 'B' the lower front edges of louvres meet the frame angles effectively. These points are also shown in the Vertical Section to further clarify what is to be achieved. By geometry it has been established that with the head of the frame sloping at $22\frac{1}{2}°$, one louvre would intersect with it at 230 mm, and the second at 460 mm as shown.

The other problem to be solved in the workshop is the bevelled cut at the ends of louvres in contact with the head. The principle of this was shown earlier in this chapter, and is pursued here in the lower part of the drawing. The louvre is shown in section and in elevation, then by developing the true shape of surfaces, the required bevels are found. Finally, the positions of louvres against the head are found by projection from the elevation below.

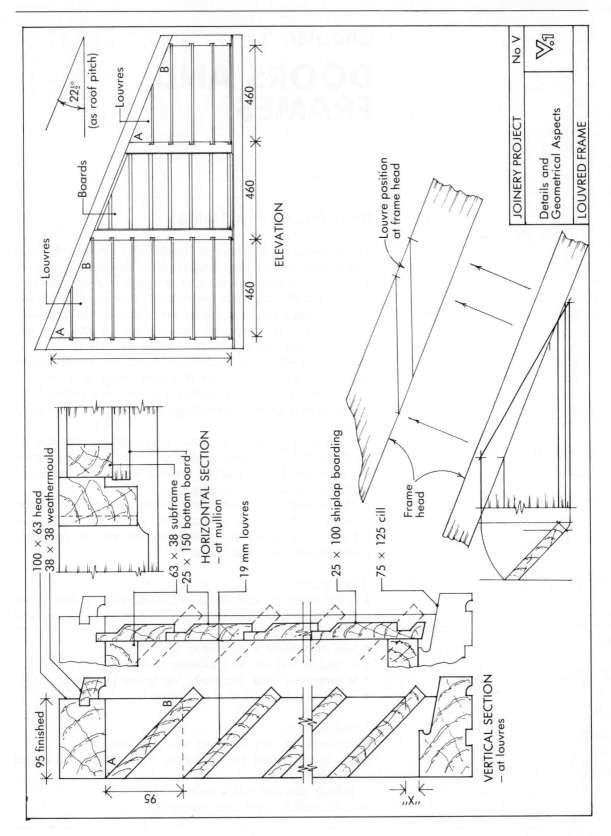

ELEVATION

22½° (as roof pitch)

Louvres

Boards

Louvres

460
460
460

A
B
B
A

Louvre position at frame head

Frame head

JOINERY PROJECT   No V

Details and Geometrical Aspects

LOUVRED FRAME

HORIZONTAL SECTION – at mullion

100 × 63 head
38 × 38 weathermould
63 × 38 subframe
25 × 150 bottom board
19 mm louvres
25 × 100 shiplap boarding
75 × 125 cill

VERTICAL SECTION – at louvres

95 finished
95
"X"
A
B

Chapter 5

DOORS AND FRAMES

Door Frames and Linings

The construction of frames or linings for purpose-made doors is most often treated as an integral part of the production of the doors designed to fit into them, even though in many cases they will be fixed or 'built-in' to the building fabric some time before the doors are hung. The joinery manufacturer will have been provided with drawings and specifications for the door and frame, showing general design criteria, dimensions, mode of hanging and design details. Where there are a considerable number of doors and frames of various kinds in a contract, much of the necessary information will have been collected and presented in a Door Schedule together with the other contract documents.

A frame or lining is designed to complement the door in satisfying the performance needs already discussed and it must also allow the door to function properly in the way determined by the chosen mode of hanging.

The following notes and diagrams show the principal features found in the basic range of frames and linings and will serve as a basis in satisfying any new problems met in producing purpose-made doors and frames.

A door frame:
- is essentially a frame, usually of wood, which is fixed to the fabric around an opening, to provide a means of hanging and fastening the door;
- may be situated in external or internal walls;
- is usually 'built-in' as brickwork proceeds;
- is sometimes fixed afterwards, but before plastering;
- is occasionally fixed after plastering.

A door lining
- performs the same functions as a door frame;
- also serves to 'line' the surfaces or reveals of the wall around the opening;
- is fixed after the wall is built;
- is occasionally fixed after plastering.

The simplest form of door frame is of the kind used for *domestic outhouses* or *stores* where there is little concern for weather protection or security, although there is growing concern for the latter.

Doors in these situations are typically of Ledged and Braced, or Framed, Ledged and Braced construction, and in the majority of cases will open outward to avoid waste of space within the building.

These frames will not have cills, and in most cases will have planted stops as shown in Fig. 5.1, where the pictorial view shows the simple mortice and tenon joint draw-bored and pinned, and the horn cut back so as not to be seen when built into the brickwork. Other frame fixings are galvanised iron frame ties, screwed to the back of the frame and built in at about each sixth course, and a galvanised iron dowel at the foot of each jamb secures it to the concrete floor or paving.

Also in Fig. 5.1, the sectional details show firstly the normal plain frame with planted stops where the door opens outward, and secondly where the door opens inward, the solid rebated frame offers better weather protection and greater security. The complete small-scale elevation and plan would indicate the form of door to be used and its main dimensions.

For larger doors on buildings such as garages and workshops, the details shown here would form a good basis for the construction of the frames, although the timber sizes would be increased

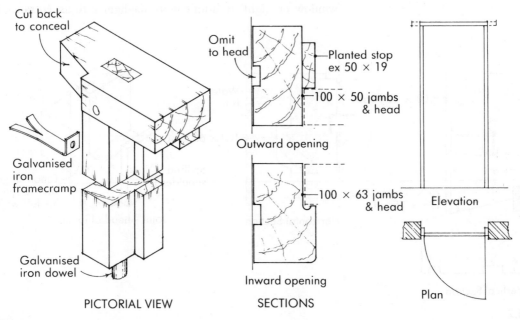

Cut back to conceal

Galvanised iron framecramp

Galvanised iron dowel

PICTORIAL VIEW

Omit to head

Planted stop ex 50 × 19

100 × 50 jambs & head

Outward opening

100 × 63 jambs & head

Inward opening

SECTIONS

Elevation

Plan

Fig. 5.1
Door frames – domestic outhouses

accordingly and timbers in the region of 150 to 200 × 75 mm are necessary and double or twin tenons and dowels would be used. Such a frame would also require two dowels at the foot of each jamb.

Fig. 5.2 shows frames to *domestic entrance doors*, or front and back entrance doors, which in most cases open inward. These frames have cills of hardwood, while the other members are most commonly of softwood. The door rebates are normally 12 mm deep, and in exposed positions may be increased to 15 mm. The moulding is usually the same depth as the rebate, and should be one that is easily scribed at the shoulders.

The Vertical Section shows how water is prevented from entering the building at the bottom edge of the door, where the water bar, usually of galvanised iron, is positioned at about the centre of the door thickness. The door will be rebated over it, and will have a weather board to direct the water forward, so as to drip onto the weathered portion of the cill.

The Horizontal Section shows the additional features of a groove for a vertical damp-proof course, and a plaster rebate.

In the pictorial view showing the joint at the head of a jamb, it will be seen that the tenon has been positioned off-centre to allow it to be the full width of the jamb. The scribed shoulder shown is produced on the tenon machine, but in small quantities it may be more economical to scribe part-way through by hand. This is true also of the bevelled scribe onto the cill, where in small numbers these shoulders are left long for hand scribing.

Front entrance door frames are often made to include a window or 'light' to admit more daylight into an entrance hall

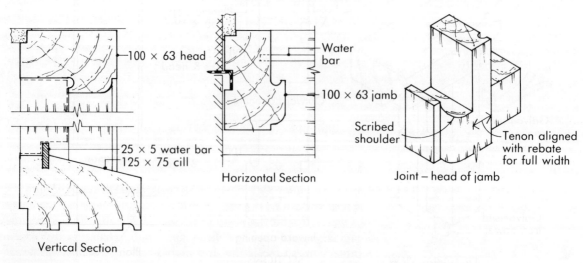

100 × 63 head

25 × 5 water bar
125 × 75 cill

Vertical Section

Water bar

100 × 63 jamb

Scribed shoulder

Horizontal Section

Tenon aligned with rebate for full width

Joint – head of jamb

Fig. 5.2
Frame – inward opening entrance door

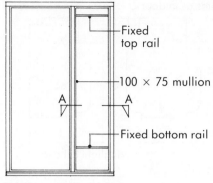

(a) Frame with sidelight

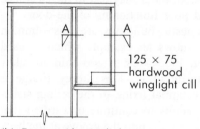

(b) Frame with winglight

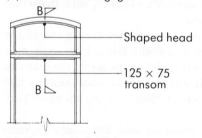

(c) Frame with fanlight

Fig. 5.3
Entrance frame with lights

and for decorative effect in the front elevation of the building. Fig. 5.3 shows three of the large number of examples of such frames.

In example (a) the frame has a sidelight which is infilled to match the door, which in this case will be fully glazed without glazing bars. Fixed rails to the sidelight match the top and bottom rails of the door, and all rebates in the sidelight will be for internal direct glazing.

Example (b) shows a frame with a single winglight which could accommodate an opening sash, but is more likely to be direct-glazed internally. This frame could of course be to the other 'hand' or it could have a winglight on both sides. It should be observed in this elevation that with a direct-glazed winglight, there will be a change of rebate sizes in the head, either side of the mullion. In the mullion itself there will be no rebate or moulding on the outer surface below the winglight cill, so involving 'stopping' or 'dropping-in' on the spindle moulder. The inner shoulder at this point will be diminished, but an alternative approach would be to reduce the mullion thickness below the cill, to align with the features above, so allowing square shoulders.

Example (c) shows a frame with a fanlight, which will either open inward (bottom-hung in this case) or will be direct-glazed. The head could have been square (straight) or one of a number of alternative shapes.

In all three frames shown, most members could be to the sectional details given in Fig. 5.2, but the additional members in these more complicated frames are detailed in Fig. 5.4. The Vertical Section B–B shows the transom and the details above it in frame (c) where the depth of the glazing rebate is made the same as the door rebate below, so avoiding a diminished shoulder at this point. In the Horizontal Section A–A the sections shown for frames (a) and (b) apply to both other frames, where the glazing rebate is made to match the door, and the fixed rails to the sidelight. Note again the comments above regarding changes in section and the effects on shoulders.

The Pictorial View illustrates the jointing of the winglight cill to the mullion where the stopped rebate leads to a diminished shoulder.

Occasionally, an entrance door is made to open outward and this is likely to be a rear entrance door when saving of internal space is important. Features in the frame details are simpler where, as seen in Fig. 5.5, it is less difficult to prevent the entry of water around the edges of the door. The addition of an anti-capillary groove to the head and jamb rebates is an added protection, so too is the drip moulding tongued into the head. The cill section should be as plain as possible, to avoid features vulnerable to damage by foot traffic passing over it.

Note that the door itself is more exposed to weather when

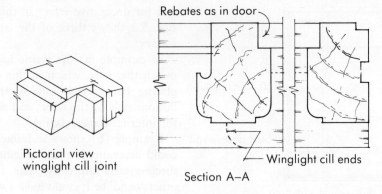

Rebates as in door

Winglight cill ends

Section A–A

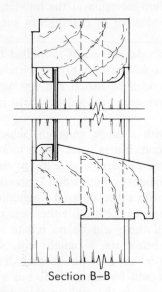

Section B–B

Fig. 5.4
Entrance frames – some details

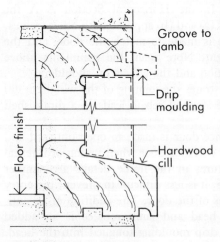

Groove to jamb

Drip moulding

Hardwood cill

Floor finish

Fig. 5.5
Frame – outward opening entrance door

Pictorial view
winglight cill joint

designed to open outward, where water may rest in the clearance joints to lead to swelling and poor functioning of the door.

Interior door frames to domestic buildings are less common than door linings. Fig. 5.6 shows an example which is used mainly because the partition blockwork is too thin to allow linings to be fixed satisfactorily to it. This Storey Frame is employed so as to gain a substantial fixing to the ceiling structure above, by allowing the jambs to continue upward to that level. Surrounding blockwork is built into the groove at the back of the frame to 'tie' the two elements together, then plastering is finished flush with the frame.

Above the transom there are two possible treatments to the frame. The Elevation shows a fanlight formed to serve as a borrowed light. As an alternative, the jambs above the transom may be reduced to block thickness, to be concealed by the plaster finish to the blockwork as shown in the pictorial view of the head detail.

Frames of this kind are plumbed and fixed into position before the partition wall is built and, where the floor is of concrete, before the floor screed is laid. When such frames leave the workshop, the jambs may have been cut to length at the finished floor level and dowelled. If they are not cut to length, the finished floor level must be clearly marked on the back of the jambs to ensure that they are cut accordingly before being fixed and built in.

More commonly, interior doors are hung on *door linings*, which serve the additional purpose of lining the wall reveals around the opening.

Delivered either assembled or in sets ready for assembly on site, door linings are fixed into the opening after the wall is built and must be accurately positioned and plumbed so as to ensure that the door can be hung properly.

Fig. 5.7 shows two forms of door lining where in (a) the linings consist of plain material of such a width that its projecting edges will determine the thickness of the plaster which will be applied after the linings are fixed. The planted stops will

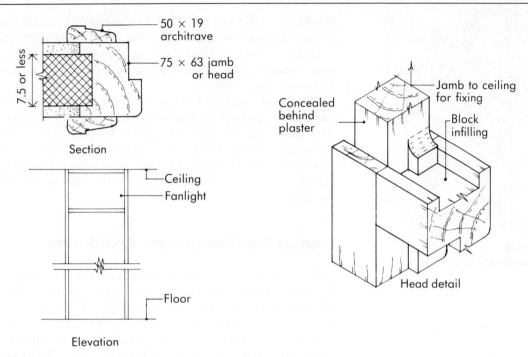

Fig. 5.6
Storey frames

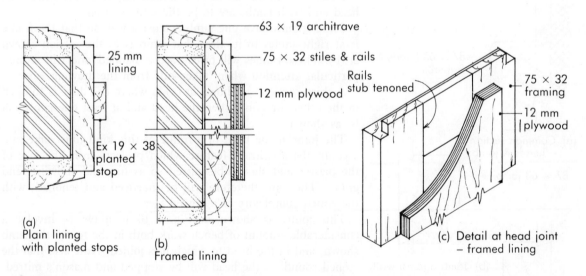

Fig. 5.7
Door linings
(**a**) Plain lining with planted
      stops
(**b**) Framed lining
(**c**) Detail at head joint –
      framed lining

be permanently fixed at the time of hanging the door. An alternative would have been to use thicker material to be rebated to receive the door, although this is less common. Parts (b) and (c) show details of Framed Linings, which are more suitable where the wall thickness, and therefore the width of linings, could result in excessive shrinkage or distortion in the material.

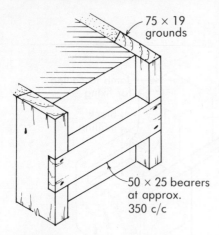

Fig. 5.8
Grounds to door linings

75 × 19 grounds

50 × 25 bearers at approx. 350 c/c

Where the wall is 'one brick' thick (nominally 225 mm) or more, Framed Linings are more appropriate, and the detail shown is a simple one with plywood glued on to form rebates. More elaborate examples have sunk, decorative panels held in grooves within the framework.

Linings of hardwood could be seriously damaged by the staining effect of wet plaster, so their fixing may be delayed until after plastering has been completed, by the use of softwood grounds as shown in Fig. 5.8. Such grounds must be carefully prepared and fixed since they will determine the accuracy of plaster as well as providing fixings for the high quality joinery to follow.

Frames that incorporate Architraves

Some buildings have frames or linings which are designed to eliminate the need for architraves, with the intention of reducing the amount of 'second fixing' work. Fig. 5.9 shows sections of frames required for a contract involving doorways in a range of situations. The frames are to be positioned before the erection of the 100 mm partition walls, and will be secured by galvanised frame ties built into the partitions. The frames do not extend to storey height.

Detail (a) shows the most common requirement, where the head and both jambs are to be the same section.

Some frames have one jamb against a wall so that the frame is at right-angles to it, then that jamb is to the section shown at (b). These frames will of course be 'handed' and will require particular attention when 'taken-off' from the drawing.

A third section, as shown at (c) is where the door is to open in the other direction, then the head and at least one jamb will be as shown.

The joint at the head of a frame of this kind must take into account the architrave feature which projects from the face of the plaster and should be mitred so as to avoid showing 'end grain'. The joint therefore will be morticed and tenoned, with the added complexity of a mitred face.

This joint, as shown in Fig. 5.10 is likely to involve a considerable amount of bench work both in the top of the jamb shown, and in the head to which it is joined. Note also that the 'pencil round' to the head will be stopped and mason's mitred.

Where considerable numbers are involved and the frames are to be painted, a compromise may be made by tenoning the head between jambs, so as to allow the jambs to pass upward and expose end grain above eye level. Fig. 5.10 (b) shows the jamb prepared for this kind of joint. The jamb has been fully prepared by machine to receive the tenoned head, so that the benchwork seen in the previous example has been eliminated.

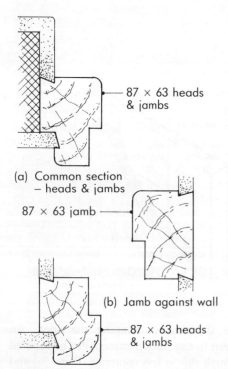

(a) Common section – heads & jambs

87 × 63 heads & jambs

87 × 63 jamb

(b) Jamb against wall

87 × 63 heads & jambs

(c) Head or jamb – reversed opening

Fig. 5.9
Frames incorporating architraves

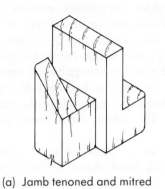

(a) Jamb tenoned and mitred

(b) Jamb to receive tenoned head

Fig. 5.10
Joints – frames incorporating
architraves

Linings that incorporate Architraves

These present similar problems, except that here the mitred portions are associated with the tongue and housing joint normally met in linings.

Fig. 5.11 gives three sections of such linings. At (a) the lining with planted stops has both edges projecting and these are bevelled for decorative effect. The mitres are taken to such a depth as to include the plaster groove so that the grooves will be continuous around the joint.

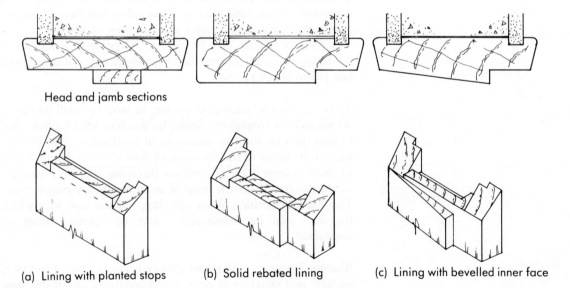

Head and jamb sections

(a) Lining with planted stops   (b) Solid rebated lining   (c) Lining with bevelled inner face

Fig. 5.11
Door linings with architrave
effect

The detail at (b) shows the thicker, rebated lining with one edge left square. The work involved here is slightly more complicated, and it will be seen that the rebate to the head is effectively 'stopped' by the portion left on the jamb. In painted work this joint could have been simplified by omitting the mitre to the square edge, where that portion could have been left parallel, to pass to the upper edge where the end grain would be above eye level. The pencil round would then have been mason's mitred.

The third detail, at (c) shows a more complicated joint resulting from the long bevel shown in the section. This joint is similar to the last, except for the scribed intersection of this bevel.

Some other examples of door frames will be found in the continuation of the chapter, in association with particular types of door.

Doors – design criteria

This section summarises the general principles underlying the design and manufacture of doors. Later sections then deal with examples of special interest or designed for a particular function.

It will be appreciated that there is a very wide range of situations demanding the use of doors and frames, each having features which will satisfy well defined requirements. Before deciding on the design features of any door and frame it is necessary to determine what is expected of this item of joinery and to put these requirements into an order of priority.

A door and frame may be required to perform a number of the following functions and the order of priority will differ from one job to another.

Access.   The easy passage of people, in large or small numbers, occasionally or frequently. Similarly, goods or vehicles may need to pass through with the minimum of obstruction. Priority may need to be given to the direction of flow of traffic by arranging the door to open in the appropriate direction, and this is particularly so where the door is situated on an emergency escape route. The size and position of the opening, and the ease with which the door and its ironmongery may be operated must be considered.

Weather Protection.   The door may be exposed to wind and rain, sunlight and extremes of outdoor temperatures, and at the same time afford protection to the interior of the building and its occupants. With such differing conditions on either side of it, the door is required to give satisfactory performance and endure for a reasonable length of time. These considerations will lead to the choice of materials and details of construction including glazing and ironmongery.

Security. The door may be required to restrict entry, or possibly exit, to those who are intended to use it. From this will come the need for soundness of construction and again the selection of suitable ironmongery.

Light Admission.   This will determine the need for some of the door or frame to be glazed, possibly with 'obscure' glass where through vision is not required. Vision through a door is most vital where for safety reasons it is necessary to see whether the door may be pushed open without injury to anyone on the other side. This applies mostly to 'swing' doors in public buildings where heavy usage is anticipated, when an area of clear glass is necessary.

Appearance.   A door and frame are likely to be a focal point of attention demanding some consideration for appearance. This may lead to the choice of material, design features, standards of manufacture and the choice of finish.

Fire Resistance.   The door and frame may be situated in a wall designed to separate a building into compartments to contain a possible fire on one side and afford protection to whatever is on the other. In most cases, such a demand arises from a statutory requirement which stipulates the degree of resistance as the length of time that the door is to be capable of serving as a fire-check. Timber doors and frames may be designed to give half-hour or one-hour protection.

Additional possibilities in the functions that a door may be required to provide are thermal insulation, sound insulation and in some cases permanent ventilation, even when closed.

Some applications demanding specialised design, where those listed properties will be needed in differing orders of priority, include entrance doors, vestibule doors, interior communicating doors, fire-check doors, emergency exit doors, garage doors and industrial doors, each of which may be made up in a variety of ways to satisfy the main functional requirement and give some freedom of choice in appearance.

Basic Forms of Door Construction

Basic forms of construction in doors may be listed as ledged and braced; framed, ledged and braced; panelled; flush; and glazed. The first of these is the simplest and cheapest to produce and has limited applications which the reader will already be familiar with. Each of the others gives scope for the introduction of details for variety in design and manufacture to satisfy a wide range of applications.

The *framed, ledged and braced door* is basically a very functional door, generally of painted softwood and favoured more for its utility than its beauty. Usually associated with rear entrances, garages and industrial buildings this form of construction can be adapted to more decorative situations. The greatest problem occurs where the door is fully exposed to weather conditions and the resultant changes in the board widths can put considerable strain on the framework of the door. Fig. 5.12 shows four alternative sections through the stile and boards. Fig. 5.12 (a) shows the common 'vee-jointed' and (b) the less common, traditional 'beaded'. It should be noted that the tongued and grooved joints are left free to move with shrinkage; in painted work they are merely primed before assembly. The boards are preferably of narrow width so that the greater number of joints will each show less shrinkage. Figs. 5.12(c) and (d) are more modern, but suited only to clear finished work, since if painted, any shrinkage would be highlighted by the broken paint surface.

Variations to the basic door can also be seen in the shaping of the top rail. In Fig. 5.13 it will be seen in (a) and (b) that the inner edge only of the rail may be shaped to leave the outer edge as normal for rectangular frame. For greater elaboration, each of these could have been similarly shaped on the outer edge, forming a parallel rail, and requiring the door frame to be shaped also. A common example of this is shown in Fig. 5.13(c), which illustrates the top of a pair of doors of Gothic design commonly seen in churches. Two associated joints are also shown in the figure.

In each of those illustrated, the door would be framed together, then the heads of the boards individually fitted to the curve to be driven up into the groove.

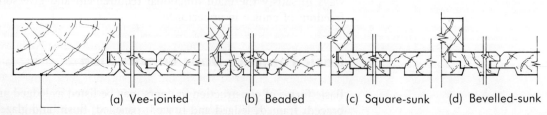

(a) Vee-jointed   (b) Beaded   (c) Square-sunk   (d) Bevelled-sunk

Fig. 5.12
Alternative board details

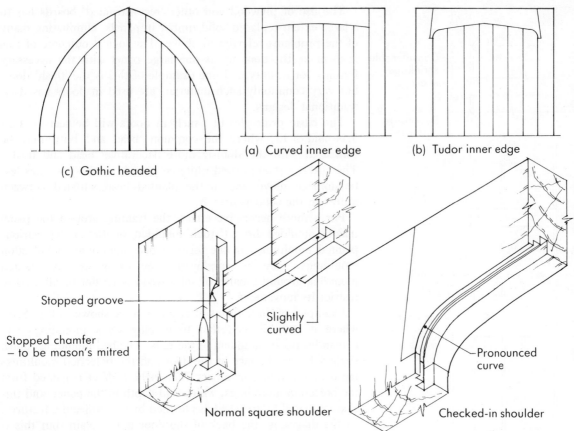

(a) Curved inner edge

(b) Tudor inner edge

(c) Gothic headed

Stopped groove

Stopped chamfer
– to be mason's mitred

Slightly curved

Pronounced curve

Normal square shoulder

Checked-in shoulder

Fig. 5.13
Shaped heads – framed, ledged and braced doors
(**a**) Curved inner edge
(**b**) Tudor inner edge
(**c**) Gothic headed

Panelled Doors

In panelled doors, a substantial framework of stiles, rails and muntins provides strength and stability while the areas between are filled with boards or panels to fulfil whatever protective and aesthetic functions the door is expected to provide. Panels also contribute to holding the door 'square' and this, together with rigid joints in wide rails, eliminates the need for braces.

In the past, panels were of solid timber, generally with the grain running vertically, and the design details were largely a result of the need to allow moisture movement horizontally across the width of the panel. Muntins were introduced partly to avoid the need to edge-joint boards to make up wide panels, but more to avoid the damaging and unsightly effect of movement in wide boards (see Fig. 1.14). Panels of solid timber must be contained and held flat by the framing, but they must at the same time be given freedom to shrink or swell as moisture content changes. Various decorative features may be added to the panels, the framework, or both, and this may serve partly to conceal movement in the panels.

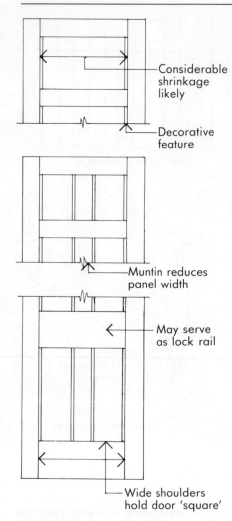

Considerable shrinkage likely

Decorative feature

Muntin reduces panel width

May serve as lock rail

Wide shoulders hold door 'square'

Fig. 5.14
Panelled door principles

The use of plywood and other 'reconstructed' boards has to a large extent replaced solid timber in panels, eliminating many of the problems referred to above. The logical outcome of this is to make the door up as one large panel with the necessary framing for rigidity and one example of this is the 'flush' door, but very commonly such materials are used in doors based on traditional designs.

The basic principles of panels in doors will be seen in Figs 5.14 and 5.15, where the common 'bead and butt' may be compared with the slightly more decorative 'bead and flush'. The latter, although used quite commonly in the past, has less freedom to move due to the planted bead situated between mitres in the solid panel.

For a more decorative effect, the framing around the panel may be moulded direct ('stuck' moulded) or alternatively various planted mouldings, in the form of bed mouldings or bolection mouldings, may be employed. The fixing of any planted moulding around a panel of solid wood must not be allowed to restrict its movement.

Examples of these forms of decoration are shown in Fig. 5.16, where it will be seen that to employ stuck mouldings will demand scribed shoulders to the rails. The bed mouldings finish slightly below the face of the door and the bolection mouldings lap over the frame members. The richest effect is gained from the bolection mouldings, which add depth to the panel, and this is accentuated by the shadows formed by the projecting features. In the diagrams, the back of the door is left plain, but this is not necessarily so: the stuck moulding could easily be produced on both sides, and the other examples would probably have bed moulds on the reverse side.

In painted softwood work, the planted mouldings would be fixed by 'skew' nailing to avoid as far as possible the restriction of movement of solid wood panels. Where the work is to be clear

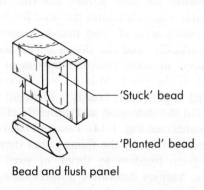

'Stuck' bead

'Planted' bead

Bead and flush panel

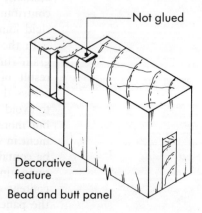

Not glued

Decorative feature

Bead and butt panel

Fig. 5.15
Panels to conceal shrinkage

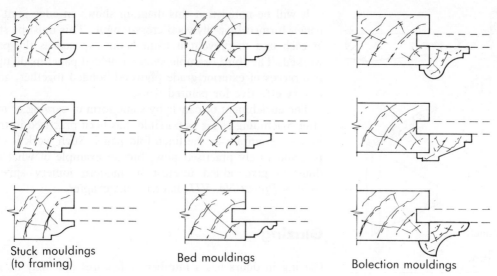

Stuck mouldings
(to framing)

Bed mouldings

Bolection mouldings

Fig. 5.16
Decoration around panels

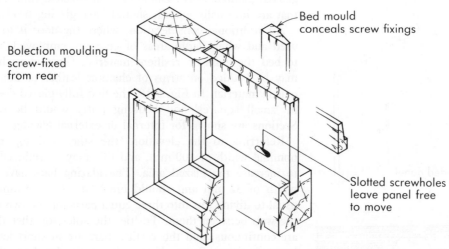

Bed mould
conceals screw fixings

Bolection moulding
screw-fixed
from rear

Slotted screwholes
leave panel free
to move

Fig. 5.17
Bolection mould fixing

finished, mouldings on the face of the door will be fixed by screwing through the panel from behind. Screw holes will be slotted or elongated to allow panel movement. Fig. 5.17 illustrates this and the bed moulding fixed internally to conceal the screw heads.

The panels themselves may be made more decorative by working various forms of embellishment on one or both faces. Fig. 5.18 shows two examples made from solid timber, the raised panel and the raised and fielded panel. The second of these is generally worked on the spindle moulder, using the slotted french head and with the rear, flat face of the panel downward. Thus the thickness of the 'tongue' that will enter the framework is controlled.

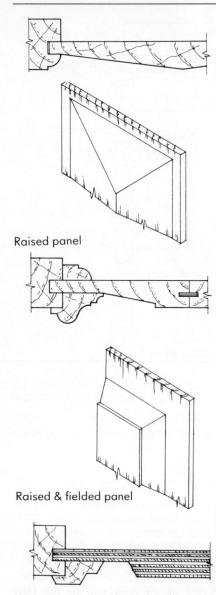

Raised panel

Raised & fielded panel

Raised & fielded panel of plywood

Fig. 5.18
Decorative panels

It will be noted that this diagram shows an edge joint in the panel, formed by a plywood cross-tongue. This must be stopped at each end to prevent it from being exposed as the panel is worked. The third example shows a fielded panel made up from two pieces of exterior grade plywood bonded together, and this is very effective for painted work.

The enrichment of panels by some form of carving or tooling, after machining as far as possible, has been practised in the past in such examples as the linen-fold panel. Such work is expensive, and rarely practised now, but an example of what can be done to give added interest in modern joinery appears in *Joinery Project No. VII*, later in this chapter.

Glazing

Glazing in doors has a number of features that may be related to windows, and much of Chapter 4 could be equally applied to doors. The use of face putty is suitable only for externally glazed, painted work. Doors of clear finished timber, and those that are internally glazed, should have glazing beads.

An additional consideration, where the door is to be heavily used and where large areas of glass are employed, is the need to bed the glass on resilient material. Glass in such situations may be bedded on strips of chamois leather or non-hardening mastic material. In Fig. 5.19, the first fully-glazed door is glazed in 'small squares' and bedding putty would be satisfactory. Sections are shown for internal or external glazing.

Referring to the elevation, the stiles and top rail have a nominal width of 100 mm, and this may be reduced to 85 mm to increase the glazed area. The glazing bars have a nominal width of 32 mm and should finish at 28 or 29 mm, and it is usual to divide this into three equal parts for the two rebates and the web between them. To 'tie' the stiles together the lay bars are continuous, and the vertical bars are in short lengths fitted between them. Some, if not all, of the lay bars should have tenons passing through the stiles to be wedged, and in this case the two nearest the centre of the height would be treated in this way. Others would be stub tenoned.

Ovolo moulding may be considered rather dated, but the resulting scribed shoulders contribute to the strength of the joints at the intersection of glazing bars where the stub tenons are very short. The 'flat' in the centre has a width equal to the tenons, so the whole section is very functional. Doors of this form of construction can be varied by differing the arrangement of glazing bars to produce decorative patterns or effects.

The other door shown in Fig. 5.19 is also fully glazed, but in this case with one piece of glass which is likely to be 6 mm thick. The two sections shown illustrate that the rebate may be

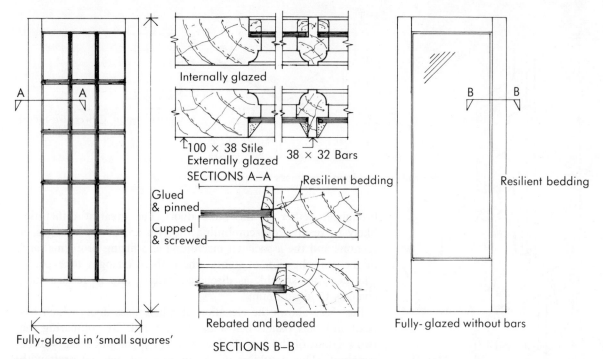

Internally glazed

100 × 38 Stile
Externally glazed
SECTIONS A–A

Glued & pinned
Cupped & screwed

38 × 32 Bars

Resilient bedding

Resilient bedding

Rebated and beaded

Fully-glazed without bars

SECTIONS B–B

Fully-glazed in 'small squares'

Fig. 5.19
Fully-glazed doors

eliminated by using two glazing beads, one of which may be glued and pinned for security and weather resistance if required. To shed water it would be necessary to bevel the outer bead. The second section shows the glass set in a rebate. Each of these should be on a resilient bed and the securing bead fixed with cups and screws. The bottom rail is in this case wider than normal so as to hold the door square, and such rails are sometimes as wide as 375 mm.

This is an appropriate stage to discuss tenon sizes as applied to a door of this nature. Fig. 5.20 shows at (a) how the thickness of the tenon is determined together with the influence that rebates (or mouldings) have on its position.

It is important next to determine the width of a haunched tenon, and this is shown at (b) firstly as applied to the top rail. Traditionally, the ratio of tenon to haunch has been taken as two-thirds to one-third of the rail width. For some years now, to reduce weakness due to short grain occurring above the tenon, this has been changed by many joiners to *equal widths of tenon and haunch*, and this same rule can apply to middle rails and bottom rails. Maximum width of tenons relative to their thickness is 5:1, and this too is illustrated in the figure; this sometimes results in three tenons in an exceptionally wide rail.

Part-Glazed Doors

A part-glazed door is one that is partly panelled or flush, glazed over part of its area so the details discussed elsewhere are

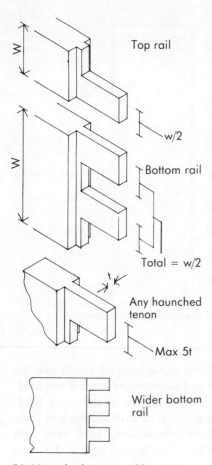

Top rail

w/2

Bottom rail

Total = w/2

Any haunched tenon

Max 5t

Wider bottom rail

(b) Haunched tenon widths

Fig. 5.20
Haunched tenons
(**a**) Tenon thickness and position
(**b**) Haunched tenon widths

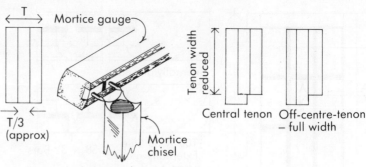

T

Mortice gauge

T/3
(approx)

Mortice chisel

Tenon width reduced

Central tenon   Off-centre-tenon – full width

(a) Tenon thickness and position

brought together in the same door. The greatest difficulties likely to result from combining the two are in the changes of sections and the associated machining and fitting problems, and in the complication of joints where these changes take place. The designer should, as discussed earlier, aim to reduce such changes to a minimum.

Fig. 5.21 shows the elevation of a half-glass door, which has bead and butt panels below the middle rail. By comparing the two sections of the stile A–A and B–B the complications will be apparent. The shoulders of the middle rail may be dealt with in a number of ways, as was discussed earlier in Chapter 1. For economy of production, the stile section below the middle rail may be modified to allow square shoulders to the middle rail. Fig. 5.21 also illustrates a half-glass door where the stile (and top rail) are reduced in size to increase the glazed area. The considerable change in the stile section results in a *gunstock stile*.

Flush Doors

Purpose-made joinery sometimes includes the manufacture of flush doors, but this is likely only where the doors required have features that are not available in the standard mass-produced range of doors. To produce flush doors effectively demands the use of a press for the gluing of hardboard or plywood faces to the cores. Ideally, a drum sander or a wide belt sander is used to flatten the faces of assembled cores prior to gluing the faces. Many joinery works producing purpose-made joinery are so equipped, and are prepared to manufacture flush doors.

The approach to this work differs from one producer to another, and Fig. 5.22 shows one form that is easily adapted to either skeleton, semi-solid or solid construction. The basic framework takes either form of core, and all members are of 50 mm wide material. The thickness depends on the required thickness of the door and the exact thickness of the face panels. The whole core must be capable of being handled for flatting

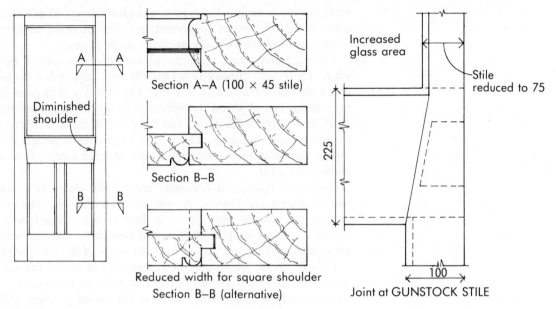

Fig. 5.21
Half-glass entrance door

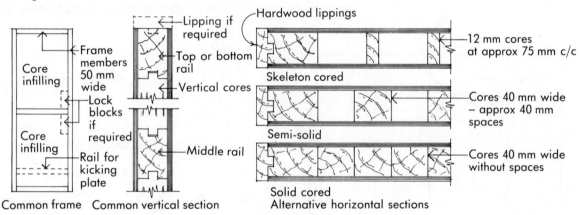

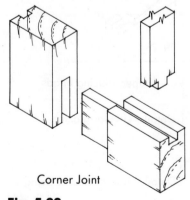

Corner Joint

Fig. 5.22
Flush doors

and pressing and it is mostly for that reason that the members are jointed together. Once completed, the glued face panels will contribute adequate strength. The skeleton cored door is the lightest and is adequate for most work but fixing blocks are required for ironmongery other than hinges.

It is important that the core material is stable, otherwise its movement will be seen in any gloss finish on the door faces and for this reason it should be reasonably free from knots and have a moisture content in the region of 10–15%. Western Red Cedar, British Columbian Pine and Swedish Redwood are all favoured for this work.

Glazing in flush doors in a common requirement in public buildings for the reasons already described, and such glazed areas are often designed also to give added interest to otherwise plain doors. The doors concerned are often in pairs, although similar features may equally apply to single doors.

Fig. 5.23 gives three examples of such doors as seen in elevation. The height dimension is typically 1981 mm (6 ft 6 in) but could also be 2032 mm (6 ft 8 in). The width will depend on the volume of traffic and the nature of goods or equipment that must pass through the doors, and the given dimension is typical in this type of building. The height of glazing is designed to satisfy the need to see through easily at 1525 mm (5 ft 0 in) above floor level.

Additional framing is necessary around the glazed area, and two examples are shown. It will be seen that the blocking around the circular opening is in four pieces, shaped before assembly. Two examples of glazing details show that the beads are designed to conceal and protect the edges of the face panels.

Pairs of doors, which may be constructed in any of the ways discussed, may be rebated together at their meeting edges so that one may be secured or bolted in the closed position while the other is free to be opened or closed independently. Such doors are said to be 'hung-folding', and some alternative treatments of the rebated edges are illustrated in Fig. 5.24 where the

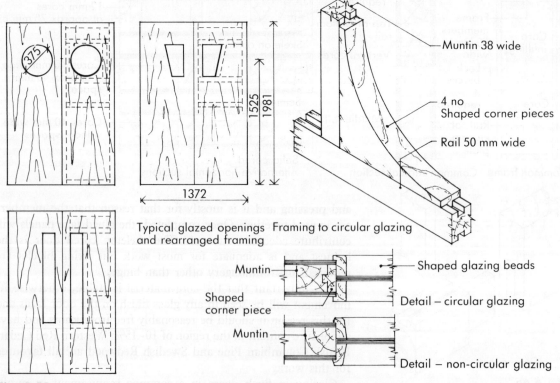

Muntin 38 wide

4 no
Shaped corner pieces

Rail 50 mm wide

Typical glazed openings Framing to circular glazing
and rearranged framing

Muntin — Shaped glazing beads

Shaped
corner piece — Detail – circular glazing

Muntin — Detail – non-circular glazing

Fig. 5.23
Glazing to flush doors

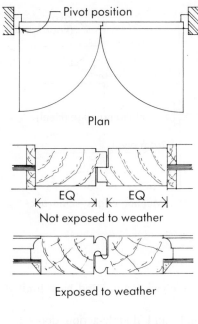

Plan

EQ   EQ

Not exposed to weather

Exposed to weather

Pivot   Pivot

Where projecting or Parliament hinges

Fig. 5.24
Rebated meeting edges

right-hand leaf is designed to open first. The details of the joint arise from the need to secure the doors together using the selected ironmongery, to prevent penetration of rainwater where this is appropriate, to allow the doors to operate freely (this may be influenced by the type of hinge to be used) and to provide a decorative finish to the joint.

The first two details are common, and the third necessary when the hinge pivot is situated forward of the door face as with parliament hinges. This detail may also be used with the more common hinges, to allow a tighter clearance joint at the meeting edges in an attempt to achieve dust-free or draught-free conditions.

Note that parliament hinges would be used for the doors shown in the plan of Fig. 5.24, to allow the doors to open through 180° without coming into contact with the brickwork.

Swing Doors

In the interior of public buildings, doors are more commonly required to function as swing doors, where either door may be opened independently of the other, or they may be opened together, to close again automatically. When hung in a rebated frame, to open in one direction, they are said to be single-action swing doors. These are often situated across an escape route, when they must open in the direction of escaping traffic.

Fig. 5.25 illustrates firstly a pair of single-action swing doors, where it will be seen that the meeting edge of each door is shaped to coincide with the path it travels as it is opened. In this way neither door will obstruct the other. Single-action swing doors may be hung on ordinary butt hinges, and a variety of automatic closers are available for use with them, most of which include a check mechanism which slows the door when it is almost closed. One that does not is the spring-load butt. For the better-class door, 'floor springs' are used: these serve both as a pivot and as a closer, and are housed within the floor, near the hanging edge of the door.

The second example in Fig 5.25 shows a pair of double-action swing doors, which are hung in the centre of a frame that has no rebates. Almost without exception, double-action swing doors are hung on floor springs that have a pivot point situated at the centre of the door thickness, and both edges of the door will rotate about that point. Both edges of the door are shaped to coincide with the path of travel. When setting-out a workshop rod for doors of this kind it is important to have exact details of the ironmongery to be employed, since this will determine a number of the joinery details.

Double-action swing doors may, as an alternative, be hung on double spring-loaded butt hinges that have two pivots, one each

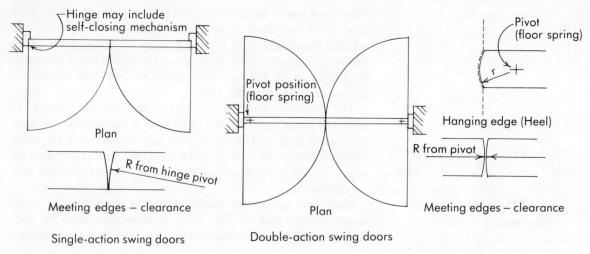

Fig. 5.25
Swing doors – geometry

side of the door. These have no 'check action' and have limited applications.

A situation where both single and double-action doors are often employed is at the entrance and vestibule of a public building, and an applied example appears as *Joinery Project No. VII later* in this chapter.

Fire-resisting Doors

These doors exist within walls or partitions designed as separating or protective elements in case of fire, with the intention of controlling the fire and protecting people or property likely to be affected by it. The need for such walls arises either from a potentially hazardous area, which must be contained or separated from the rest of the building, or from the need to provide particular protection to a part of a building to ensure a safe means of escape for the occupants.

Fire-resisting doors provide access through walls or partitions of this kind, and are therefore part of a fire-resisting element and should not significantly lower its protective properties. The need for the door to be closed in the event of a fire is an obvious one which generally leads to a requirement that the door must be self-closing. In some cases they are held open by a 'fusible link', which will break down in case of fire and allow the door to close automatically.

At the design stage, the degree of protection or resistance to fire is determined and expressed on a time scale, and timber doors and frames may be required to resist fire for either half-hour or one-hour periods.

The rate at which timber is consumed by fire, and its readi-

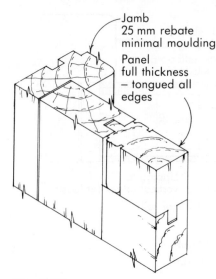

Jamb
25 mm rebate
minimal moulding

Panel
full thickness
– tongued all
edges

Fig. 5.26
Fire-resisting door

ness to ignite in the first place, depend to some extent on its natural characteristics, its bulk and its surface area. The denser timbers of the least resinous or 'oily' nature will resist fire most effectively. Substantial sections may allow the consumption of some bulk, so that the formation of charcoal over the surface will protect the remaining useful substance within. By avoiding unnecessary decoration or moulding, the surface area is kept to a minimum, and this too will be beneficial in terms of fire resistance.

Fire retardents may be applied to timber to increase its natural resistance in a number of ways. These are commonly in the form of chemical solutions applied to penetrate the surface by vacuum/pressure treatment, and the effect is to raise the ignition temperature, to reduce the rate of burning and to encourage the formation of protective substance around the material.

The design of fire-resisting doors and frames may be determined in consideration of the points discussed, and the result could be in the form of that shown in Fig. 5.26. The door construction is solid and the surfaces are as far as possible plain and free from decorative features. The frame is substantial and the rebate is 25 mm deep. If the material throughout were of a dense hardwood (Afrormosia, for example) and the door hung with joints not exceeding 3 mm this door would in all probability adequately provide one hour's resistance.

The need to satisfy statutory requirements and convince those who need to be convinced that a door will provide the specified degree of resistance has led to the use of doors and frames designed through experiments and tests to be described in a positive specification which is readily acceptable. Fire-check flush doors and frames are commonly made to BS 459: Part 3 and these are illustrated in Fig. 5.27 where the principal points of construction are shown. The framework of the door is the same for half-hour or one-hour resistance and each has four panels of plasterboard, nailed into rebates 25 mm wide. The 3 mm plywood face panels are glued and pressed and must not be nailed. For the additional resistance of the one-hour door, a panel of 5 mm asbestos millboard is glued on beneath each plywood face. The door frames each provide a rebate 25 mm deep and in the case of the half-hour door this may be formed by a screwed-on stop. The one-hour door frame must be solid-worked and then impregnated with a 15–18% solution of mono-ammonium phosphate to a depth of 12 mm. These are the principal points of construction from the specification, but there would be a need to refer to the document for the necessary further information in order to make doors to conform to it. Note too that the dimensions given here are close approximations of those given in the specification which are in Imperial units.

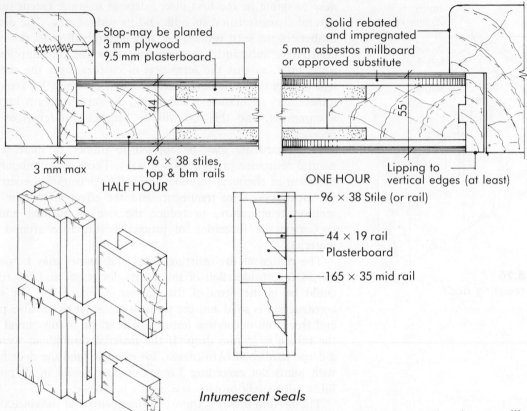

Stop-may be planted
3 mm plywood
9.5 mm plasterboard

44

3 mm max

96 × 38 stiles,
top & btm rails

HALF HOUR

Solid rebated
and impregnated
5 mm asbestos millboard
or approved substitute

55

ONE HOUR

Lipping to
vertical edges (at least)

96 × 38 Stile (or rail)

44 × 19 rail

Plasterboard

165 × 35 mid rail

Fig. 5.27
Fire-check flush doors to BS
459: Part 3

Intumescent Seals

The necessary clearances or joints around a door are likely to be a weakness in the fire-resisting construction, where the fire will make its first penetration. Such clearances will also allow the penetration of smoke, which is itself of increasing concern as a source of danger to people. Intumescent seals are manufactured as strips for insertion into grooves formed in door edges or within frame rebates. These strips are designed to expand rapidly as temperatures increase to a point that indicates that fire is imminent and, in so doing, seal the gap to prevent smoke and fire penetration.

Desirable properties in intumescent strips in door edges are that they should not interfere with the normal functioning of the door, and that they should be neat and unobtrusive and reasonably tamper-proof. In the event of fire they should be activated quickly, and should produce enough material to prevent loss of seal through consumption by fire for the designed period. The expanded intumescent material should seal the gap without preventing the opening of the door for rescue purposes.

'Pyromaster' intumescent seals are in strips contained in specially designed channels of aluminium alloy which, as a good conductor of heat, will lead to early activation. Strips are available for half-hour or one-hour rated doors, and have a neoprene blade which serves as a draught excluder in everyday use, and

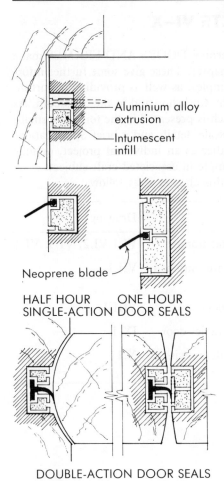

HALF HOUR   ONE HOUR
SINGLE-ACTION DOOR SEALS

DOUBLE-ACTION DOOR SEALS

Fig. 5.28
Intumescent seals to doors

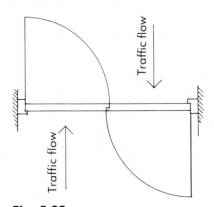

Fig. 5.29
Alternative to double-action
doors

as a smoke-stop in the earlier stages of a fire before the intumescent filling is activated.

Fig. 5.28 shows examples of the 'Pyromaster' strip, some with the neoprene blade and an improved feature designed to give better protection to the intumescent filling.

Where double-action swing doors are required to serve as fire-check doors, they can be constructed in the way already described, and according to BS 459: Part 3. There is, however, a problem in the fact that 25 mm rebates in the frame are generally required, and this is not possible with double-action doors. It is sometimes permissible to form doors of this kind, employing intumescent strips to the pivot edges, meeting edges and head, and there are Pyromaster strips specially designed for the purpose. Fig. 5.28 illustrates these strips as applied to the hanging and meeting edges of such doors. The upper edge would be sealed with one of those described earlier. It would of course be necessary to consult the manufacturer's literature to determine the exact details of appropriate strips for any particular application.

An alternative to the pair of double-action swing doors, where considerable traffic may pass in either direction, is to use two single-action doors opening in opposite directions as shown in Fig. 5.29. This arrangement has the advantage of allowing a smooth flow of people in both directions at the same time, and is also more satisfactory from the point of view of fire resistance since the meeting edges of the door, and all frame members, are rebated. The frame will of course have reverse rebates formed in the head and for continuity of line should have a moulding feature worked in the faces, to the same depth as the rebates.

Glazing in fire-resisting doors is usually permissible where the rating is not more than one hour. The period achieved will depend upon the type, thickness and area of glass, and generally acceptable are:

(a) 6 mm wired glass up to 1.2 m² in area;
(b) Copper-light glazing with 6 mm unwired glass where individual panes do not exceed 0.015 m² in area, and the whole area does not exceed 0.4 m²;
(c) 6 mm unwired glass in vision panels up to 0.065 m².

The acceptability of glazed areas in fire-resisting doors and all associated details depend on local conditions and the risks involved. Glazing will generally be required to conform to CP 153: Part 4: 1972, which includes details of glazing bars, rebate sizes and glazing beads as necessary features of the joinery involved.

JOINERY PROJECTS VI–X

Five joinery projects concerning DOORS AND FRAMES make up the remainder of the chapter. These give some further information on a variety of examples, as well as providing opportunities for student work in the workshop and in the classroom. As in the previous chapter, each is presented in the form of a small-scale drawing with larger-scale details and a brief Specification. Each may be pursued further as an individual project, or may be used as an applied example in associated craft subjects.

The list of projects for this chapter is as follows:

No.	Item	Drawings
VI	Vestibule doors and frames	VI.1, VI.2, VI.3, VI.4
VII	Hardwood door with enriched panels	VII.1
VIII	Emergency exit doors	VIII.1
IX	Inward opening 'stable' door	IX.1
X	Industrial sliding doors with wicket	X.1

Project No VI
Single and Double-action Swing Doors and Framing
in Library Vestibule

Brief Specification

This item of joinery is to comprise two pairs of swing doors and associated framing to form a fully-glazed vestibule to the entrance of a Public Library.

The outer frame is to be 4.150 m long between brickwork, and 2.600 m to the full storey height at roof soffit level, and is to include one pair of single-action swing-doors hung on 'Close-check' S/A 2001 floor springs to open outward.

The inner frame, having a floor to ceiling height of 2.600 m, is to be in two portions fitted together on a right-angled plan so as to enclose a rectangular vestibule area 4.115 × 2.100 m, and will include one pair of double-action swing doors hung on 'Closecheck' D/A 2002 floor springs.

Framing generally is to be of 150 × 75 or 63 material and the doors of 125 × 50 with wider middle and bottom rails, all as shown in drawing VI.1.

Doors and frames are to be prepared to receive 6 mm clear Georgian wired glass bedded on mastic compound and secured with glazing beads fixed with brass screws and cups as indicated in the sectional details in drawings VI.2 and VI.3.

The work throughout is to be of selected clear Afrormosia having a moisture content in the range of 10–15% at the time of assembly. Nominal sectional sizes shown must not be reduced by more than 2.5 mm for each prepared face when measured in the finished product. The finished thickness of doors is to conform accurately to the specified ironmongery. All is to be properly framed together with close-fitting mortice and tenon joints well glued, cramped and wedged and brought to a high standard ready for a clear varnish finish.

Fixing of the outer frame may be at an appropriate stage in the works, prior to plastering subject to adequate protection from damage due to following works. The fixing of interior framing is to be delayed until all plastering is complete and the building substantially dried out.

The first of three coats of clear varnish is to be applied in the workshop, before delivery.

Interpretation

It is seen in Drawing VI.1 that the frame is to be in three portions which connect together on site to form the vestibule. Critical dimensions, particularly of the outer frame which relates to the brickwork opening, must be confirmed by close liaison between workshop and site. Dimensions of the internal frames, which will be fixed after plastering, will result from the dimensions of the outer frame.

Workshop rods will be produced by reference also to Drawings VI.2 and VI.3 and will show the plan sections of the three frames in length (length rods) and the four variations of vertical sections (height rods). The rods will be similar to these given sections except that all dimensions must be shown fully and exactly as the work is intended to finish, including precise timber sizes and exact details of sectional features.

It is noted that in the designed sections the 150 mm material width will require double tenons, and that the shoulders may be easily scribed.

There will be problems resulting from changes in section firstly in the transoms over doors and adjoining lights as seen in the vertical sections, and this will necessitate 'stop' operations in moulding, and additional work in fitting the joints at the top of door jambs. Similar problems occur in the outer jambs where the glazing rebates differ above and below transoms. The given plan details of both inner and outer frames show where glazing rebates differ above and below transoms.

Joint details are designed at marking-out stage, and the resulting operations must be considered carefully at this stage. As examples of what the setter-out has in mind, two frame joints are illustrated in Drawing VI.4. In the same drawing sheet, the corner assembly detail of the interior framing is shown, where the cill is mitred together and adjoining jambs secured by softwood blocks screwed into position. The heads will also be mitred together. To complete the work at this point, the tongued casings will be fitted between head and cill and fixed over the softwood blocks.

On completion of the workshop rods it is necessary to produce the cutting list. For a job of this kind, where there are a considerable number of pieces of material involved, it is important to adopt a systematic approach to 'taking-off' the requirements from the rods to avoid omissions from the list. For this project it would be logical to deal with the three frames separately, followed by the doors, and take off all horizontal pieces from the length rods at the same time before dealing with vertical pieces from the height rods. The list produced at this stage will appear as identifiable groups of pieces related to particular parts of the job, and this serves as a very useful reference at marking-out stage to ensure that each piece is used for the intended component part.

The list, as taken off, will appear as follows except that the additions to lengths, allowed as necessary waste are shown here for the reader's benefit:

Outer Frame		*Waste Allowance (mm)*
1	4.300 × 150 × 75 Head	150 (Horns)
1	4.200 × 150 × 75 Transom	50
2	1.425 × 150 × 75 Cills	75 (Horn)
2	1.400 × 275 × 50 Mid Rails	50

Rear Frame		
1	4.420 × 150 × 63 Head	150 (Horn and Mitre)
1	4.320 × 150 × 75 Transom	50
1	1.425 × 150 × 75 Cill	75 (One Horn)
1	1.525 × 150 × 75 Cill	75 (Mitre)
2	1.400 × 275 × 50 Mid Rails	50

Return Frame		
1	2.400 × 150 × 63 Head	150 (Horns and Mitre)
1	2.300 × 150 × 75 Transom	50
1	2.400 × 150 × 75 Cill	150 (Horn and Mitre)
1	2.300 × 275 × 50 Mid Rails	50

Jambs and Mullions		
5	2.650 × 150 × 63 Outer Jambs	50
1	2.650 × 105 × 63 Jambs	50
4	2.130 × 150 × 75 Mullions	50
4	0.620 × 150 × 75 Mullions	50
2	2.550 × 85 × 25 Casings and linings	50
1	2.550 × 75 × 25 Casing	50

Doors		
8	2.085 × 125 × 50 Door Stiles	50 (Horns)
4	0.750 × 275 × 50 Mid Rails	25
4	0.750 × 225 × 50 Btm. Rails	25

Glazing Beads above transom	
4	4.150 × 32 × 19
2	2.100 × 32 × 19
14	0.570 × 32 × 19

Sidelights	
6	1.350 × 25 × 19 (Horizontals)
8	1.350 × 25 × 12.5 (Fixed rails)
8	1.600 × 25 × 19 (Verticals)
2	1.350 × 32 × 19 (Outer cill)

Doors	
8	1.600 × 25 × 12.5
8	1.400 × 25 × 12.5

The list is now rearranged into an orderly cutting list as shown in Fig. 5.30.

NO.	LENGTH	NOMINAL		FINISHED		MATERIAL	COMPONENT	UNITS
		Width	Thickness	Width	Thickness			
1	4.320	150	75	145	70	Afrormosia	Transome	
1	4.300	"	"	"	"	"	Head	
1	4.200	"	"	"	"	"	Transome	
1	2.400	"	"	"	"	"	Cill	
1	2.300	"	"	"	"	"	Transome	
4	2.130	"	"	"	"	"	Mullions	
1	1.525	"	"	"	"	"	Cill	
3	1.425	"	"	"	"	"	Cills	
4	0.620	"	"	"	"	"	Mullions	
1	4.420	150	63	145	58	"	Head	
5	2.650	"	"	"	"	"	Jambs	
1	2.400	"	"	"	"	"	Head	
1	2.650	105	63	100	58	"	Jamb	
1	2.300	275	50	270	45	"	Mid. Rails	
4	1.400	"	"	"	"	"	" "	
4	0.750	"	"	"	"	"		
4	0.750	225	50	220	45	"	Btm. Rails	
8	2.085	125	50	120	45	"	Stiles	
4	0.750	"	"	"	"	"	Top Rails	
2	2.550	85	25	80	20	"	Casings/Lining	
1	2.550	75	25	70	20	"	"	
4	4.150	32	19	28	15	"	Glazing beads	
2	2.100	"	"	"	"	"	" "	
2	1.350	"	"	"	"	"	" "	
14	0.570	"	"	"	"	"	" "	
8	1.600	25	19	18	15	"	" "	
6	1.350	"	"	"	"	"	" "	
8	1.600	25	12.5	18	10	"	" "	
8	1.400	"	"	"	"	"	" "	
8	1.350	"	"	"	"	"	" "	

CUTTING LIST FOR JOB NUMBER _____ 128 _____ DATE _____
JOB _____ VESTIBULE DOORS & FRAMES
CONTRACT _____ INVICTA PUBLIC LIBRARY

Fig. 5.30
Cutting List Project No. 6

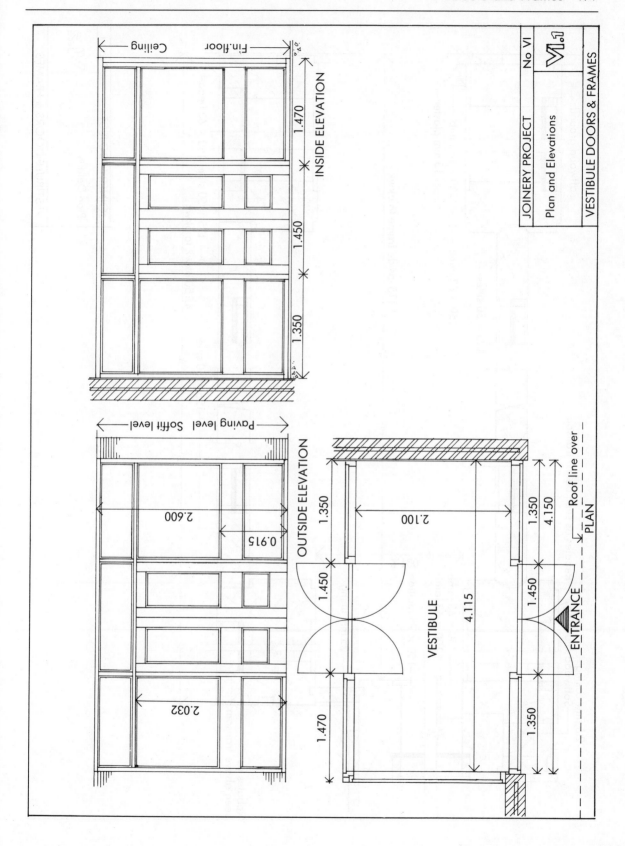

INSIDE ELEVATION

Ceiling

Fin. floor

1.470

1.450

1.350

OUTSIDE ELEVATION

Soffit level

Paving level

Ceiling

2.600

0.915

2.032

PLAN

VESTIBULE

ENTRANCE

Roof line over

1.350

2.100

1.350

4.150

4.115

1.450

1.450

1.470

1.350

JOINERY PROJECT No VI

VI.1

Plan and Elevations

VESTIBULE DOORS & FRAMES

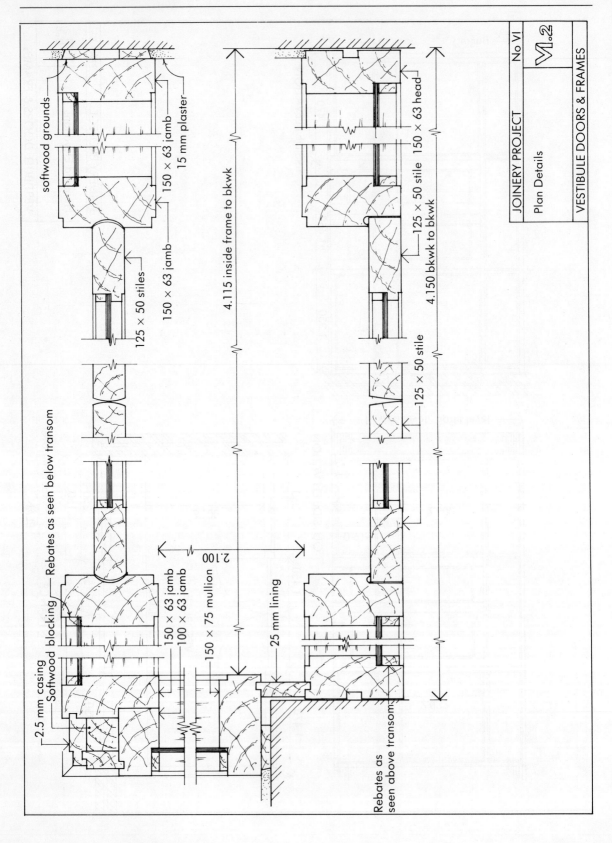

softwood grounds

150 × 63 jamb
15 mm plaster

125 × 50 stiles
150 × 63 jamb

4.115 inside frame to bkwk

150 × 63 head
125 × 50 stile

125 × 50 stile

4.150 bkwk to bkwk

Rebates as seen below transom

2.5 mm casing
Softwood blocking

150 × 63 jamb
100 × 63 jamb
150 × 75 mullion

25 mm lining

2.100

Rebates as seen above transom

JOINERY PROJECT   No VI

VI.2

Plan Details

VESTIBULE DOORS & FRAMES

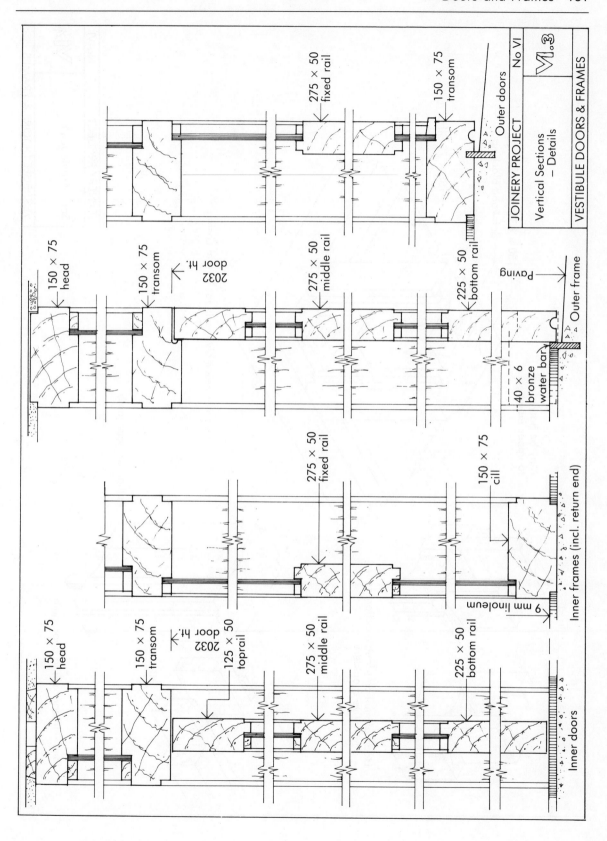

JOINERY PROJECT   No VI

VI.3

Vertical Sections
– Details

VESTIBULE DOORS & FRAMES

275 × 50 fixed rail

150 × 75 transom

Outer doors

150 × 75 head

150 × 75 transom

2032 door ht.

275 × 50 middle rail

225 × 50 bottom rail

Paving

Outer frame

40 × 6 bronze water bar

275 × 50 fixed rail

150 × 75 cill

9 mm linoleum

Inner frames (incl. return end)

150 × 75 head

150 × 75 transom

2032 door ht.

125 × 50 toprail

275 × 50 middle rail

225 × 50 bottom rail

Inner doors

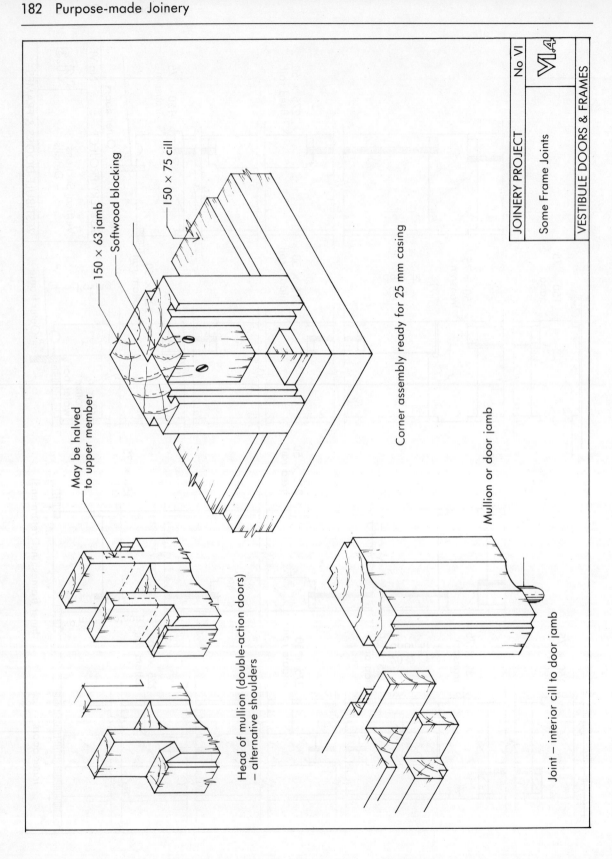

150 × 63 jamb

Softwood blocking

150 × 75 cill

May be halved
to upper member

Corner assembly ready for 25 mm casing

Mullion or door jamb

Head of mullion (double-action doors)
– alternative shoulders

Joint – interior cill to door jamb

JOINERY PROJECT   No VI

Some Frame Joints   VI 4

VESTIBULE DOORS & FRAMES

Project No. VII
Hardwood Doors to Front Elevations of high quality apartments

Specification

5 no. Hardwood Entrance Doors 2032 × 813 × 45 mm, and 5 no. 1981 × 762 × 45 mm matching doors to adjacent stores, each door being framed so as to include 21 panels, all as shown in Drawing VII.1. (The drawing shows the smaller doors, sized 1981 × 762 mm).

The framing is to be prepared to accommodate square panels, and any fine adjustment to material widths is to be restricted to intermediate rails and muntins. The sight sizes of panels are to be 150 × 150 mm for the smaller doors, and 170 × 170 mm for the larger doors.

All is to be of clear selected Brazilian Mahogany, properly morticed and tenoned together, well glued, cramped and wedged with close-fitting shoulders and brought to a high standard of finish ready for the application of clear varnish.

Interpretation

The work will demand accurate setting-out and machining, and it is evident from the dimensions on the drawing being shown as finished sizes that the design depends very much on the precision of the square panels and the openings to receive them.

The workshop rod will confirm the stated sizes of frame members, particularly the intermediate rails and muntins. Those for both doors would have been checked by calculation at design stage to arrive at the stated panel sizes.

The framing presents few technical difficulties, since the shoulders can be scribed, although it would enhance the appearance if the intersecting mouldings were mitred (discounting any shrinkage). Mitring can be ruled out here in view of the additional labour and subsequent cost.

Production of the panels presents some interesting machining operations, and one proved sequence is as follows (see also Fig. 5.31).

Firstly, panels are accurately brought to the square dimensions, then

(a) The recessed margin around the four edges is produced on the tenoner. Since the spur cutters will leave marks across the worked surface at each corner, the recessed margin is left slightly thick, by 1 or 2 mm, at this stage;

(b) The 'enrichment' of the raised field is carried out by four passes over the spindle moulder, dealing with the two cross-grain passes first;

(c) The margin is now brought down to its finished thickness (mulleted) to fit the grooved framing (also removing the spur marks) and at the same time producing the bevelled edge to the raised portion, in one spindle-moulder operation.

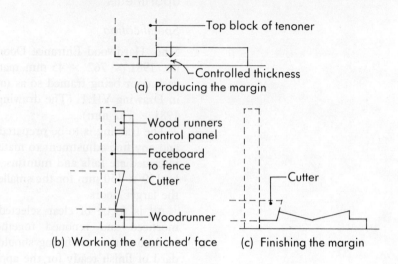

(a) Producing the margin

(b) Working the 'enriched' face

(c) Finishing the margin

Fig. 5.31

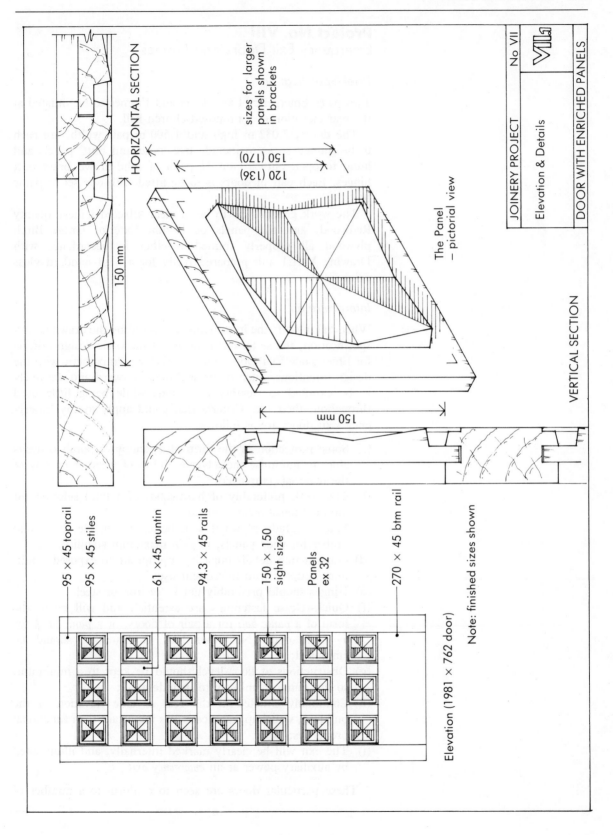

HORIZONTAL SECTION

sizes for larger
panels shown
in brackets

150 (170)

120 (136)

150 mm

The Panel
– pictorial view

VERTICAL SECTION

150 mm

JOINERY PROJECT   No VII

Elevation & Details

VII

DOOR WITH ENRICHED PANELS

95 × 45 toprail

95 × 45 stiles

61 ×45 muntin

94.3 × 45 rails

150 × 150
sight size

Panels
ex 32

270 × 45 btm rail

Note: finished sizes shown

Elevation (1981 × 762 door)

Project No. VIII
Emergency Exit Doors and Frames

Brief Specification

Two pairs Emergency Exit Doors and Frames to be situated at the rear elevation of a proposed church hall.

The doors, 2.032 m high and 1.500 m pair width, are each to be framed so as to include five 'bead and butt' panels and hung to open outward on 1½ pairs of solid-drawn brass butt hinges. Each pair of doors is to be fitted with one set of panic bolts.

The work generally is to be of clear selected joinery quality Redwood, and the panels of 19 mm Exterior Grade Birch plywood all properly framed together in accordance with Drawing VIII.1 and prepared ready for a high-standard gloss paint finish.

Interpretation

When 'taking-off' the information conveyed by the drawings and specification, the setter-out is aware of the basic design criteria for Emergency Exit Doors and is therefore sympathetic with the design intentions. Such doors will open outward and are likely to be exposed to weather conditions while being little used throughout their life. Criteria that could apply to any Emergency Exit doors are as follows:

(a) Some protection in the form of a canopy or porch is desirable, to minimise the adverse effects of weather on any of the materials employed;

(b) The work preferably of hardwood, of a kind selected for minimal moisture movement;

(c) Exterior grade plywood is a better alternative than solid timber for wide panels, to gain maximum stability;

(d) Construction details must be appropriate to exposed conditions coupled with infrequent use;

(e) Hinges should preferably not be of iron or steel;

(f) Quick-release fastenings are essential, and will be in the form of a *panic bolt* for a pair of doors, or a *panic latch* for a single door. No other lock or fastening should be employed;

(g) Obstructions at floor level should be kept to a minimum, so the frame is unlikely to include a cill;

(h) Commonly situated at the rear or side elevation of the building, visual appearance is less important than functional properties;

(i) The exit will be clearly marked internally, and illuminated by auxiliary power as an *emergency exit*.

These particular doors are seen to conform to a number of

those criteria, and one outstanding feature of their design is in the plywood panels made to appear as traditional bead-and-butt panels but without the excessive shrinkage or considerable swelling that could put severe stress on the framework, had solid timber been used for panels of this width.

The frames are to be 'built-in', and the feet of the jambs should be provided with projecting metal dowels to be enclosed within the concrete screed or paving at a later stage. These dowels are commonly of galvanised iron, but for a longer life are occasionally of copper or bronze. All should be knotted and primed before delivery which, in the case of the doors, should be delayed to an appropriate later stage in the site work to avoid damage.

100 × 63 head

100 × 50 top rails

19 mm exterior grade plywood panel

225 × 50 bottom rail

50 × 6 non-ferrous water bar

Paving

Cement/sand screed and floor finish

Plywood panel

Meeting edges

JOINERY PROJECT   No VIII

Plan, Elevations and Details

VIII 1

EMERGENCY EXIT DOORS

INSIDE ELEVATION and panic bolt arrangement

100 × 63 jamb
100 × 50 stile

Lipping to panel

HORIZONTAL SECTION A–A – Details

2.032

1.500

OUTSIDE ELEVATION

Plan

Project No. IX
Domestic Rear Entrance 'Stable' Door and Frame

Brief specification

Inward opening Rear Entrance Door and Frame to a new dwelling house; the door to comprise an upper and lower leaf in the style of a stable door.

The door, 2032 high, 813 wide and nominally 50 mm thick is to be in two portions, each framed so as to receive a panel of tongued, grooved and vee-jointed boards in face widths not exceeding 100 mm, and properly braced. The finished thickness of the door must not be less than 44 mm.

The frame is to be solid rebated and moulded from 100 × 63 mm joinery quality Redwood and a 150 × 75 mm Iroko cill, grooved to receive a 25 × 5 mm galvanised water bar. The lower edge of each leaf is to be protected by a 63 × 50 mm tongued weather board.

All is to be in accordance with Drawing IX.1, properly framed together with close-fitting mortice and tenon joints, well glued, cramped and wedged together. Concealed surfaces associated with the boarded panels are to be thoroughly primed before assembly. Exposed surfaces are to be brought to a high standard of finish ready for the application of high gloss paint to softwood and preservative stain to hardwood.

Intrepretation

The doors are seen to be of normal Framed, Ledged and Braced construction except that the bottom rail to each leaf is to the full door thickness to allow the meeting rails to be rebated together, and effective weathering details to be employed at the cill. The curved inner edge of the top rail can be finished and grooved by the use of a plywood template against a ring fence. Rebates to the meeting rails and to the bottom rail will be worked before assembly. Chamfers to the stiles must be stopped so that their intersections at the rails may be mason's mitred. (Alternatively, they may be left entirely until after assembly, to be worked with a portable power router).

The tongued and grooved boards are shown on the drawing as all being to the same width, and this means that they will have to be specially produced to the exact width required. An alternative approach would have employed standard boards, so leaving just the outer boards to be specially tongued to the stiles, so reducing their width to less than the other boards. The shaped upper ends of the boards, to fit the curved top rail, can be marked out by being cramped together so that the plywood template already referred to can be applied to them. At the lower ends, the boards will be fixed by being skew-nailed into the rebate.

Each leaf will be braced to suit the 'hand' indicated on the drawing, using 100 × 32 mm material and thicknessed so that measured together with the board thickness, they will be equal to the thickness of the stiles and rails.

Grooves for the weather boards will be machined before assembly, then continued across the stiles by hand after assembly. These grooves should be stopped at approximately 20 mm from the edges of the doors for neatness of appearance. The weather boards will be delivered separately, to be fixed after the doors are hung, and to be fully effective their ends should be recessed into the door jambs, as shown in the drawing.

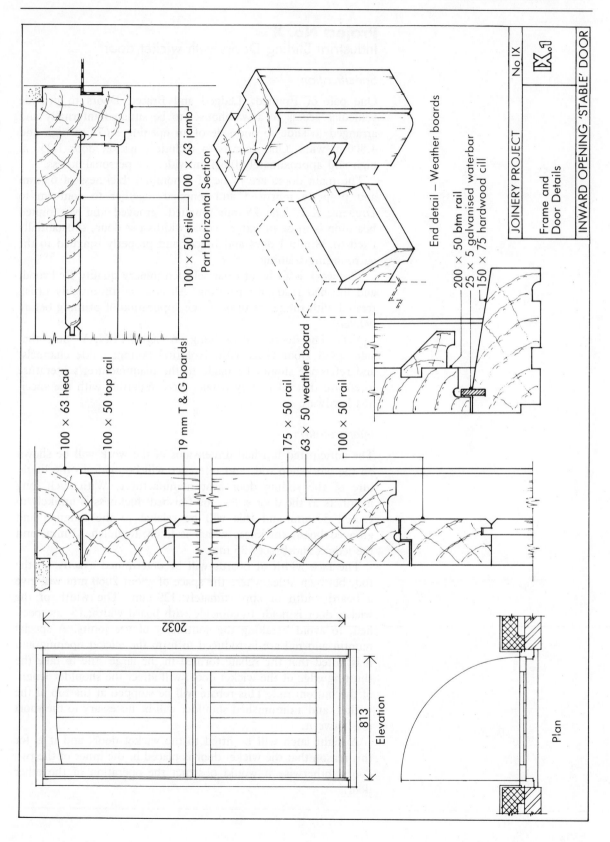

JOINERY PROJECT   No IX

IX.1

Frame and
Door Details

INWARD OPENING 'STABLE' DOOR

Part Horizontal Section

100 × 63 jamb
100 × 50 stile

End detail – Weather boards

200 × 50 btm rail
25 × 5 galvanised waterbar
150 × 75 hardwood cill

100 × 63 head
100 × 50 top rail
19 mm T & G boards

175 × 50 rail
63 × 50 weather board
100 × 50 rail

2032

813
Elevation

Plan

Project No. X
Industrial Sliding Doors with wicket door

Specification

One pair of Framed, Ledged and Braced Doors to provide vehicular access to a warehouse, to be situated internally and arranged to slide to one side of an opening 3.675 m high and 4.800 m wide. One door is to include a wicket door 1.250 m high and approximately 0.650 m wide, for personal access.

The main doors are to be of a nominal thickness of 63 mm and properly morticed and tenoned together to conform to Drawing X.1. The 25 mm tongued, grooved and vee-jointed boarding is to be in sixteen equal widths per door, substantially fixed to 38 mm ledges and braces and properly tongued to the surrounding framing.

The work is to be of clear selected joinery quality Redwood, and finished ready for painting. All is to be thoroughly brush treated with fungicide prior to the application of priming before delivery.

Note: The doors will be hung on COURTENAY 'Smootha-side' 1838 Door Gear with 'Holdtite' bottom guide channels, and reference should be made to the manufacturer's literature to ensure that all joinery details are compatible with the specified hardware.

Interpretation

The anticipated finished dimensions of the work will be shown on the workshop rod, and reference will be made to the literature of the sliding door gear manufacturer. With such long members as the door stiles, the finished thickness is unlikely to exceed 57 mm and this will be related to the tongued and grooved board thickness which is likely to finish 22 mm, and the ledges and braces 35 mm.

The face width of boards will be determined exactly on the rod, between stiles where the space of about 2060 mm will give a board width of approximately 129 mm. The width of the wicket door is made to coincide with board widths (5) as specified, to avoid breaking the continuity of vee joints. A special muntin and rail are introduced to form the wicket opening and it is noted that the rebate formed in the large stile to take the shutting edge of the wicket door, will affect the shoulder length of the bottom rail. This rebate will be stopped at the top of the wicket, and a diminished shoulder will be necessary to the short rail above it.

A night latch will be fitted to the wicket door, and it is for this reason that the wicket door is placed in the inner of the two doors, otherwise it would obstruct the operation of the other door.

The specified sliding gear will have been selected to cope with the weight of the doors, and comprises a double upper track (approximately twice the length of the opening) and a guide channel set into the concrete floor.

To estimate the weight of each door, its approximate volume is calculated by:

Overall volume	$3.675 \times 2.400 \times 0.060$	$= 0.5292$
Deduct volume behind boards	$2.675 \times 2.060 \times 0.040$	$= \underline{0.2204}$
		$= 0.3088$
Add braces	$2 \times 3.600 \times 0.175 \times 0.040$	$= \underline{0.0504}$
	Approximate volume of each door	$= 0.3592$ m^3

At a moisture content of 18% the Redwood will weigh about 545 kg/m^3, and each door therefore will weigh approximately $545 \times 0.3556 = 193.8$ kg.

Each door will be suspended on two hangers, and these must be positioned at the top of the stiles and not within the length of the top rail because this would put excessive stress on the upper joints of the door.

No detail is given of the fixing of the boards to the full-thickness bottom rail and it is determined that they will be skew-nailed into a rebate, and a vee joint added for visual effect. The boards will not be too tightly fitted in their width, otherwise seasonal swelling will exert considerable stresses on the framing. The boards and hidden surfaces should be fungicide treated before the boards are fixed.

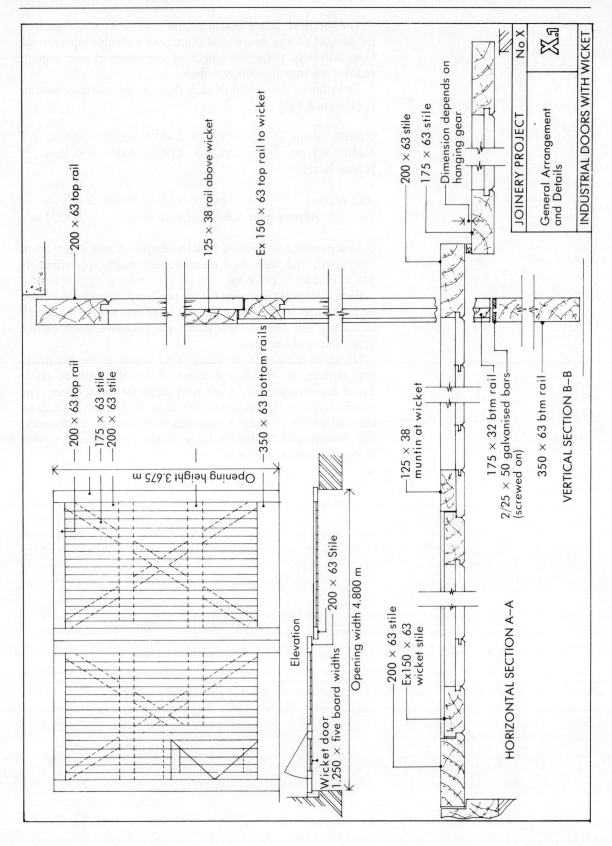

200 × 63 top rail

125 × 38 rail above wicket

Ex 150 × 63 top rail to wicket

200 × 63 stile

175 × 63 stile

Dimension depends on hanging gear

JOINERY PROJECT   No X

General Arrangement and Details

INDUSTRIAL DOORS WITH WICKET

X.1

350 × 63 bottom rails

200 × 63 top rail

175 × 63 stile

200 × 63 stile

Opening height 3.675 m

Elevation

200 × 63 Stile

Wicket door
1.250 × five board widths

Opening width 4.800 m

200 × 63 stile

Ex150 × 63
wicket stile

125 × 38
muntin at wicket

175 × 32 btm rail

2/25 × 50 galvanised bars
(screwed on)

350 × 63 btm rail

VERTICAL SECTION B–B

HORIZONTAL SECTION A–A

Chapter 6

WALL PANELLING, WORK SURFACES AND COUNTERS

WALL PANELLING

This aspect of joinery is concerned with the finish of interior wall surfaces by the application of areas of timber or other materials mainly for decoration. The aim is often to achieve a particularly luxurious effect by the selection of timbers for their beauty and the way in which they are put together; work of this kind is likely to be restricted to rooms where the considerable expense can be justified, although in the long term the cost of upkeep will usually be small.

Traditional panelling made from solid timbers was of necessity constructed from pieces of limited size for reasons of moisture movement, and held within a framework of narrow members to form *framed panelling*. The alternative approach, less demanding in terms of cost and work content, was to cover the area with narrow strips of tongued and grooved boards fixed vertically to the wall and this too was designed to allow freedom of movement. This approach, known in the past more for its utility than its beauty, is referred to as *strip panelling*. For each of these there are modern versions which offer advantages in manufacture and performance, and allow design details which appeal to present-day tastes. Many of these developments are made possible by the use of manufactured boards, which do not place the restrictions on design that are associated with solid timbers, and where these materials are used to their best advantage a third type of wall panelling is employed, known as *sheet panelling*.

Wall panelling therefore may be of three basic types, framed panelling, strip panelling or sheet panelling, each of which may be detailed in a variety of ways, but before looking into examples of these the properties that might be desirable in any example of this work will be summarised.

Depending on the location, the panelling may be required to:

• Conceal the structure or background material,
• Produce a decorative or even a luxurious effect,
• Require the minimum of maintenance,
• Offer sound absorptive or acoustic properties,

- Provide thermal insulation,
- Resist flame spread,
- Provide fire resistance,
- Be hygienic,
- Resist particular forms of 'wear and tear'.

It is also generally expected that the panelling will be prepared as much as possible 'off-site', and this will include assembly and to some extent finishing. Prefabricated areas of panelling will be as large as practicable, and the limitations in size are most likely to be from problems of handling and manoeuvring into the building.

As an interior finish, the work is often to a high standard and fixing will be delayed until the building is sufficiently dry to avoid damage from moisture (the timber is likely to be kiln dried to a specific moisture content), and to a time when there is least likelihood of physical damage from other building operations. Wet trades, particularly plastering, will have been completed some time before the panelling is fixed. 'Fixings' for the panelling will have been prepared before plastering, and these are most often in the form of *softwood grounds* (See Figs 1.42 and 1.43 and associated notes).

Softwood grounds may in some cases be in the form of separate strips, or they may be framed together to provide a considerable number of fixings for the panelling with a fewer number of fixings to the wall. Commonly, part of the wall adjoining the panelling is plastered, in which case the grounds must be of the right thickness and so accurately fixed as to control the thickness and flatness of the plaster which is applied afterwards. Fig. 6.1 shows an example where separate grounds

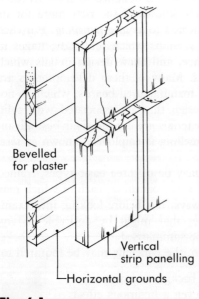

Bevelled
for plaster

Vertical
strip panelling

Horizontal grounds

Fig. 6.1
Softwood grounds

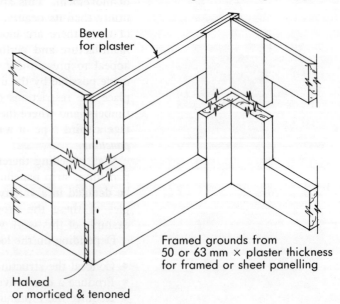

Bevel
for plaster

Halved
or morticed & tenoned

Framed grounds from
50 or 63 mm × plaster thickness
for framed or sheet panelling

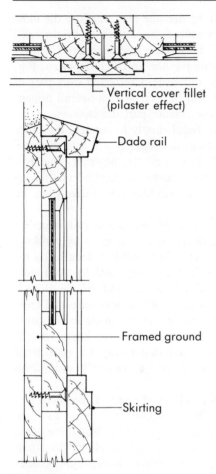

Vertical cover fillet (pilaster effect)

Dado rail

Framed ground

Skirting

Fig. 6.2
Fixings concealed by cover mouldings

fixed horizontally provide fixings for vertical strip panelling. Also illustrated is an example of framed grounds which provide fixings for framed or sheet panelling. The thickness of the grounds determines the thickness of plaster and it will be appreciated that great care must be taken to ensure that the grounds are plumb and accurate. Packings will be necessary behind the grounds to gain this accuracy, as they are fixed by plugging and screwing or by hard steel nails which may be driven by a cartridge tool. The grounds, which may be required to be pretreated with fungicide or insecticide, must be positioned to provide the designed fixings, and they will be shown on the workshop rod of the panelling to ensure this.

The fixing of the panelling itself to the grounds will be as unobtrusive as possible, and a number of alternative methods are employed in an attempt to achieve 'secret fixings'. In Figs 6.2 and 6.3 the following are shown:

Cover Fillets, generally fixed with panel pins and concealing the screwed fixings of the panellings. This cover fillet may be in the form of a prominent moulding or feature which occurs at a point between assembled units of panelling (as shown) or at the upper or lower edge of the work. Examples of this are in pilasters, cornices, frieze rails, dado rails and skirtings.

Pellets made from the same material as that being fixed, and glued into place over the screw so that the grain is continuous. Accuracy in the work and careful matching of grain can produce good results, and this is a popular method of concealing fixings.

Slot Screwing, where the joinery has keyhole slots prepared so as to be located over projecting screws, then driven along the length of the slot to provide a completely secret fixing. This has been used a good deal in the past for the fixing of hardwood architraves and plinth blocks, but it does demand a high degree of accuracy and is time absorbing.

Slotted Plates are similar in principle to the last but simpler to apply. Their use is more likely to be found in the fixing of isolated items of high-class joinery than in the greater number of fixings for wall panelling.

Interlocking Blocks, where the lower block is fixed to the wall (between grounds) and the upper block is fixed to the back of the panelling. As the panelling is lowered into place the blocks interlock and secure the work.

The workshop rod is made up by reference to the drawings provided, showing the general arrangement of the panelling together with large-scale details, but it will be essential to take accurate site dimensions.

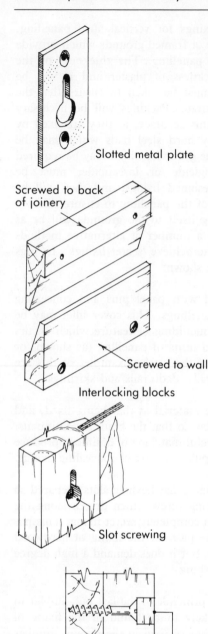

Slotted metal plate

Screwed to back
of joinery

Screwed to wall

Interlocking blocks

Slot screwing

Glued matching pellets

Fig. 6.3
Alternative secret fixings

Of the dimensions taken from site, the plan sizes are the most critical, and these will be measured 'brickwork to brickwork'. Each portion of the wall will be given a reference letter, generally in a clockwise order starting at the entrance doorway. Fig. 6.4 shows an example of the dimensions recorded over part of a room to be panelled and it will be seen that an overall dimension is taken as a check on the smaller part dimensions.

The diagonal check is also useful, firstly to confirm the other dimensions taken, since any large discrepancy will lead to measurements being taken again. It is unlikely, however, that this dimension will be perfectly accurate when checked mathematically, since the angles of the building are unlikely to be perfectly 'square'.

The workshop rods will consist of one height rod, together with additional ones for particular features, such as windows which interrupt the panelling, and there will be a length rod for each wall face. The brickwork dimensions will be accurately inserted first, then the panelling details will be developed, paying particular attention to angles, where adjoining wall faces come together. Reasonable tolerances will be made in the panel dimensions where gaps can be concealed by cover fillets, mouldings and pilasters. It is at this stage that fixings are considered so that the grounds may be positioned accordingly and shown on the rod.

The height of panelling depends on the use of the room and the furniture and fittings to be accommodated in it. In some cases it will be to the full height of the room, but more often it will finish with a cornice moulding (at or above door and window frame height) and a plaster frieze above it. Sometimes it is only to dado height, to suit the height of furniture such as counters and display cases in the region of 0.9–1.1 m and finished with a capping or dado rail.

Framed Panelling

Figs 6.5 and 6.6 show some details of framed panelling which may be related to the walls F, G, H and J in Fig. 6.4. The sections shown on plan are as they would appear on the workshop rods, except that on the rod they would not be 'broken' in length. The brickwork would be shown first, as measured on site, then the ground thickness inserted. Panel frame members are then detailed, with an attempt to achieve equal face widths as indicated. Joints at angles are designed to assemble in a clockwise order, and the tongues arranged to conceal any shrinkage. Ground members are inserted last and located to provide the fixings required.

The vertical section shows alternatives, either to frieze or dado height, and the rod would show precise details. Note that if the

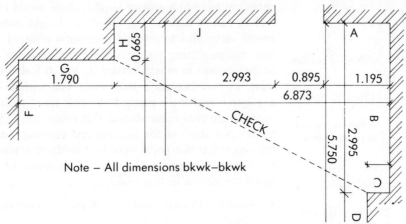

Fig. 6.4
Site dimensions

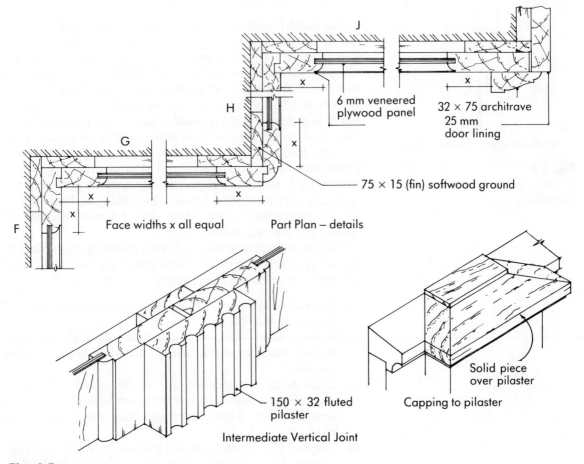

Fig. 6.5
Horizontal details – framed panelling

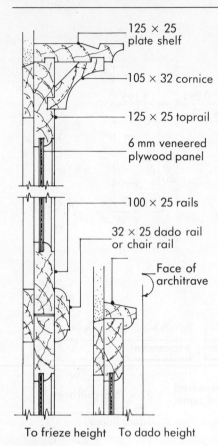

125 × 25 plate shelf

105 × 32 cornice

125 × 25 toprail

6 mm veneered plywood panel

100 × 25 rails

32 × 25 dado rail or chair rail

Face of architrave

To frieze height   To dado height

Fig. 6.6
Vertical section details – framed panelling

panelling were to a greater height, there would probably still be a chair rail or dado rail at about the height indicated, and this would serve also to cover a horizontal joint, if required. Note that the projecting mouldings are thinner than the architrave, so they would fit neatly against it. Fig. 6.5 also shows a vertical joint, as necessary in a long wall. The joint is concealed with a pilaster which is planted on the face, then skirtings and capping are continued around this projection. The flutes would be stopped short of the skirting and capping, and as illustrated the capping at this point would probably be worked 'in the solid' to avoid short-grained pieces. The sizes of the principal members shown in this example are:

- *Grounds*, 15 mm thick × 50 mm minimum, wider where lapped.
- *Framing* to panels 25 × 75 mm or more. Bottom rail 95 mm on face, extra for overlap of skirting.
- *Panels*, 6 mm veneered plywood.

The panel framing is morticed and tenoned together, glued, and in most cases secured by screwing from the back. An important part of work of this nature is that it must be finished to a high standard, and this includes the inner edges, mouldings and panels, from which all machine marks and blemishes must be removed before assembly, and in readiness for the applied finish to follow. Finishing trades, and in the past this would most often be the polisher, may prefer to work on panels before they are finally secured into the framing, and for this reason panels may be set in rebates, rather than grooves, and secured from behind. This is less important now with the more common approach of brush-applied finishes, but could still be an advantage in consideration of the whole process of work necessary in achieving a high standard of finish.

Various alternative details in framed panelling appear in Fig. 6.7 where it will be seen that some panels are capable of being polished or varnished independently of the framing.

(a) Is a simple approach, using 5 mm veneered plywood, and planted mouldings;
(b) Reduces hand work to a minimum since the machine-worked stuck moulding allows shoulders to be machine scribed;
(c) Could be more expensive due to the mitred solid pieces which are tongued and glued to the laminboard. The panels here are 12 or 15 mm laminboard with edge pieces 75 mm wide;
(d) Employs 9 or 12 mm veneered plywood panels held in place by bolection mouldings which are screwed from behind.

In work of this kind it is usual not to allow moulded architraves to pass down to the floor level, where they are likely to

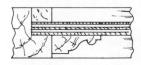

(a) Planted bed moulding

Dust-free lower edge

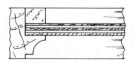

(b) Stuck moulding

(c) Solid edge to laminboard panel

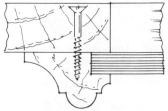

(d) Reversed bolection moulding
     to veneered plywood panel

Fig. 6.7
Framed panel details

be damaged and difficult to keep clean. Plinth blocks, situated at the base, are plain in section and therefore do not present the problems that moulded members would create. Another reason for using plinth blocks in this kind of situation is that when the skirting is as thick, or thicker, than the architrave the plinth block will effectively 'master' the end of the skirting. Fig. 6.8 illustrates a plinth block, and shows the architrave and skirting adjoining it. A barefaced tenon at the foot of the architrave is screwed and glued into a recess which may be prepared on the spindle moulder (alternate feeding onto the spindle, then cutting to length). Architraves are prepared in the workshop, in pairs, leaving only the mitre cuts to be worked on site. Note too that the end of the skirting is recessed into the block to conceal shrinkage.

Internal angles in framed panelling, where the adjoining stiles meet, should be adequately supported by properly positioned grounds behind. Tongued and grooved joints are generally employed here to locate the members effectively and conceal shrinkage. A mitre would be wrong here, since, as the panelling is drawn back to the grounds in fixing, the mitre would open. Fig 6.9 illustrates a rebated joint and the more effective tongued and grooved joint at such an internal angle.

External angles are more difficult, since they are more noticeable than internal angles. A mitre offers the advantage of placing the joint precisely at the corner, or arris, but it will need some form of tongue to locate its position and to secure the joint. To allow one member to pass by the other to tongue and groove the joint creates imbalance in the appearance of the joint, so a decorative feature is added to overcome this. Several alternative joints at external angles are also illustrated in Fig. 6.9.

Strip Panelling

Strip panelling, employing simple tongued and grooved boards, presents few problems to the joinery producer since the work in manufacture entails only the moulding of material to be fixed on site. This approach to panelling has been revived in recent years and made more interesting by imaginative designs in sections and by a wider selection of materials.

Generally fixed vertically, this panelling must be in narrow strips to minimise the unsightly effects of shrinkage, and in many cases only one edge of each board is fixed, while the other is free to move with moisture content changes. In some cases alternate strips are made from veneered manufactured boards, which may be in wider strips. Angles are easier to deal with where the boards are vertical, and any bold features are less likely to create cleaning problems than they would in horizontal boards. Horizontal strip panelling is sometimes used where there

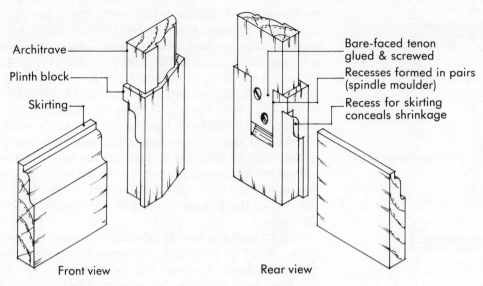

Fig. 6.8
Plinth blocks to architraves

Architrave
Plinth block
Skirting
Front view

Bare-faced tenon glued & screwed
Recesses formed in pairs (spindle moulder)
Recess for skirting conceals shrinkage
Rear view

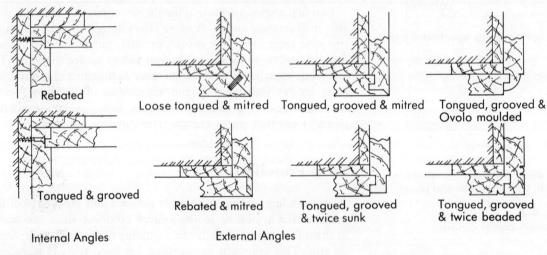

Rebated
Tongued & grooved
Internal Angles

Loose tongued & mitred
Rebated & mitred
External Angles

Tongued, grooved & mitred
Tongued, grooved & twice sunk

Tongued, grooved & Ovolo moulded
Tongued, grooved & twice beaded

Fig. 6.9
Alternative corner details

is an intention to influence the visual impression of a wall by making it appear longer than it is, and vertical strip panelling has the opposite effect, making the wall appear higher.

Fig 6.10 shows several approaches to strip panelling by illustrating a number of details to indicate typical sections of strips and the chosen materials each could be made from.

1. Tongued and grooved boards ex 112 × 19 Swedish Redwood;
2. 100 × 19 white ash kiln dried to 12% moisture content, both edges fixed to softwood grounds. Loose tongue of matt black

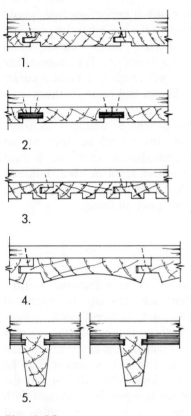

Fig. 6.10
Strip panelling – some examples

melamine on plywood inserted from above (vertical boards, to dado height);

3. 125 × 25 tongued, grooved and moulded Brazilian Mahogany.

Note that each of the above could serve as horizontally fixed boards, but the following are only suitable as vertical strips.

4. 150 × 32 tongued, grooved and moulded Afrormosia;
5. 63 × 38 Utile pilasters at approximately 300–400 centre to centre. Panels of 12 mm plywood faced with Moroccan Leather PVC.

In considering the details at angles, a decision must be made as to which prominent feature is to occur at the change of direction. Taking the last two cases, each has two prominent features. No. 4 has a recess and a hollow face, and either of these could be made to coincide with both the internal and the external angle. No. 5 presents a similar choice.

Fig. 6.11 shows both angles as applied to the last example, where it is considered that the pilaster should occur at the inner angle, and a special section is devised for it from 63 × 63 mm material. At the external angle the best effect is gained from allowing the panel to occur at that point. There pilasters could

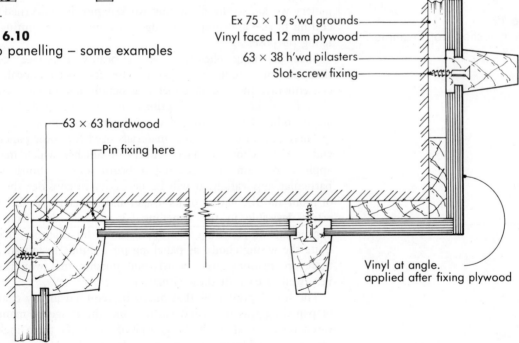

Fig. 6.11
Details at angles
(for Example 5)

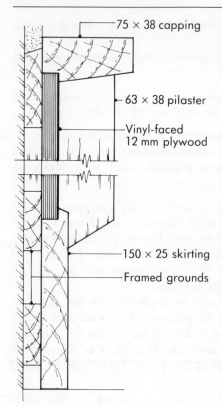

75 × 38 capping

63 × 38 pilaster

Vinyl-faced
12 mm plywood

150 × 25 skirting

Framed grounds

Fig. 6.12
Vertical section (for Example 5)

be fixed by slot screwing, since the number involved would justify the making of keyhole slots in the workshop by precision drilling to a template. Accuracy of screw positions on site would be ensured by the use of a similar template. The grounds are shown as being framed since this will result in a more accurate background, even though most fixings will be in the horizontal ground members.

Vertical sections through the panelling, which is to frieze height, are given in Fig. 6.12 from which it will be observed that the skirting would be fixed immediately after the framed grounds are fixed. Panels and pilasters are then fixed, followed by the cornice which completes the work. Much of the polishing or varnishing could be carried out prior to fixing.

Sheet Panelling

Sheet panelling is almost entirely of manufactured boards, taking advantage of the facts that such materials are capable of covering wider expanses than solid timbers, with greater stability, and that craft work is reduced because the greater part of the manufacture of this form of panelling is in the production of the board itself. Where a decorative face or veneer is to be applied, this is most likely to be done before delivery to the joinery works, so the remaining work is mostly concerned with cutting to size and preparing edges as required for jointing and fixing purposes.

Sheet panelling relies more on the beauty of its face veneers than on intricate joinery features for its visual appeal, and consequently the overall effect is generally one of flat surfaces with the minimum of interruptions. In some cases joinery details are introduced purely to add visual interest to the work.

There is a range of board materials used for sheet panelling, and a wider choice of face veneers or finishes which may be applied to them. In selecting a board and its finish for a particular application, it will be necessary to consider the type of room and the nature of its usage, and to determine the properties desirable in the panelling. A material that would be appropriate as panelling in a board room, for example, may be quite the wrong choice as panelling for a public restaurant, but there are manufactured boards and finishes that would serve very well in each of these situations.

The list of properties that might be required in any example of panelling was discussed earlier, and the range of manufactured boards that might be employed to satisfy them includes plywood, blockboard, laminboard, chipboard, fibreboard, plasterboard and proprietary fire-retardant boards. Each of these may be made more decorative by finishes applied *in-situ*, but particularly for panelling work boards are available with moulded, 'sculptured' or textured faces, or with factory-applied veneers of decorative timbers, laminated plastic or metals.

When an important feature of wall panelling is that it should improve the acoustic properties of the room, then it could involve highly specialised design criteria, beyond the realms of joinery technology.

The practical implications that it could have on the production of panelling are likely to be concerned with the choice of materials to be used for the sheeting or boarding, in the applied finishes to be attached to them, in the area of panelling to be produced and in the location or part of the room that is to be so panelled, relative to the noise source. The principle to be employed is that of sound absorption, so as to reduce the reverberation that may occur with hard, unyielding surfaces.

Absorptive materials used in panelling will be of low density and, to enhance their effectiveness, some have a textured surface which produces an increased surface area. The sheeting or boarding will typically be of insulation fibreboard (acoustic board) medium hardboard, or cork, all of which have very limited strength and may need to be bonded to a stiffer board material. Although this work is not concerned with preventing sound from being transmitted through the material, it may still be a requirement that the boards are glued into place and that metal fixings should be kept to a minimum.

The acoustic properties of other boards may be improved by an applied surface of materials such as cork, linoleum, flexible PVC, quilted upholstery materials or even carpet.

Many of the soft materials referred to are vulnerable to impact or abrasion damage and should be protected from such wear and tear by strategically placed frame members or appropriate mouldings.

Balancer veneers are sometimes applied to the reverse side of boards of reconstructed timber to avoid distortion due to moisture content changes, but the need for these depends upon the stability and thickness of the board, and how well it is fixed.

The first example, in Fig. 6.13 shows a form of sheet panelling that does not gain the fullest possible advantage from the use of sheet materials, since there is some joinery framing involved, but the form of construction is simple and economy

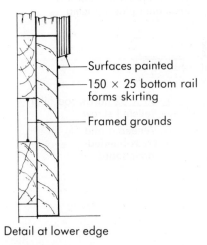

Surfaces painted

150 × 25 bottom rail forms skirting

Framed grounds

Detail at lower edge

Fig. 6.13
Framed sheet panelling

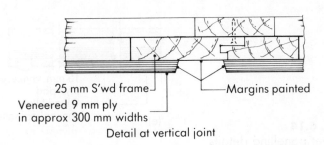

25 mm S'wd frame

Veneered 9 mm ply
in approx 300 mm widths

Margins painted

Detail at vertical joint

is achieved in the use of softwood for the framing and in the relatively thin panelling material employed.

It will be seen in the given details that the exposed surfaces of the softwood, and the edges of the plywood, are painted in a colour chosen to complement the veneered panels, and the bottom rail of the framing serves as a skirting. A vertical joint between assembled units of the same panelling is also shown. The sizes and arrangement of plywood panels in this last example are variable and largely a matter of taste.

Several examples of sheet panelling are shown in Fig. 6.14 as seen at vertical joints between panels, and the brief descriptions following are typical of the materials that could be employed.

(a) 18 mm wood-veneered chipboard screwed to softwood grounds with joints and fixings concealed with moulded hardwood cover fillets;

(b) 18 mm blockboard with hardwood lippings and laminated plastic facing. Tongued hardwood fillet between panels provides fixing by pins, punched home and stopped;

(c) 15 mm laminboard, hardwood lipped and hardwood veneered. Screw fixings concealed by plastic faced plywood tongue inserted from the top (dado height);

(d) 18 mm veneered and cross-banded laminboard, grooved to receive loose tongue of plywood, 38 × 32 mm grooved and moulded hardwood fillet screwed and pelleted to softwood grounds;

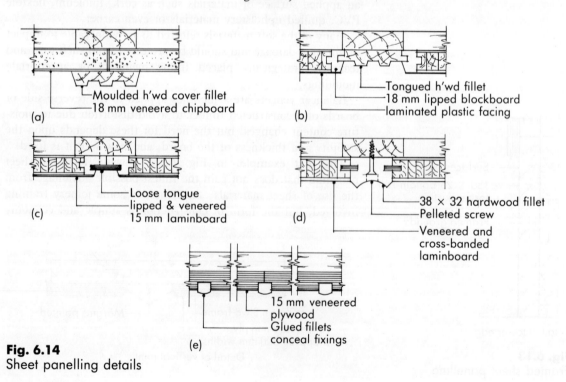

(a) Moulded h'wd cover fillet
18 mm veneered chipboard

(b) Tongued h'wd fillet
18 mm lipped blockboard
laminated plastic facing

(c) Loose tongue
lipped & veneered
15 mm laminboard

(d) 38 × 32 hardwood fillet
Pelleted screw
Veneered and cross-banded laminboard

(e) 15 mm veneered plywood
Glued fillets conceal fixings

Fig. 6.14
Sheet panelling details

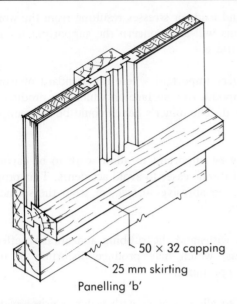

50 × 32 capping
25 mm skirting
Panelling 'b'

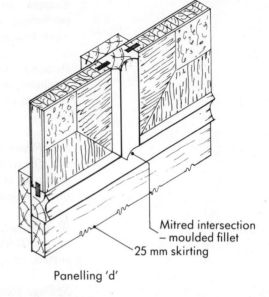

Mitred intersection
– moulded fillet
25 mm skirting
Panelling 'd'

Fig. 6.15
Pictorial details at skirtings

(e) 15 mm veneered plywood grooved to receive contrasting hardwood fillets, glued in after polishing. Fixings by screws or pins beneath glued fillets, which are finished at 15 × 10 mm and spaced at 75–100 mm centres.

Associated with each of those details would be the need to consider how to deal with internal and external angles, top and bottom edges as discussed for the other forms of panelling. Panelling (b) for example could have, as its lower edge detail, that shown in Fig. 6.15 where the skirting and its capping would be fixed first, to hold the lower edge of the panels which would be fixed after it. Panelling (d), with its screwed and pelleted hardwood mouldings, could rest directly on the skirting since the joint between the two is masked by the projection, and this is illustrated in the same figure.

WORK SURFACES

Work surfaces, which occur on tables, benches, cupboards, desks and counters, are mainly functional, although in some cases appearance may be almost as important as performance.

The functional requirement of a work surface will determine the choice of material, the construction details and applied finishes. Function may also dictate some dimensions, particularly the height of the surface, for reasons of anthropometry as discussed in Chapter 1.

Properties that may be required in a work surface in order to perform the functional requirements expected of it may include a number of the following.

Strength to withstand loads or stresses resulting from the work performed on it. This will also concern the supporting framework beneath the surface.

Accuracy may be very important where the standard of work produced depends upon a true surface on which the product is prepared or assembled. The joiner's bench could be an example of this.

Slip Resistance may be important to allow work to be carried out effectively, and in some cases to avoid accidents. This property may come from an abrasive surface, or from the softness of a 'resilient' surface.

Wear Resistance to withstand the rubbing and abrasive effect of the work process, which may produce distortion of the surface or spoil its appearance.

Spillage Resistance to allow contact with water, spirits, acids, grease or oil associated with the designed use of the surface. Failure to resist such contact may result in a breakdown of finishes, materials and adhesives, leading to structural or visual deterioration.

Heat Resistance so as not to be damaged by contact with heat from materials or tools associated with certain occupations, or from nearby heat-producing appliances.

Hygiene as necessary where food is prepared or handled and where the work process demands the use of sterile materials and equipment. This property is likely to be achieved only where the surface is hard, non-absorbent and free from open joints or crevices. Timbers are unlikely to satisfy this requirement.

Heat Conductance, depending on the use of the surface, may or may not be desirable. For example, the use of cast iron in machine surfaces, chosen because it can be manufactured to precision, has the undesirable property of being a ready conductor of heat, and feeling cold to the touch, which in excess could be dangerous. On the other hand, a cool surface is considered to be an advantage for the preparation of pastry in a kitchen.

Of the materials used as work surfaces, timbers probably satisfy more of the requirements discussed than any other, and the timbers selected are most commonly species of hardwood.

It is most likely that the width of surface being produced will demand edge jointing of the material, and there are several approaches to this. There is generally some form of tongue and groove employed, principally to ensure that the faces are kept flush during assembly, and not as a necessary aid to the strength of the glued joint. Dowels and slot-screwing, used in association with glued joints in the past, can rarely be justified with the more efficient glues now in use. Various types of machine-made edge joints are in use in larger production works, but for small production joinery the plywood cross-tongue is very effective. Earlier chapters included some points of interest in the need to consider moisture movement in edge jointed boards as in table tops, and methods of fixing were discussed. Fig. 6.16 shows further details related to solid wood work surfaces, as in the tops to counters. The *clamped end* is used to hold the top flat, and to avoid showing end grain, and the mitre would occur at the front edge, possibly both edges, of the top. End-to-end joints in such a top are sometimes necessary for practical purposes and these are best fitted in the workshop ready for assembly on site. Tongued or dowelled to retain a flush surface, joints of this kind are cramped and held together by *counter keys* which remain in place beneath the worktop. It will be seen in the diagram that, as the folding wedges are driven through the staggered housings in the keys, the joint is drawn together, then the remaining six screws are inserted.

Solid wood worktops of the kind shown are not suitable where cutting or chopping operations are carried out on the surface, since the material would soon be eroded. An extreme example, where activity of this kind is to be provided for, is the butcher's chopping block in which the top is made from end-grain blocks of hardwood, which for obvious reasons will withstand constant contact with cutting edges for a much longer period. This principle is used on a smaller scale where culinary cutting boards are made from end-grain blocks glued together side-by-side.

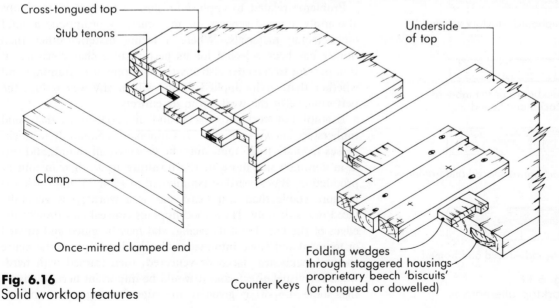

Cross-tongued top

Stub tenons

Underside of top

Clamp

Once-mitred clamped end

Fig. 6.16
Solid worktop features

Counter Keys

Folding wedges through staggered housings proprietary beech 'biscuits' (or tongued or dowelled)

The species of solid wood used as a work surface will have been selected for its visual appeal and ability to withstand the rigours of its designed use. Most softwoods, and some of the lower density hardwoods, will soon become unsightly as a result of the slight pressure or impact from relatively light use, as is being experienced in the currently popular use of pine as domestic table tops which need continuous care to prevent their rapid deterioration. Some timbers soon become stained as a result of contact with moisture and may appear to be unhygienic, and for this reason oak is generally considered to be unsuitable as a bar top.

With the exception of the butcher's end-grain cutting block (which is never in contact with water, but is regularly scraped or wire-brushed for cleanliness) solid wood work surfaces need to be sealed to prevent them from becoming soiled or ingrained with dirt or grease from the work process and from general handling. The sealant or applied finish to a worktop must itself be capable of withstanding the effects of the work with which it comes into contact, as has already been discussed. The traditional 'French polish' is recognised as being a superior finish, but is suitable only in a limited number of situations since it will not withstand water, spirits or moderate heat. Other traditional finishes which gave better performance in those situations were costly in terms of the labour involved and have consequently been superseded by a number of finishes developed in recent years, which are easier to apply and are reliable. Polyurethane varnish is in popular use, and depending on the standards of workmanship is capable of being brought to a very good finish in either gloss, matt or semi-matt forms to resist contact with water, spirits and heat.

Problems related to applied finishes to timbers in worktops also apply to wood veneers and to framework or lippings around other facing materials. Where a facing material other than timber has been selected for its performance characteristics, it is important to consider also any timber lippings or framings and whether that, or its applied finish, will in any way reduce the performance of the worktop in its entirety.

Examples of workstops that include materials other than solid timbers are shown in Fig. 6.17. Chipboard, commonly in thicknesses from 12 to 25 mm, must be veneered all round, and this is in common use more in the furniture trade than in joinery production. Blockboard or laminboard in 18 or 25 mm thickness is more stable than chipboard and as a worktop is generally faced one side only. Hardwood lippings conceal and protect the edges of the board and its facing, and may be glued and pinned or tongued and glued into place. The third example in the figure shows blockboard, faced or veneered, then framed with hardwood for visual effect, and it would be important here to ensure that some support is given to the edge framing rather than to

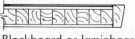

Chipboard – factory veneered

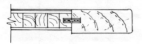

Blockboard or laminboard
– faced and lipped

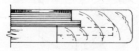

Blockboard – faced and framed

Plywood – faced and framed

Fig. 6.17
Worktop alternatives

allow its whole width to project beyond the work beneath. Plywood, although available in the greater thicknesses equal to blockboard or laminboard, is rarely used in those thicknesses for worktops because of its expense. The fourth example shows plywood as commonly employed for this work, in 9 or 12 mm thickness, framed in hardwood and supported at intervals by cross-rails.

The face materials referred to are very commonly of laminated plastic, under a number of trade names and comprising a number of melamine-bonded laminates of kraft paper. As a facing material to a worktop, this is available in a wide range of colours and patterns, is hygienic, resistant to water, spirits, grease, oils and moderate heat. Where there is constant contact with water, the face materials should be bonded to the board with water-resistant glue, and latex 'contact' glue is unsuitable. The surface is not designed to withstand cutting or abrasive operations, and has a limited life in those conditions.

Surfaces designed for the purpose of reading or writing are required to be slightly resilient and warm or comfortable to the touch, and these generally occur on desks, lecterns and some service counters. Typical finishes are leather, flexible PVC, linoleum and cork, and either of these could be applied to the last three examples in the last figure. Fig. 6.18 shows further examples where either leather or PVC is used in a desk top. In the first, the 9 mm plywood has battleship grade 'lino' bonded to it to finish flush with the framing. The second example shown, is where the leather or PVC is wrapped around the edge of a 4 mm plywood panel, then bonded down to the under-panel with contact adhesive.

The third example has similar facing material bonded to thicker plywood. Heights, and to a lesser extent widths, of worktops may be critical to their function, but since the people using them will differ in stature some compromise is necessary in determining the dimensions that will suit the majority. Worktops are in most cases associated with items of furniture which

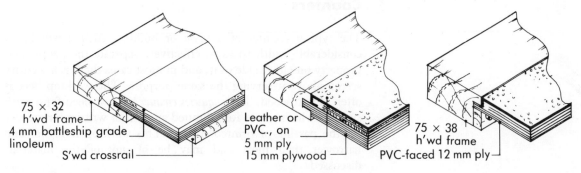

75 × 32
h'wd frame
4 mm battleship grade
linoleum
S'wd crossrail

Leather or
PVC., on
5 mm ply
15 mm plywood

75 × 38
h'wd frame
PVC-faced 12 mm ply

Fig. 6.18
Further worktop details

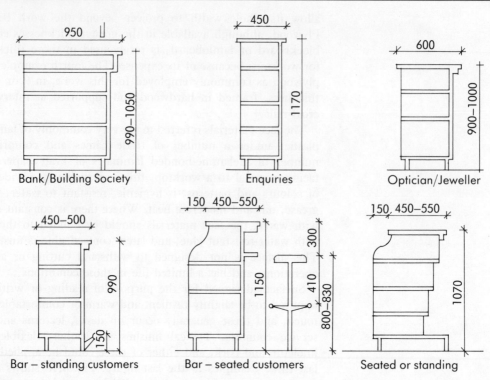

Fig. 6.19
Worktop dimensions – counters

serve other purposes as well, and examples are seen in the home where the surface is designed for food preparation, dining, writing and cosmetics. In industry and commerce work surfaces provide for a wide variety of functions, and in every case ideal dimensions will depend not only on the stature of the user, but on the nature of the function he performs and whether he is standing or sitting. Some examples of such dimensions applied to common items of joinery are shown in Fig. 6.19 which illustrates a number of service counters.

Counters

The typical counter at a bank or building society will be of considerable width so as to effectively separate the people and property on either side of it, and in most cases there is a security screen above it serving the same purpose. The worktop here is often of hardwood. The *enquiries counter* has less need for a work surface, which serves for a limited amount of writing but mostly for the passing of printed matter. This worktop is higher and narrower than most and may be of any of the materials discussed.

The example indicated for an optician or jeweller is of dimensions suited to persons standing on either side and needing to inspect and discuss small items in some detail. Soft non-slip surfaces would be appropriate for either of these businesses.

The bar counter needs to withstand contact with liquids, including spirits, and constant abrasion from glasses and coins. Traditionally, solid hardwoods are used for these, and they are probably still the best choice for long service, although laminated plastics are a very popular choice. It will be seen that the height of a bar counter, which is intended to be a comfortable 'leaning height', depends on whether the customer is standing or seated on a bar stool. In the second case, the bar top is 300 mm above the stool top. In the last example, the height is a compromise, to be used in reasonable comfort by the standing or seated customer.

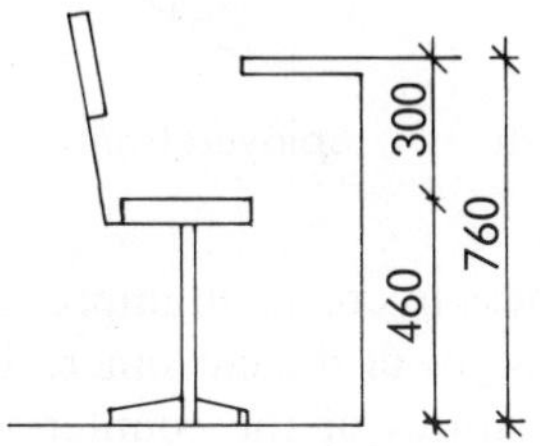

Desk tops, similar to dining tables, should also be to a height relative to the seat height, and the seat height relative to the floor or footrest. A standard seat or chair height of 460 mm is intended to allow the average-sized person to rest the feet firmly on the floor without fatigue, and a desk height of 760 mm should leave the forearms in a horizontal position when the hands are resting on the desk or table top (see Fig. 6.20).

Worktops in laboratories are most often of hardwood, Teak or Iroko being ideally suited, and are generally 920 mm high to suit work which is not of a strenuous nature. This dimension is also used as the standard height for worktops in domestic kitchens, probably with more concern for aesthetics than effectiveness in use. Such a height would be unsuitable without mechanical aids which have dispensed with much of the physical effort in cutting or mixing food by hand. The joiner's bench is an example of a work surface having a height which is critical to its function, and the joiner may find a need to stand on a duckboard or conversely may need to place blocks under the bench legs to achieve the correct height to work effectively. Benches produced commercially are standardised at 840 mm high.

Surfaces designed purely for reading purposes may be higher than those used also for writing, and consequently may be made to slope to afford better vision. An example of this is the lectern, which may rest upon a table or desk, or be free-standing. In either case the function is the same, and the height at the lowest point of the slope is at about waist height to the reader. The slope should be no less than 1:3 to give reasonable vision to readers of average height, and not steeper than 1:2. These dimensions, as illustrated in Fig. 6.21 would lead to considerations on the aesthetic proportions, and other dimensions. The width of such a lectern is likely to be between 450 and 625 mm.

Service counters are used by a number of trades or businesses for the purpose of providing a point, or meeting place, at which the business transaction takes place, or the service is provided by the trader for his customer. Although the counter may serve as a barrier between the private and public sides of the estab-

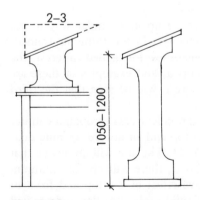

Fig. 6.20
Relative seat and desk heights

Fig. 6.21
Lectern dimensions

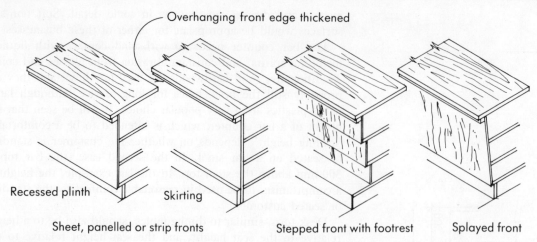

Fig. 6.22
Counter top to front profiles

Overhanging front edge thickened

Recessed plinth

Skirting

Sheet, panelled or strip fronts

Stepped front with footrest

Splayed front

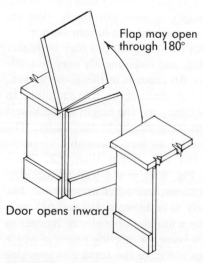

Flap may open through 180°

Door opens inward

Fig. 6.23
Access through counters

lishment, it may be used by the business to create an impression that will enhance its reputation in the eyes of the customer. The choice of materials and the design features of the counter will be used to create an impression appropriate to the nature of the business. The counter in a bank or building society is generally used to confirm a state of financial well-being, that in a saloon bar an air of warmth and comfort, and in a trade concerned with handling food, an impression of hygiene.

A service counter consists of the worktop, as already discussed, and a counter front, and it is these two that create the impression on the customer. On the business side of the counter is its structure, which is generally designed also to satisfy some functional requirements of the trade, such as the storage, preparation and packaging of goods. Fig. 6.22 shows how the counter top and front come together, and that at the bottom edge there will be either a skirting or a recessed plinth. The top is allowed to overhang at the front to reduce the possibility of damage through accidental kicking, and the projecting edge is thickened to improve its appearance by an additional piece screwed on beneath it.

The counter front may be made up in a similar way to the wall panelling shown in this chapter, in the forms or framed, strip or sheet panelling. Sometimes for added interest the counter front is splayed or stepped, and examples of these are also illustrated in Fig. 6.22 where it will be seen that the third also provides a footrest.

It is sometimes necessary to provide access through a counter by forming a hinged flap in the top and an inward opening door in the front, as shown in Fig. 6.23. The aim will always be that when the flap and door are closed, there will be the minimum of interruption in the decorative effect of the top and front of the counter, although where of solid timber the flap and top will be clamped, as shown earlier in Fig. 6.16. The flap will in many

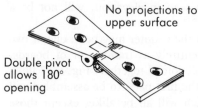

No projections to upper surface

Double pivot allows 180° opening

Counter flap hinge

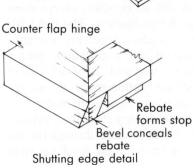

Rebate forms stop

Bevel conceals rebate

Shutting edge detail

Fig. 6.24
Flap details

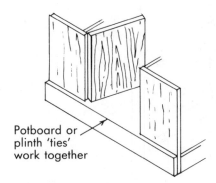

Potboard or plinth 'ties' work together

Fig. 6.25
Threshold gives continuity

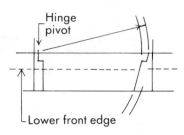

Hinge pivot

Lower front edge

Fig. 6.26
Door geometry

cases be required to open through 180° to rest flat on the counter top, and the *counter flap hinge* allows this without projection above the surface of the counter when the flap is closed. The hanging and meeting edges of the flap are rebated to the counter top to ensure a flush surface, and these rebates should be stopped short of the front edge and finished as a bevel, as shown in Fig. 6.24. The door, hung on butt hinges, will also be rebated on both edges to be effectively 'stopped' in the closed position. Problems arise as a result of differential movement either side of the door, and it is good practice to reduce this by allowing the plinth of the counter to pass across the doorway to form a threshold which will serve to tie the two portions of counter together, as shown in Fig. 6.25.

The door to either of the last two counters shown in Fig. 6.22 would present particular problems as a result of their profiles. The pivot points of the hinges must be in a perpendicular line, otherwise the door will swing upward as it opens (a principle used where a large gate is to clear an upward sloping driveway). Each door in such counters must be constructed so that its inner face is in a vertical plane, while its outer face follows that of the counter front.

Fig. 6.26 shows the geometry concerned and its effect on the door construction. The outline of the door shown represents its structure without the front panel, and it will be seen that the door is of considerable thickness with the result that there is a positive need for a clearance bevel to the shutting edge. The hanging and shutting pieces are fixed to the counter framing or 'standards' at either side of the door opening, so the counter front will conceal them. As a point of interest, the joint at the

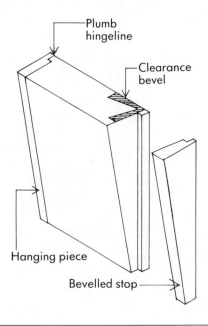

Plumb hingeline

Clearance bevel

Hanging piece

Bevelled stop

shutting edge of the door, as seen in elevation, will not be a vertical line.

The structure, or carcase, of the counter may be in one of two basic forms, made up either entirely as framing or of boards, in standards and shelves suitably joined together. Fig. 6.27 illustrates a framed carcase where the first parts to be assembled will be the framed standards, which will all be alike, except those which need to be panelled in, as at the doorway. The standards must be at suitable spacings for the shelves, which are in lengths which join together at each standard, and a maximum spacing of 1.200 m would suit both the stiffness and the sheet sizes of 18 mm blockboard. The top rails are continuous; so too are the front rails and the potboard which would be screwed to the standard from below. The counter front is screwed on from behind, through the front rails; similarly the top is fixed through the top rails. The plinth is assembled separately and fixed up from beneath by pocket screwing.

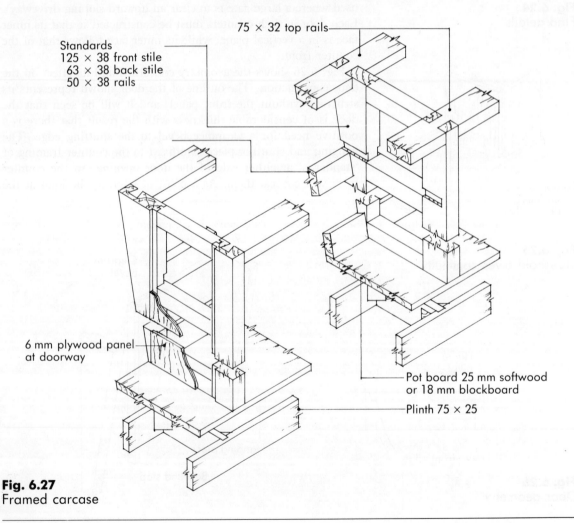

75 × 32 top rails

Standards
125 × 38 front stile
63 × 38 back stile
50 × 38 rails

6 mm plywood panel
at doorway

Pot board 25 mm softwood
or 18 mm blockboard

Plinth 75 × 25

Fig. 6.27
Framed carcase

In Fig. 6.28 the alternative approach to the construction of the carcase is illustrated. In the past this would have entailed the work of building up the necessary board widths in solid material, in most cases softwood, by edge-jointing and employing cross-tongued joints. The problem of moisture movement in such construction was considerable, particularly where any members were joined together in differing grain directions, and this occurred mostly where shelf bearers or drawer runners were attached to divisions or standards. In the example shown, the only members presenting this problem are the cross-bearers beneath the potboard, so this would have been treated in the same way as a table top, by using buttons or shrinkage plates to fix the potboard to the bearers. The use of solid timbers in this form of construction is now unlikely, because of the advantages offered by the use of 18 mm, or possibly 25 mm, blockboard (with exposed edges lipped with hardwood) for all of the wide board members shown.

As in the previous example, the potboard and the two top rails are continuous, so that they will effectively tie the carcase together. Joints between board members are formed by housings

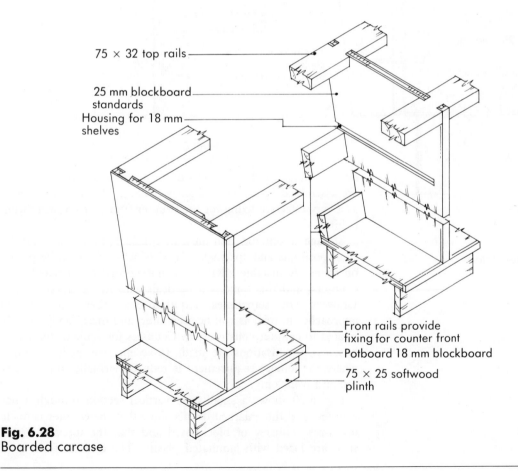

75 × 32 top rails

25 mm blockboard standards

Housing for 18 mm shelves

Front rails provide fixing for counter front

Potboard 18 mm blockboard

75 × 25 softwood plinth

Fig. 6.28
Boarded carcase

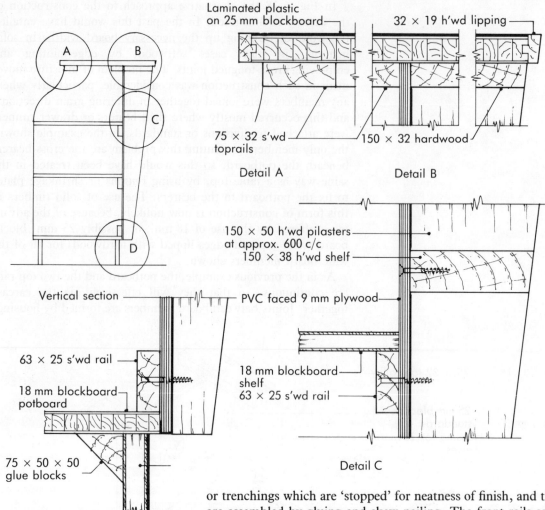

Laminated plastic
on 25 mm blockboard

32 × 19 h'wd lipping

75 × 32 s'wd
toprails

150 × 32 hardwood

Detail A

Detail B

150 × 50 h'wd pilasters
at approx. 600 c/c
150 × 38 h'wd shelf

PVC faced 9 mm plywood

Vertical section

63 × 25 s'wd rail

18 mm blockboard
potboard

18 mm blockboard
shelf
63 × 25 s'wd rail

75 × 50 × 50
glue blocks

Detail C

Detail D

Fig. 6.29
Bar counter details

or trenchings which are 'stopped' for neatness of finish, and they are assembled by gluing and skew nailing. The front rails serve as a very effective fixing for the counter front, by screwing from behind.

Storage accommodation must be considered carefully, and the shelf positions and spacings related to whatever is to be placed on them. Adjustable shelves are not normally associated with counters, and this topic will be dealt with in the next chapter. Drawers are sometimes required and there are several approaches to this, as will be seen later, and these can be readily related to counter construction. Counters for some of the larger business organisations are made to accept steel pedestal units, where the joinery requirement is reduced virtually to a counter top and front only.

Fig. 6.29 shows a small-scale vertical section through a bar counter, and the enlarged details show that the counter is made up almost entirely of blockboard and that the top and upper shelf are faced with laminated plastic. The counter front is of

12 mm plywood, faced with 'leathergrain' PVC, and fixed from behind. Superimposed on the counter front is a framework of hardwood with vertical members or 'pilasters' at about 600 mm centre-to-centre. This spacing is taking into account the widths of plywood in the front, and is designed to cover the joints between sheets. This hardwood framing would be assembled independently of the counter, then fixed by screwing through the counter front.

The setter-out would produce a length rod, showing the horizontal section of the counter and the exact positions of standards (ends and divisions). The rod would also show the positions of the hardwood pilasters, equally spaced within the overall length and in consideration of the front panel sizes. A height rod would also be produced, similar to the vertical section given but to the exact full size, and showing all related details as finished.

Sometimes the plan of the counter includes angles, when it will be necessary to consider the construction of the top, shelves, potboard and front at the point where the direction changes. There may also be some geometrical development necessary, and Fig. 6.30 shows an example of this where the counter has a right-angled intersection on plan. From the plan and vertical sections, the true shape of the division and of the corner pilaster are developed, as at the mitre line. The section of the pilaster includes a vee groove at the back edge and a double bevel at the front, and although these all appear as 45° on plan the bevels to the front edge will not be so when applied to the member itself. The geometry for this was shown earlier, as part of *Joinery Project No. I* but a simpler approach is possible here.

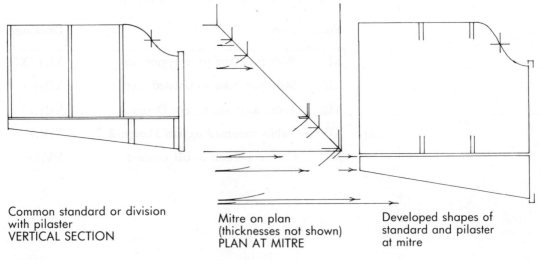

Common standard or division
with pilaster
VERTICAL SECTION

Mitre on plan
(thicknesses not shown)
PLAN AT MITRE

Developed shapes of
standard and pilaster
at mitre

Fig. 6.30
Developed shapes at corner

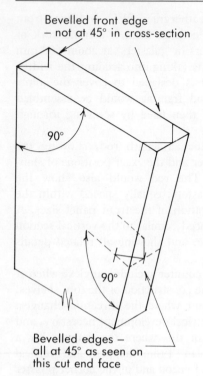

Bevelled front edge
– not at 45° in cross-section

90°

90°

Bevelled edges –
all at 45° as seen on
this cut end face

Fig. 6.31
Corner pilaster sectional shape

In Fig. 6.31 it will be seen that by applying the 45° bevel to the horizontal cut at the end of the material, there is no need for further geometry, and that lines extended down the faces of the shaped member will show the true extent of the bevels.

There are no complications in the construction of the counter at this point. The counter top and potboard would be mitred and tongued together, and the shelves cut to 45° to fit into the housings in the corner division. In most cases the angle of the counter would be fitted together in the workshop, then taken apart for transportation, to be finally assembled on site.

Other plan shapes of counters include curves, generally circular curves, where the counter has a constant cross-section with divisions 'normal' to the curve. In these conditions all divisions or standards are of identical shape, and offer no difficulties. The counter top, shelves and potboard are shaped, and since these are likely to be of blockboard (or other reconstructed boards) there are few problems in these. The potboard, as a continuous member and to the full width of the counter, can usefully serve as a workshop rod, for the development of the shelves and counter top above it.

An example of a counter that is curved on plan appears as one of the Joinery Projects that make up the remainder of this chapter.

JOINERY PROJECTS XI–XV

As in previous chapters, five related joinery projects follow, both to convey some further information and to provide opportunities for applied student activities.

The list of projects for this chapter is as follows:

No.	Item	Drawings
XI	Wall panelling to reception area	XI.1, XI.2
XII	Strip panelling to isolated pier	XII.1
XIII	Table-mounted lectern Design 1	XIII.1
XIV	Table- mounted lectern Design 2	XIV.1
XV	Curved portion to bar counter	XV.1

Project No. XI
Wall Panelling to Reception Area

As part of the Reception Area in a large commercial office building, a small area at the foot of a stairway is to be developed as a waiting area. The work is to comprise two principal parts, the first being panelling to the walls, and the second being the installation of wall seating. The wall panelling is the subject of this Joinery Project, and the seating will form the subject of another in the following chapter.

Specification

The walls to be panelled consist of two adjoining plastered areas, one 3.80 m long with a raking height conforming to the pitch of the stairs where the lowest dimension is 0.880 and the highest is 2.230 m. The other is 1.770 m long and is to be panelled to a constant height of 2.230 m, all as shown in Drawing XI.1. The given dimensions are to be checked on site.

The panelling is to be of 12 mm Birch plywood faced with leather-grain expanding PVC to approved colour and screwed to framed softwood grounds; 63 × 45 mm twice splayed hardwood pilasters are to be fixed to the face of the panelling at approximately 350 mm centre-to-centre. The lower edge is to be finished with a 150 × 25 mm hardwood skirting, and the upper edge with a 50 × 32 mm hardwood capping, all as detailed in Drawing XI.2.

Hardwood is to be clear. selected Brazilian Mahogany with a moisture content in the region of 12–15%. As far as possible, fixings are to be concealed, and all is to be brought to a high standard of finish ready for the application of clear varnish.

Intrepretation

In Drawing XI.2 the plan at each wall is shown as it would appear full size on the workshop rod. The dimensions shown on these Drawings are slightly different from those on the first drawing, as a result of the site check. The corner piece occurring at the angle between the two walls is necessarily of square material so as to align with the pilasters on both walls, and for balance of appearance those at the outer ends are of the same dimensions.

On the workshop rods, the grounds and plywood panels are inserted first, before showing the pilasters to their finished sizes and accurate spacings. Finished sizes of all members must be anticipated, and the principal ones are as follows: Corner pieces 58 × 58, Pilasters 58 × 33, Plywood 12, Grounds 18. The spacing of the pilasters will be determined on the rods by geometrical means, but using the finished sizes stated, the spacings at wall A can be calculated as 341.5 mm, or 374.5 centre-to-centre. At wall B, 12 mm is added to the overall length for the purpose of scribing at the right-hand end, then the spacing is calculated as 302 mm, and the centre-to-centre dimension as 335 mm.

The skirting and the PVC-faced plywood will be fixed to the grounds first, followed by the fixing of pilasters. Concealed fixings for the pilasters may be achieved by slot-screwing, where they are driven downward over projecting screws, to come to rest on the skirting. Since it is intended to fix wall seating as a second part of the project, the lower ends of pilasters, and the skirting will be largely concealed and pelleted screws could be appropriate fixings in those cases.

The framed grounds are to serve firstly to receive fixings of the plywood panels, and these screws will be positioned so as to be concealed by the pilasters. The screws securing the pilasters, are likely to be spaced at 300–400 mm centres, therefore horizontal members of the framed grounds are required in these positions. (It would be unreasonable to provide a vertical ground to every pilaster). Vertical members will be more widely spaced since they serve only to 'frame' the grounds together.

The drawing also illustrates the special details at the heads of the corner piece, and of those pilasters occurring at the stair pitch.

Cappings will be the last pieces to be fitted, and it will be noted that the width is designed to allow scribing to the soffit of the stairs above wall A.

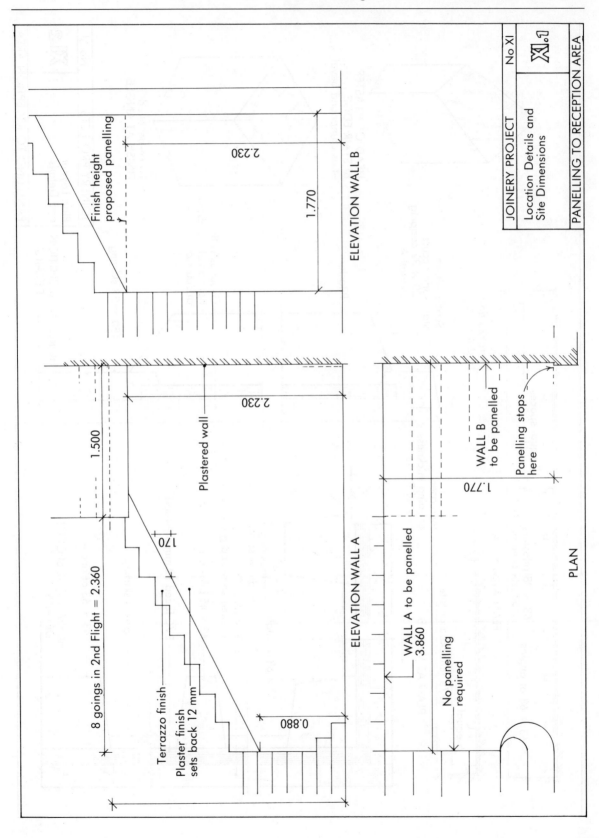

Finish height
proposed panelling

2.230

1.770

ELEVATION WALL B

1.500

2.230

Plastered wall

170

8 goings in 2nd Flight = 2.360

Terrazzo finish

Plaster finish
sets back 12 mm

0.880

ELEVATION WALL A

WALL B
to be panelled

1.770

Panelling stops
here

WALL A to be panelled
3.860

No panelling
required

PLAN

JOINERY PROJECT   No XI

Location Details and
Site Dimensions   XI.1

PANELLING TO RECEPTION AREA

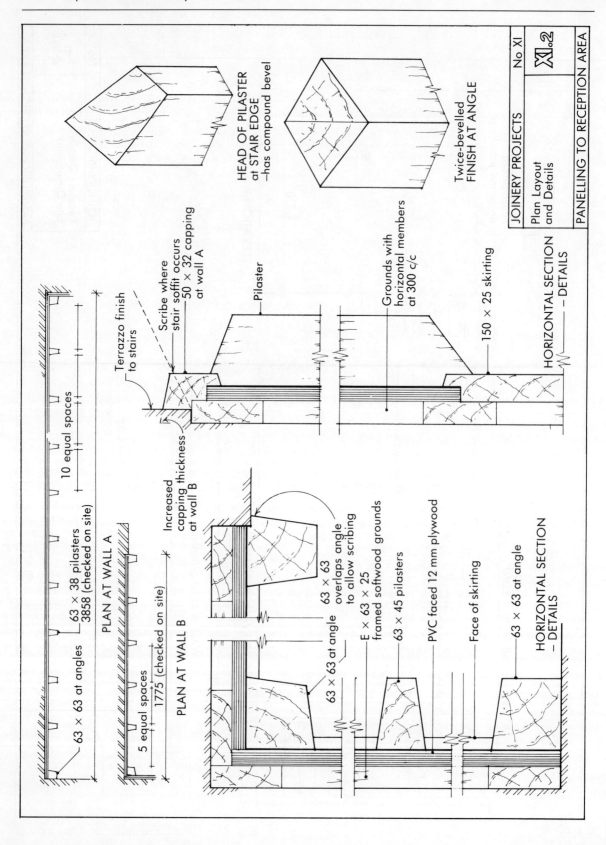

HEAD OF PILASTER
at STAIR EDGE
–has compound bevel

Twice-bevelled
FINISH AT ANGLE

Scribe where
stair soffit occurs
50 × 32 capping
at wall A

Pilaster

Grounds with
horizontal members
at 300 c/c

150 × 25 skirting

HORIZONTAL SECTION
– DETAILS

Terrazzo finish
to stairs

Increased
capping thickness
at wall B

10 equal spaces

63 × 38 pilasters
3858 (checked on site)

PLAN AT WALL A

63 × 63 at angles

5 equal spaces
1775 (checked on site)

PLAN AT WALL B

63 × 63
overlaps angle
to allow scribing

63 × 63 at angle

E × 63 × 25
framed softwood grounds

63 × 45 pilasters

PVC faced 12 mm plywood

Face of skirting

63 × 63 at angle

HORIZONTAL SECTION
– DETAILS

Project No. XII
Vertical Strip Panelling to Isolated Pier

Description

As part of the refurbishment of a large hotel, the walls to the entrance hall and main staircase are to be finished to dado height with vertical strip panelling. Drawings and Specifications for the work will have been provided, and may be summarised as requiring 25 mm Iroko strips in widths 90 to 125 mm, fixed to 63 × 19 mm framed softwood grounds. The joints between the strips are designed to allow screw fixings to be concealed by exposed tongues of 4 mm plywood faced with laminated plastic, this being of approved colour to complement the matt-finished natural hardwood. Vertical and Horizontal details of the work are shown in Drawing XII.1.

As an integral part of the work, an isolated brick pier, situated within the lower flight of the staircase is to be similarly panelled, and it is this item that is the subject of this Joinery Project.

Intrepretation

The horizontal details of the panelling are noted and it is appreciated that each flank of wall will be divided into equal widths of strip panelling each to come within the dimension 90 to 125 mm. The joint detail allows both boards to be secured, but gives freedom for movement in width. The loose tongue will slide into place from above. Vertical details show that the hard-wood capping to the painted skirting or string may be screwed into place, so that the fixings are concealed by the panelling resting on its upper surface. The panelling to the hall will require a large number of boards of the same length, and these could be machined elsewhere to reduce site work.

Strips of laminated plastic, cut precisely to width, will conceal the fixing of the dado rail, and these strips will be fixed with contact adhesive.

The pier will have been shown on the architect's drawing as being situated within the flight of stairs, and the dimensions of the pier together with the stair pitch will have been included. The plan dimensions of the pier, in brick sizes are noted as 788 × 562 mm, with the greater dimension parallel to the 'going' of the stair. The pitch of the stair is shown as having a rise of 156 mm and a going of 265 mm. These dimensions must all be checked on site.

Drawing XII.1 is devoted mostly to the geometry associated with the mouldings around the pier. Pitched or 'raking' mould-ings which intersect with level mouldings in this way cannot all be of the same section. The raking mouldings are parallel to the stair pitch, and will be to the common given section, used else-where. The level mouldings which intersect with them will be to special sections found by geometrical development.

Referring to the drawing, the given section and elevation of the raking mouldings are drawn first, to the stair pitch. The important features are the mitred ends, as seen in elevation. For clarity, the cut ends are shown hatched so that their outline shapes may be seen although in this elevation these cut ends would of course be hidden.

The level mouldings, which must intersect with the raking mouldings will have mitre cuts to exactly the same outline shapes though in reverse form, or 'mirror image'. These reversed outlines are drawn next, by projection, ensuring that all thickness dimensions (numbered) are retained. Elevations of level mouldings are projected from these reversed outline shapes. The special sections required are true cross-sections of the level mouldings, and these are shown for positions A and B on the column.

It should be noted that these sectional shapes, *in level mouldings*, are exactly the same as the outline of the 45° mitre as seen in elevation (this being the property used in cutting scribed intersections from mitre cuts).

To produce the special sections developed will be costly, in view of the geometrical development and the practical work involved. An alternative approach where the common moulding shapes could be used throughout is also shown on the drawing, and this may well be acceptable.

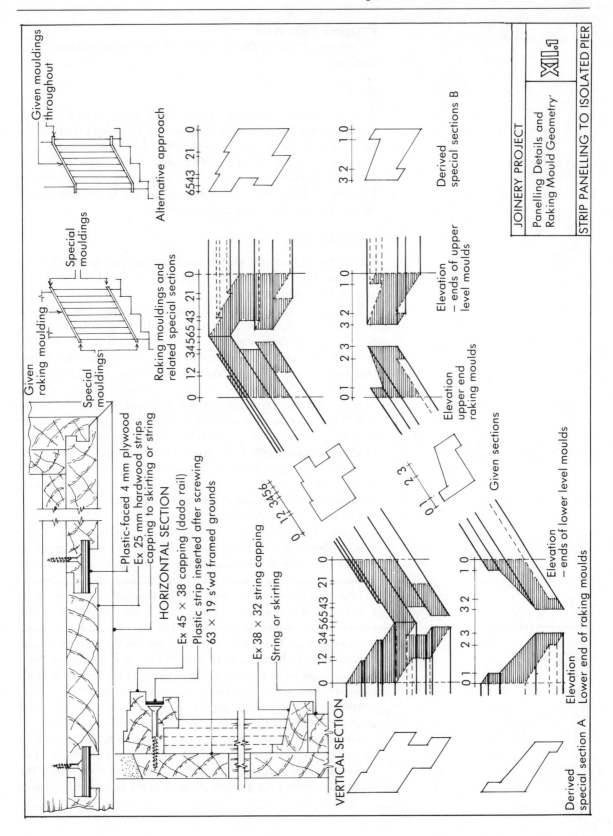

Given mouldings throughout

Alternative approach

6543 21 0

3 2 1 0

Derived special sections B

JOINERY PROJECT

Panelling Details and Raking Mould Geometry

XII.1

STRIP PANELLING TO ISOLATED PIER

Special mouldings

Special mouldings

Given raking moulding

Special mouldings

Raking mouldings and related special sections

1 2 3456543 0

0 1 2 3456 0

12 3456543 21 0

12 3456543 21 0

Plastic-faced 4 mm plywood

Ex 25 mm hardwood strips capping to skirting or string

HORIZONTAL SECTION

Ex 45 × 38 capping (dado rail)

Plastic strip inserted after screwing

63 × 19 s'wd framed grounds

Ex 38 × 32 string capping

String or skirting

VERTICAL SECTION

Derived special section A

Elevation – ends of upper level moulds

Elevation upper end raking moulds

Given sections

Elevation – ends of lower level moulds

Elevation Lower end of raking moulds

1 0

3 2

2 3

0 1

2 3

1 0

Project No. XIII
Table-mounted Lectern – first of two alternative designs

Brief

Two alternative sketch proposals have been provided, each giving overall dimensions and showing the aesthetic features to be produced. From the given sketches the construction details and work content are to be determined. This project concerns the first alternative design, which appears in sketch form in Drawing XIII.1, from which the details are to be determined before the Specification can be written.

Interpretation

It is apparent from the sketch proposals and the materials to be used that the work is to be of high quality, and that cost is a secondary consideration.

The cantilevered effect in the supporting standards would be difficult to achieve satisfactorily by framing solid material together, since there will be excessive stress on the joints. The most likely joint to employ would be a glued combed joint, but this would present a problem in concealing end grain. The conclusion is that the most satisfactory results will come from building up the standards to the required thickness from a number of laminates of multi-plywood, then facing all surfaces with Oak veneers. This approach will also make it possible to produce a mitred effect as shown in the pictorial view on the same drawing sheet. Veneers, cut for the purpose to a thickness of 2 to 3 mm, can be produced, fitted, glued and cramped into place by employing normal joinery techniques.

The lectern top will be framed together from solid oak, mitred together and with a plywood panel finishing flush on the under-side as shown in the Edge Detail. In order to give support to the leather-covered plywood forming the upper surface, it is decided to produce a solid effect by building up the plywood thickness as shown. The width of the framing is kept down to a nominal 50 mm so as to minimise possible shrinkage in the mitres, which would be unsightly. The back rail must be wider to accommodate the lipping, which is seen in the End Elevation.

Note that the bevelled front edge of the top is continued along the side edge so as to intersect effectively at the mitre, without exposing end grain. Similarly, the bevel to the rear edge is continued part-way along the side edges. In each case, the bevel is stopped at an appropriate place for the best visual effect.

The shaped distance pieces, made to conform to the pitch of the top of the lectern, are glued into place on the standards. The top is fixed by screwing through the distance pieces into the standards, before the leather covered panel is inserted. This is secured at four glued spots to allow removal at a later date if necessary.

The brass clips holding the glass panel in place are purpose-made, with the cylindrical portions being polished and lacquered and the bracket portions finished matt black. A suitable finish for the Oak will be to apply three coats of clear polyurethane varnish in semi-matt.

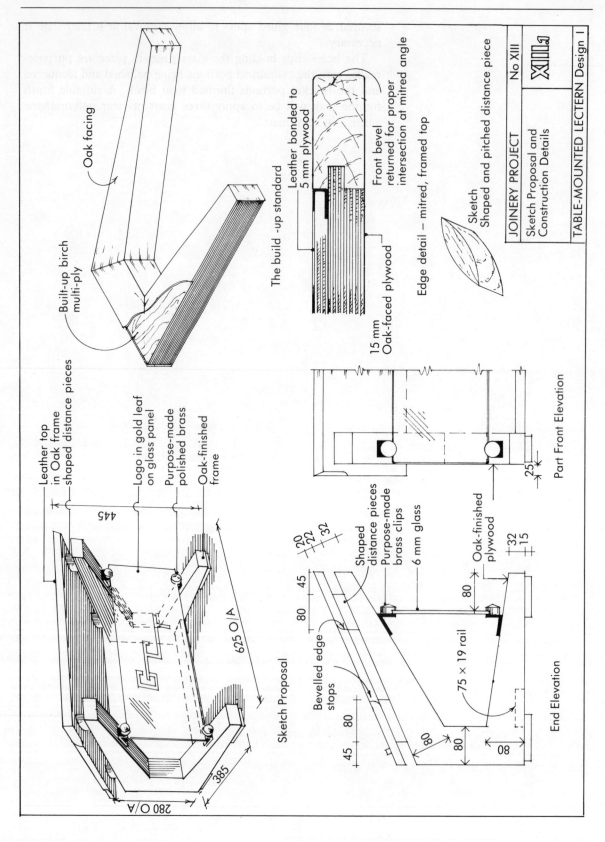

Oak facing

Built-up birch multi-ply

The build -up standard

Leather bonded to 5 mm plywood

Front bevel returned for proper intersection at mitred angle

Edge detail – mitred, framed top

15 mm Oak-faced plywood

Sketch
Shaped and pitched distance piece

JOINERY PROJECT   No XIII

Sketch Proposal and Construction Details

TABLE-MOUNTED LECTERN Design I

Leather top in Oak frame shaped distance pieces

Logo in gold leaf on glass panel

Purpose-made polished brass

Oak-finished frame

445

625 O/A

385

280 O/A

Sketch Proposal

Shaped distance pieces
Purpose-made brass clips
6 mm glass
Oak-finished plywood

20
22
32

45
80

80

80

45

Bevelled edge stops

75 × 19 rail

32
15

80

80

80

08

Part Front Elevation

25

End Elevation

Project No. XIV
Table-Mounted Lectern – second of two alternative designs

As with the first alternative design, which was the subject of the previous Project, this example is presented firstly in the form of a sketch proposal showing the main dimensions and principal features, at the stage when the construction details have yet to be determined.

Drawing XIV.1 shows the sketch illustration, then develops the construction details that result partly from practical considerations in producing the work, and partly from performance requirements in the finished lectern.

Interpretation

The supporting framework consists of two framed standards of hardwood, mitred together to produce the geometric shape required. The standards depend largely on shaped, plastic faced plywood webs for rigidity, and their proper connections to the framing is important.

The top of the lectern consists of a frame of hardwood, enclosing a veneered plywood panel supporting an inlay of linoleum. A plastic faced plywood fascia, between the two standards serves firstly to give lateral rigidity to the lectern, and secondly to carry a 'logo' of hardwood.

Front and End Elevations as shown on the drawing are produced accurately to establish precise shapes and timber sizes. These drawings are as they would appear, full-size, on the workshop rod.

The standards are determined as being made from 63 × 32 mm hardwood, mitred together to conform to the end elevation on the rod. The mitres will need to be tongued and glued. The frame members are grooved to receive the 12 mm plywood webs, and the laminated plastic faces will 'shoulder' against the hardwood. The shaped edges of the webs have hardwood strips inserted at the time of facing with plastic, so that the plywood is not exposed.

The pictorial sketch illustrates the main features of production of the standards. As an aid to cramping the mitres, triangular blocks of wood may be glued to the outer faces, to be sawn off after the removal of the cramps.

Construction of the top of the lectern is partly illustrated in the Edge Detail, which shows that it has 50 × 25 mm front and side rails, with a wider back rail to accept the lipping. The veneered plywood panel is made to produce a flush undersurface, and to support the 5 or 6 mm linoleum. The 'lino' will be glued into place after screwing the top into position. This and the necessary stopped bevels will be as described for the first example.

The plywood fascia, faced both sides with plastic, will include a hardwood insert to the top edge, and will be carefully fitted and glued into housings prepared in the framing of the standards. The hardwood logo will be produced from a twice-bevelled hardwood strip, mitred together to produce the designed pattern, after being brought to the required finish.

The colour of the laminated plastic will be chosen to complement the finished colour of the specified hardwood. As examples, the combination could be specified as:

Black (Ebonised) Ash with pale grey laminated plastic or Afrormosia with sand-coloured laminated plastic.

Hardwood is to receive three coats of clear polyurethane varnish to produce a semi-matt finish.

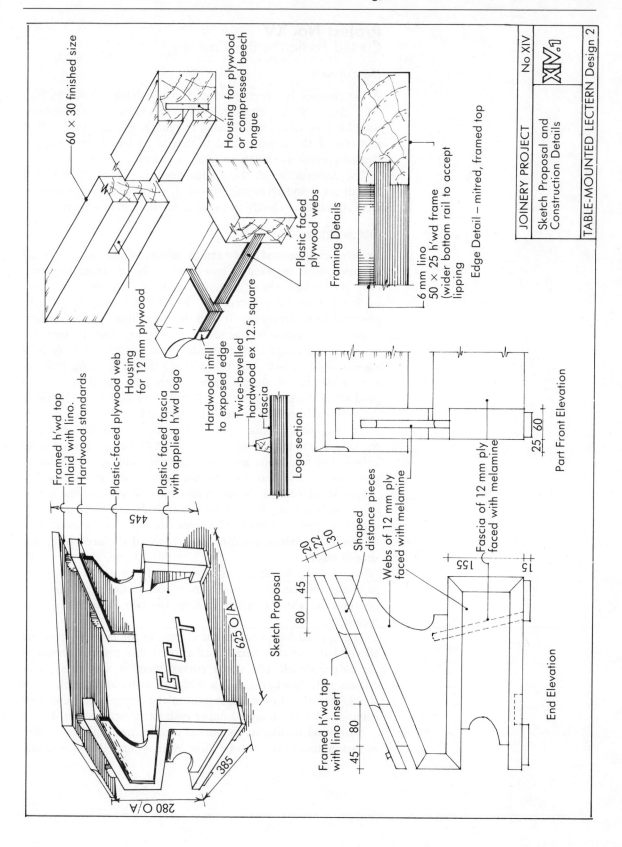

JOINERY PROJECT   No XIV

XIV.1

Sketch Proposal and
Construction Details

TABLE-MOUNTED LECTERN Design 2

60 × 30 finished size

Housing for plywood
or compressed beech
tongue

Plastic faced
plywood webs

Framing Details

Plastic-faced plywood web
Housing for 12 mm plywood

Hardwood infill
to exposed edge

Twice-bevelled
hardwood ex 12.5 square
fascia

Plastic faced fascia
with applied h'wd logo

Logo section

6 mm lino
50 × 25 h'wd frame
(wider bottom rail to accept
lipping

Edge Detail – mitred, framed top

Framed h'wd top
inlaid with lino.
Hardwood standards

445

625 O/A

385

280 O/A

Sketch Proposal

80 45
20
22
30

Framed h'wd top
with lino insert

45   80

Shaped
distance pieces

Webs of 12 mm ply
faced with melamine

Fascia of 12 mm ply
faced with melamine

155

15

End Elevation

Part Front Elevation

60
25

Project No. XV
Curved Portion to Bar Counter

Description

A bar counter has been produced to the details shown in Fig. 6.29 earlier in this chapter, and was designed to fit between walls. It has since been decided to remove the partition wall at one end of the counter, and to extend its length by adding a curved portion as shown on plan in Drawing XV.1.

The construction of the original counter was controlled by a Specification and Drawings provided, and the additional portion is to conform as closely as possible to those instructions.

Interpretation

In producing curved members in joinery of this kind, special attention must be given to how they can be produced economically yet perform their function effectively. The drawing shows in sketch form the construction details that emerge from these practical considerations. It will be seen that, as in straight counters, longitudinal members at the top and bottom are continuous throughout the length of the counter so as to hold the carcase together. The top rails are shown as being built up from a number of shaped pieces of plywood glued together to produce a thickness to match the existing counter. The inner rail may be lipped to conceal the plywood.

The potboard is also in one length and is housed to receive the centre standard shown, and is fixed by being screwed from below. The front rails are produced from bent, glued laminates and it is to these that the plywood front panels will be fixed.

End standards will be of 18 mm blockboard, and the centre one, which appears in the illustration, is 25 mm thick to accept shelf housings both sides. The inner edges of the standards have solid material edge-jointed to them to avoid the need to lip the shaped edges.

To produce the inner and outer curved plinths, an alternative to using solid laminates is shown, where a number of pieces of plywood are glued together to form the two (differing) curved members.

The applied hardwood features fixed to the counter front are all cut from solid material, and part of this work is shown in the corner detail. The upper curved member may need to be end-jointed, depending on the width of material available. This should preferably be a single joint in the centre, and joints that coincide with the tenoned upper ends of pilasters avoided.

Hardwood lipping to the curved counter top could be applied as two laminates so as to be more easily cramped into position.

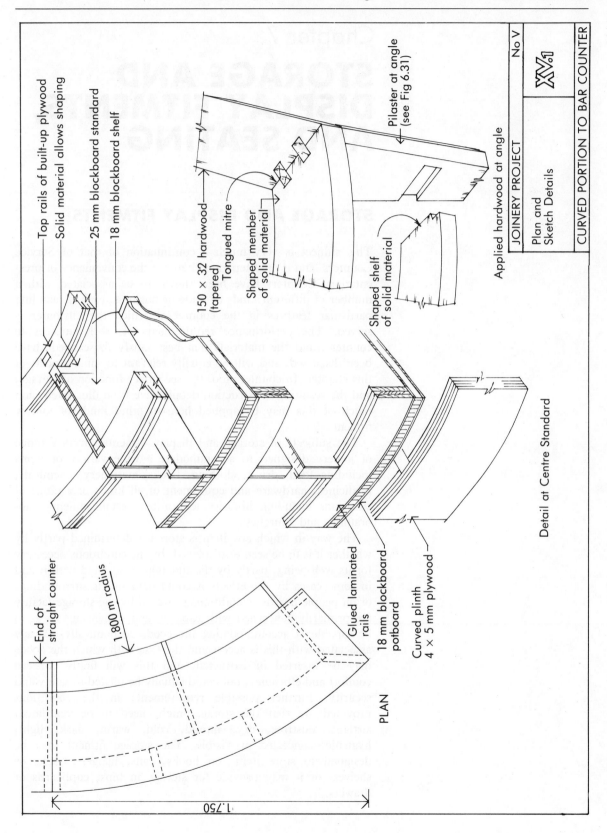

Top rails of built-up plywood
Solid material allows shaping
25 mm blockboard standard
18 mm blockboard shelf

150 × 32 hardwood (tapered)
Tongued mitre
Shaped member of solid material

Pilaster at angle (see Fig 6.31)

Applied hardwood at angle

Shaped shelf of solid material

Detail at Centre Standard

End of straight counter
1.800 m radius

Glued laminated rails
18 mm blockboard potboard
Curved plinth 4 × 5 mm plywood

PLAN

1.750

JOINERY PROJECT   No V

XV₁

Plan and Sketch Details

CURVED PORTION TO BAR COUNTER

Chapter 7

STORAGE AND DISPLAY FITMENTS, AND SEATING

STORAGE AND DISPLAY FITMENTS

This subject is very much a continuation of that of Service Counters, and is only separated here for the convenience of presentation. Counters have been shown to be associated with a number of different kinds of trade or business, each demanding particular features in the counter at which the customer is served. The performance requirements of work surfaces to counters, and the materials that best satisfy those needs have been discussed, and will be equally relevant to some aspects of this chapter. In counters too, the secondary function of storage, and the resulting construction details have been illustrated, and much of this may be applied here to other kinds of joinery fitments.

The subjects of storage and display fitments covers a range of joinery designed to accommodate a wide variety of items including food, drink, clothing, books, stationery, chemicals, medicines, hardware and equipment of all kinds in a range of situations including libraries, educational establishments, laboratories and churches.

The way in which any item is stored is determined partly by whether it is to be seen or displayed, by the conditions necessary for its well-being, partly by the functions associated with it and in some cases by the effects it could have on its surroundings or on people nearby. Conditions provided by the storage facility are primarily concerned with capacity and dimensions so as to be capable of accommodating the goods economically. Closely associated with this is access and the ease with which the goods may be inserted or extracted, and this will firstly concern comfort and efficiency, but could equally be related to safety and security. Further possible requirements in the conditions provided are that the storage might need to be ventilated, airtight, dustfree, dry, humid, cold, warm, dark, light, hygienic, concealed or visible. The storage fitment may be designed to store items on hooks, rails, hangers, racks or shelves, or it may provide for storage in bins, cupboards or drawers.

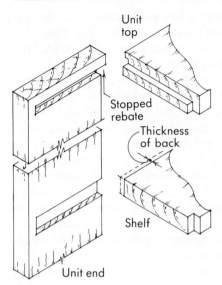

Fig. 7.1
Shelf joints

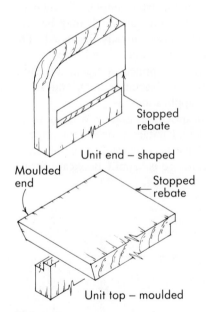

Fig. 7.2
End-grain treatment

Some of these storage requirements may best be satisfied by mass-produced units, designed for specific purposes and often employing materials other than timbers. Examples of this kind, where purpose-made joinery may not effectively compete, include domestic sink units and kitchen cabinets, office storage cupboards and filing cabinets, unless there is a need for special features in their design.

Shelving may be 'open', for ready and frequent access, as is common for the storage of books in public lending libraries, or there may be reasons for shelves to be enclosed, behind doors, in cupboards. Where the shelves are to be in fixed positions, there is a need to determine exactly what is to be stored, to space the shelves accordingly. For shelving intended to carry a range of different-sized items, the best overall economy of accommodation is gained by avoiding equal spacing.

Shelving in a simple bookcase may be entirely of solid timber, since moisture movement will occur in the same direction in all members. In Fig. 7.1 the joints in such a case are illustrated as common 'housings' stopped at the front edges. It will be seen that the plywood back is accommodated by rebates formed in the back edges of the top and ends of the unit, and by reducing the shelf width by the plywood thickness. The rebate is stopped at the upper end of the vertical member so as to prevent it from being seen on the outside.

Assuming that the bookcase is to a height above eye-level, the plywood back could have been allowed to pass to the upper edge of the unit top, instead of being set in a rebate as shown, and this would have avoided the need to stop the rebate.

If the top were visible, as in a low-level unit, the end-grain showing at the top of the unit end would not have been acceptable if finished flush as illustrated. By allowing either member to project, so as to be moulded or shaped as in the two examples shown in Fig. 7.2, simple solutions are found to make end-grain acceptable.

For the very best finish at this point, end-grain may be avoided altogether by producing the effect of a mitre between the top and end of the fitment. A plain mitre would be difficult to fix together with sufficient strength, so some form of tongued and housed joint is incorporated as in Fig. 7.3. Where the corner joint is mitred, there is of course no need to stop the rebates in order to conceal the plywood back.

Fitments of this kind, made from solid timber, are most likely to be of clear-finished hardwood, but common alternatives are veneered and lipped blockboard or laminboard, and veneered chipboard.

Jointing in reconstructed timber boards presents some difficulties in joinery manufacture, and conventional joints developed for solid timbers are not always appropriate to manufactured boards. Veneered chipboard presents particular

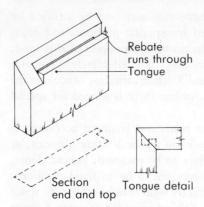

Fig. 7.3
Tongued mitre – avoids end
grain

problems in this respect and it has been necessary to develop various fixing devices, which have in some cases dispensed with the need for conventional 'worked' joints, yet have provided the means to join the material together.

One method of jointing, developed principally for the reconstructed boards, and which is proving to be a very effective and economical method of jointing solid timbers as well, is the Lamello-Minilo jointing system. The device has been accepted, and is being used to good effect by some reputable producers of purpose-made joinery, and may be very well applied to the work of this chapter. The joint is merely butted together, and secured by compressed Beech jointing tongues glued into milled slots prepared by a portable power tool. The time taken to prepare the slots is very short indeed, and compares very favourably with that taken to prepare the stopped housing and shouldered end in the conventional joint.

Fig. 7.4 illustrates the joint between a shelf and standard in a shelving unit, and shows that the tongue is similar in principle to the solid wood cross-tongued joint (now superseded by plywood) in that the grain crosses the tongue obliquely for maximum strength.

The system can be applied also to various end-to-end and edge-to-edge joints including mitres, two examples of which are also shown in Fig. 7.4, and the second of which may be seen as the top corner joint in the bookcase already discussed. The beech tongues (becoming known as 'biscuits') are compressed to encourage swelling when glue is applied, are available from the same source as the power tool (biscuit router), and are in three sizes to suit a variety of applications.

Where it is not possible to anticipate exactly what is to be placed on shelves, it may be an advantage to make their spaces adjustable. Various methods have been employed in the craft, but the most common in current use is 'Tonks Bookcase Strip',

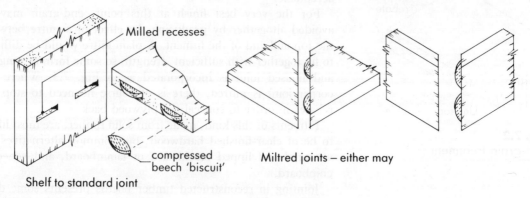

Fig. 7.4
The Lamello jointing system –
some applications

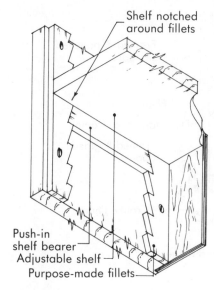

Fig. 7.5
Adjustable shelving

Shelf notched around fillets

Push-in shelf bearer
Adjustable shelf
Purpose-made fillets

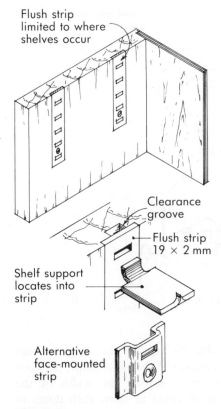

Fig. 7.6
Tonks bookcase strip

Flush strip limited to where shelves occur

Clearance groove

Flush strip 19 × 2 mm

Shelf support locates into strip

Alternative face-mounted strip

which provides a neat solution without involving a great deal of joinery work. Fig. 7.5 shows one of the older craft methods, sufficient to allow comparisons with the more popular approach, and in which there are supporting fillets cut saw-tooth fashion from close-grained hardwood to finish 35 × 10 mm, screwed to the standards. Push-in supports of the same material may be inserted at any height to support the shelf, which is otherwise free to move up or down.

Tonks Bookcase Strip in its most common form, made from iron strip 19 × 2 mm in a number of applied finishes, and designed to be recessed into the standard to produce a flush finish, is shown in Fig. 7.6. It will be seen that the strips occur only where the shelves are likely to be positioned, and stop short of the cupboard height for economy reasons. The enlarged detail shows the shelf support, and it will be seen that the groove formed in the standard, or side of the cupboard, to accommodate the strip, is designed also to allow clearance for the tongue of the shelf support. Also shown is a type of strip intended to be screwed onto the face of the material to avoid the need for grooving, so it is labour saving but not as neat in appearance as the strip that is recessed into the material.

Doors to cupboard fitments may be necessary for the protection of their contents, security or tidiness, and there are a number of alternatives with regard to the construction of the doors and the way they are hung. The doors may be of a type chosen for appearance, to suit the style of the unit to which they belong or the decor of which they are part. They may be designed to satisfy particular functional needs like robustness, security, hygiene or ease of cleaning. They are sometimes required to allow the contents to be seen, in addition to satisfying some of the other needs. Doors to cupboards are made from a variety of materials and are commonly constructed as framed and panelled, framed and glazed, flush, or frameless glass. They may be hinged or they may be made to slide. Hinged doors, when opened, give full access to the cupboard and are generally easier to clean and maintain, but they have the disadvantages associated with the fact that they project into the room when open. Traditionally, hinged doors to cupboards are set within the framing so that the appearance from the front includes the surrounding margin formed by the frame, together with the necessary clearance joint around the door. Such doors would be hung on butt hinges as in Fig. 7.7. Mass-produced cupboards often have doors with rebated edges to lap over the frame to conceal the clearance joint, in a similar way to 'stormproof' windows. Doors of this kind must have cranked hinges so as to place the pivot point in a place that will allow the door to open and this is also illustrated in the Figure. It is currently more popular to allow the door to extend to the whole width of the cupboard so as to conceal the frame completely. This

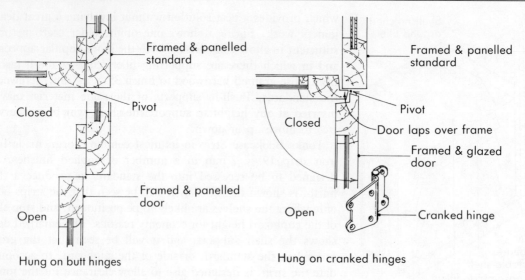

Fig. 7.7
Cupboard door hanging – two
examples

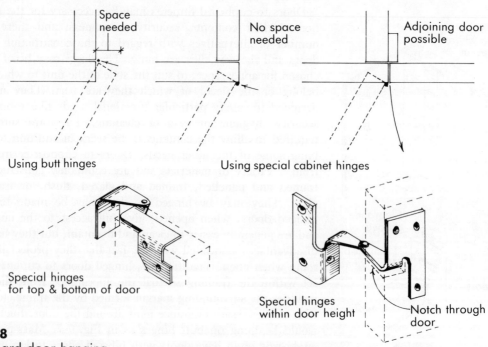

Fig. 7.8
Cupboard door hanging –
concealing the carcase

arrangement would be possible by hanging the doors on butt
hinges, but, because of the position of the pivot point, the door
when open, would occupy space beyond the width of the
cupboard. Hinges have been designed to allow such doors to
open within the cupboard width, by transferring the pivot point
to the outer face of the door, and Fig. 7.8 shows two of the

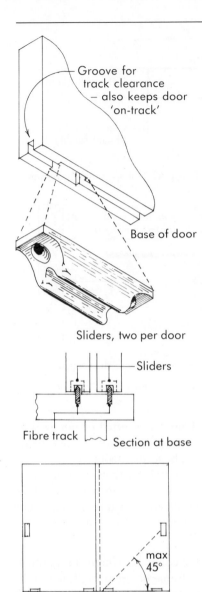

Groove for track clearance – also keeps door 'on-track'

Base of door

Sliders, two per door

Sliders

Fibre track   Section at base

max 45°

'Door-pull' height to base width

Fig. 7.9
Bottom-hung sliding doors

several types of hinge designed for this purpose. There are some that include a spring device that eliminates the need for door fastener.

These are many types of fasteners and associated ironmongery available for cupboard doors, and reference to catalogues will show mechanical and magnetic latches which simply hold the door in the closed position, cupboard locks for use where security is important and a wide range of handles and escutcheons, the selection of which is largely a matter of taste.

Sliding Doors

The design of sliding doors to cupboards is partially dependent upon, and cannot be finalised without knowledge of, the details of the track selected for the work. The doors may be 'bottom hung', where they rest and slide upon tracks fixed beneath their bottom edges, and where their top edges are kept on the designed lines of travel by some form of guides or beads. Alternatively they may be 'top hung', where they are suspended from and slide along tracks fixed above them, in which case their bottom edges will be controlled by guides.

Because many cupboard doors are relatively small and light in weight they may be bottom-hung satisfactorily on a very simple form of track, an example of which is shown in Fig. 7.9 which shows proprietary fibre tracks set into grooves in the frame or potboard. Two plastic sliders are recessed into the bottom edge of the door to such a depth as to give a neat joint between the door and frame. The groove in the door is necessary for clearance. The figure also illustrates the significance of door proportions, or, more precisely, the height of the door handle relative to the base width overall sliders, in achieving the smooth operation of the doors.

Typical details of the arrangement are shown in Fig. 7.10, where it will be seen in the vertical section that a parting bead and staff beads guide the top edges of the doors. The outer bead should be cupped and screwed, and the parting bead a 'push fit' into the groove. The upper details determine the spacing of the two bottom tracks. In the horizontal section will be seen the need to fit a dust strip between the two overlapping door edges, and this is fixed to the outer door. To allow the cupboard to be dusted out more easily, the tracks and their grooves may be stopped short of the end of the cupboard. The beads shown at the vertical edge in this section, although not necessary as door guides, serve partly for continuity and partly for dust exclusion. Note that the sizes given are nominal, and the staff beads, for example, would finish at not more than 12 mm thick.

The alternative top edge detail shown in the figure is cleaner in appearance and simpler in construction, since the beads and

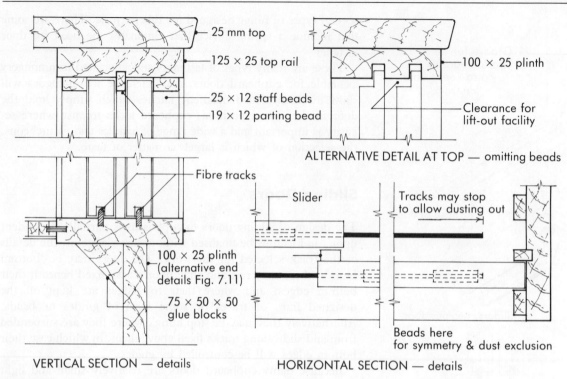

25 mm top

125 × 25 top rail

25 × 12 staff beads

19 × 12 parting bead

Fibre tracks

100 × 25 plinth
(alternative end
details Fig. 7.11)

75 × 50 × 50
glue blocks

VERTICAL SECTION — details

100 × 25 plinth

Clearance for
lift-out facility

ALTERNATIVE DETAIL AT TOP — omitting beads

Slider

Tracks may stop
to allow dusting out

Beads here
for symmetry & dust exclusion

HORIZONTAL SECTION — details

Fig. 7.10
Bottom-hung doors – details

dust strip are eliminated. The doors are inserted or removed by lifting into the upper grooves to clear the bottom tracks, hence the generous clearance indicated above the doors.

The plinth, shown in the Vertical Sections and in some counter details earlier, provides a 'toe space' to reduce the likelihood of damage from accidental kicking. In this example there are several ways that the plinth may be fitted and these are illustrated in Fig. 7.11, where:

(a) Is similar to those shown for counters, where the plinth is mitred together as a separate frame before being fitted to the counter, and produces the effect that the recessed plinth continues around the end of the unit;

(b) Shows the plinth, which would have a bare-faced tongue at each end, fitted between the ends of the unit, which are allowed to run down to floor level. The obvious disadvantages in this detail are that damage could result from acidental kicking, and the inner angle produces a 'dust-trap';

(c) Is an improvement on (b) where the front edge of the unit end is cut back to within about 3 mm of the face of the plinth. The tongued ends of the plinth would in this case be shouldered on the face;

(d) Illustrates a detail where the plinth is mitred to the unit end, producing an effect as neat and clean as the first example,

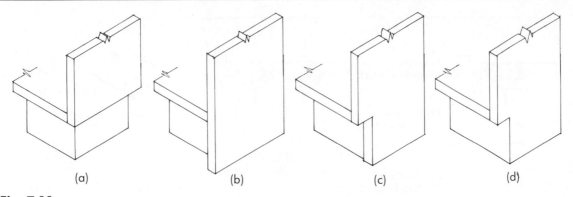

(a)   (b)   (c)   (d)

Fig. 7.11
Plinth details – alternatives

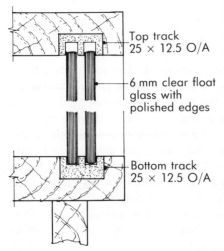

Top track
25 × 12.5 O/A

6 mm clear float
glass with
polished edges

Bottom track
25 × 12.5 O/A

Fig. 7.12
Frameless glass doors sliding in
fibre tracks

but without the continuous toe-space around the end of the unit.

In all cases, the use of glue blocks in securing the joints in the plinth, and in fixing it to the unit, is good joinery practice.

Fig. 7.12 shows the vertical section through a pair of frameless glass sliding doors, in proprietary fibre track. The grooves in the top and bottom members of the frame are identical, but in the track itself the deeper grooves above the glass enable its insertion and removal by lifting so as to clear the bottom track. Tracks are also available for 9 mm glass, and for three doors to pass each-other.

Various kinds of track and associated fittings are available for top-hung doors to cupboards, and the selection for a particular job will be largely dependent upon the weight of the doors to be carried. The proportions, height-to-width, in a top-hung door are less critical to smooth running than in the bottom-hung doors, but where there is a choice in the height of the handle it would be logical to put it as high as is reasonable to achieve the best results.

The simplest versions of track, designed for small top-hung cupboard doors, have no mechanical parts. Each door is suspended on two nylon hangers which slide in an extruded aluminium track, fixed to the framework above the doors. The track is designed to be exposed to view, but may be concealed behind a wood fillet. At the bottom edge of the door, a short guide made from aluminium or nylon angle is fixed to the lower framework so that the grooved door passes over it in a controlled line. The guide is situated at the side of the door opening to leave the base unobstructed.

This system of top-hung doors is shown in Fig. 7.13, where the first Vertical Section shows a single door which is designed to slide to the side of the door opening. The same section could be illustrating a pair of bi-parting doors running on the same track so as to open to each side of the opening. This arrangement may satisfy a particular space problem, where the resulting narrower doors can be better accommodated, but it may also be

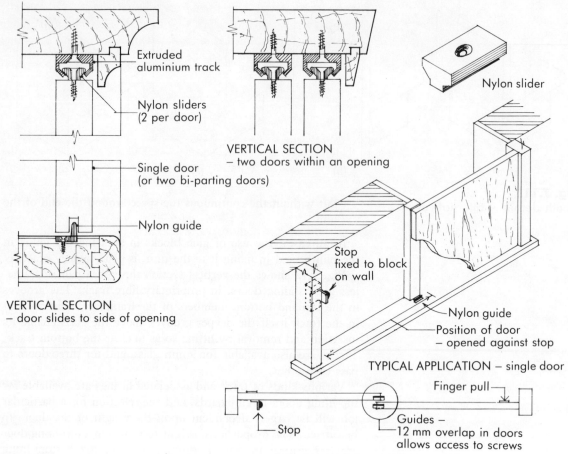

Extruded aluminium track

Nylon sliders (2 per door)

VERTICAL SECTION – two doors within an opening

Nylon slider

Single door (or two bi-parting doors)

Nylon guide

VERTICAL SECTION – door slides to side of opening

Stop fixed to block on wall

Nylon guide

Position of door – opened against stop

TYPICAL APPLICATION – single door

Finger pull

Stop

Guides – 12 mm overlap in doors allows access to screws

Plan – two doors within an opening

Fig. 7.13
Top-hung sliding doors

necessary in order to reduce the weight of each door to within the limit stated by the manufacturer and this is likely to be about 9 kg.

The pictorial view illustrates the single door to a serving hatch where an important feature of concern to the joiner is the determination of the length of the frame. The bottom guide is fixed with two screws, one of which must be exposed when the door is closed, and the other when it is fully open, so this will dictate the minimum distance between jambs. By using a door stop, fixed to a block on the wall as shown, the jambs may be set further apart so giving clear access to the bottom guide. After fixing the door stop, the guide will be concealed.

The Figure also shows the section through two doors contained within a frame, and designed to open past each other and this is further illustrated, in the plan.

Sliding door gear for heavier cupboard doors is likely to be for bottom hung doors, and catalogues will state the maximum capacity. Such systems employ bottom rollers morticed into the lower edge of the door to run on a bottom track and typically capable of carrying doors up to 20 kg in weight. The upper edge of the door is controlled by guides which locate into channel tracks set into the head of the frame.

DRAWERS

Drawers as a means of storage are generally of smaller capacity than shelves or cupboards and used to accommodate smaller items which need to be isolated from other things. The contents of drawers are concealed from sight, and this is used to advantage for the storage of groups of items which are otherwise difficult to keep in an orderly manner. A drawer may also offer security, when fitted with a drawer lock.

Related to the volume of storage provided, drawers involve more work in their construction than other forms of storage, and as a result are likely to be more expensive.

Before proceeding with details concerning the construction of drawers, it is necessary to illustrate the range of associated parts and Fig. 7.14 shows most of these. The parts illustrated in Fig. 7.14 may be briefly described as follows, and the finished sizes given are typical to joinery rather than to cabinet making.

- *Drawer front*. The only part visible when closed; 20 mm thick.
- *Drawer side*. Moves in contact with the runner, guide and kicker; 12 mm thick.
- *Drawer back*. Narrower than the sides, to allow the bottom to be fixed to its lower edge. Top edge also usually lower than sides; 12 mm thick.

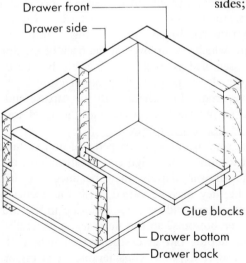

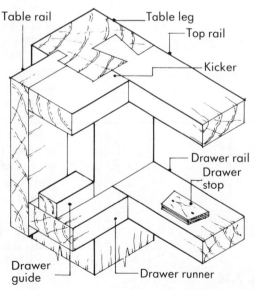

Fig. 7.14
Parts related to drawers

- *Drawer bottom.* Generally of plywood, nailed or screwed to drawer back, grooved into other three sides; 4 or 5 mm thick.
- *Glue blocks.* Square section hardwood, give rigidity to the drawer and provide a running surface beneath; 12 mm square.
- *Table leg and rail* are not particular to drawer construction.
- *Top rail and drawer rail.* Frame the top and bottom of the drawer opening; 58 × 20 mm.
- *Drawer runner.* Provides the lower running surface; 20 mm thick.
- *Kicker.* Prevents the front of the drawer from falling downward as it is drawn out; 20 mm thick.
- *Drawer guide.* Keeps the drawer on its correct line of travel; 20 mm thick.
- *Drawer stop.* Locates against the drawer front to ensure a flush finish when closed. Of plywood; 6 mm thick.

The making of a drawer on traditional lines is an opportunity to show the true skill of a craftsman, but that in itself is rarely sufficient reason for employing that form of construction. Fig. 7.15 illustrates drawer details which may still be an economical approach, particularly in small quantity production. Where all members are machined to section, the time taken in bench work in preparing and fitting the lapped dovetails to the front, and the housed joints at the back could compare favourably with that of the equivalent machining operations.

The smooth operation of drawers depends on their close fitting to the carcase rather than on an excess of freedom, and the joiner will fit the drawer front to the carcase before making the drawer.

Machine-made dovetails, produced by using a special attachment on the spindle moulder, or with a router, are very different in appearance from the hand-made dovetail. Fig. 7.16 illustrates the machined joint, which is employed at the back of the drawer also, and when assembled is easily recognisable by the equal spacing of the dovetails. This method of manufacture is ideally suited to repetitive production where both the carcase and the drawer are made to precise tolerances, and the need for the individual fitting of drawers is minimal.

Where there are several drawers in a pedestal unit or 'nest of drawers' there are a number of design and constructional details to consider. The drawer depths may be made to accept particular items, or they may be varied, with the deeper ones toward the bottom. There will be some loss due to the drawer rails and the drawer bottoms, so the designer is generally not specific on drawer depths but gives the overall height of the unit. Where the drawer depth is considerable, it is important to consider the effects of shrinkage in the material, which could result in slackness in depth, causing the drawer front to fall as it is opened, so kiln seasoning or the use of reconstructed boards

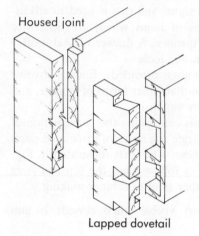

Housed joint

Lapped dovetail

Fig. 7.15
Joiner-made drawer details

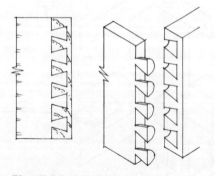

Fig. 7.16
Machine-made dovetails

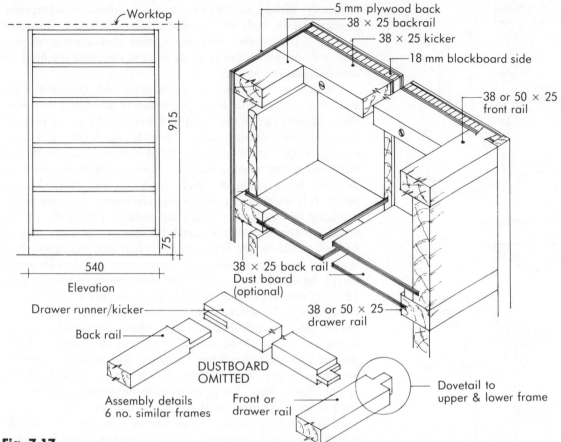

Fig. 7.17
Drawer pedestal unit

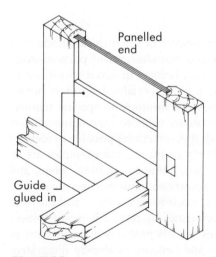

Fig. 7.18
Guides to panelled ends

could be advisable. Fig. 7.17 shows the elevation of a drawer pedestal to be made from veneered blockboard sides and hardwood framing. It will be seen that the construction is simplified by the fact that the drawer rails and runners are joined together in six almost identical frames, which differ only in that the dovetail shown could only occur on the top and bottom frames and the others would be tenoned. The blockboard sides are joined to these frames by screws, and the front rail joints already referred to. Also shown is a dustboard which is sometimes fitted to separate the drawer compartments.

The sides to such a pedestal are sometimes framed and panelled, and in such a case there would be a need for drawer guides, which may be as simple as that shown in Fig. 7.18 and simply glued and pinned into place to create the necessary flush surface.

Drawer rails are in some cases concealed by allowing the drawer fronts to project downward, and this is particularly effective where the fronts are of veneered plywood or similar material, when the face grain may be allowed to continue

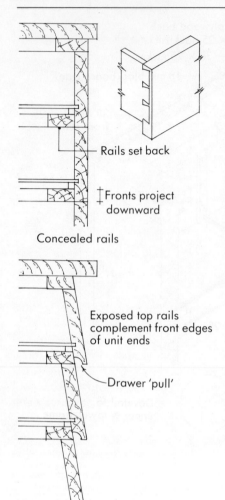

Rails set back

Fronts project downward

Concealed rails

Exposed top rails complement front edges of unit ends

Drawer 'pull'

Concealed rails and sloping fronts

Fig. 7.19
Alternative front details

vertically down all drawer fronts without interruption. Concealed rails with solid timber drawer fronts are illustrated in Fig. 7.19, together with the further alternative of sloping drawer fronts which can be made so as to eliminate the need for drawer 'pulls' or handles.

The free-running drawers which cope with continuous use and carry considerable loads as commonly associated with steel filing cabinets can be produced in joinery by the use of proprietary suspension-drawer slides. These fittings work on a telescopic principle, are made from plated steel and incorporate ball races and nylon wheels, and the various patterns available are designed for a range of weight capacities and dimensions of travel. It is necessary to consult manufacturers' literature before finalising joinery details which are affected principally in two ways. Firstly, there is no need for drawer runners, rails or kickers, so the carcase is merely a box-like unit. Secondly, there is a need for space between the drawer side and the carcase, to accept the drawer slide, and the clearance required may be from 12 to 25 mm depending on the pattern of fitting selected. To achieve this, the drawer front is allowed to project beyond the drawer side, as seen in Fig. 7.20a, where a dovetail is formed across the width of the drawer side, and this joint could be prepared by hand or machine methods. Alternatively more reliance may be placed on the glue by employing the joint shown in Fig. 7.20b. Note that in either case the groove in the drawer front must be stopped so as to conceal it from view. A further possibility is to make up the drawer as a simple box, then fix a false front with projecting ends, screwed on from behind as in Fig. 7.20c.

SEATING

Seating is generally more the concern of the furniture trade than of joinery, but the designer and manufacturer of purpose-made joinery does, to a limited extent, become involved with work of this kind, often in connection with specialised business organisations or institutions demanding furniture to specific requirements. Seating in these situations is more for communal use than for individuals, although it is sometimes possible to identify a limited range of people likely to use it, and examples are in educational buildings, churches, libraries, waiting rooms and public indoor and outdoor recreational and sporting areas.

In Chapter 1, reference was made to ergonomics, and the need to relate the physical characteristics of certain items of joinery to those of the user, and this need is probably at its greatest in the design of work surfaces and benches as already illustrated, and in the design of seating. Where it is to be used by a wide

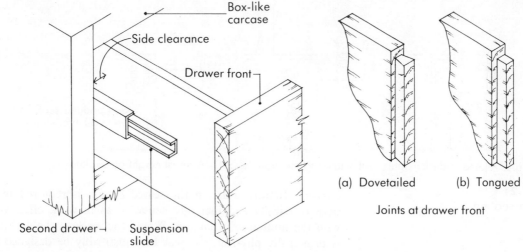

(a) Dovetailed (b) Tongued

Joints at drawer front

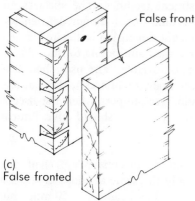

(c)
False fronted

Fig. 7.20
Drawers on suspension slides
(**a**) Dovetailed
(**b**) Tongued
(**c**) False fronted

range of people, in situations such as those listed above, seating is designed to satisfy the majority by using dimensions which are found to be most generally acceptable.

The functional aim in the design is to give as much support as possible to the body, without creating isolated pressure points, and to relieve the muscles of work to allow relaxation. A shaped or moulded seat with correct geometry, even of hard materials, is potentially more comfortable than one of poor design covered in deep, soft upholstery. In upholstery, resiliency rather than softness gives more complete contact with, and therefore better support to, the body.

The seat height is also vitally important, as measured in relation to the floor or to any footrest provided, so that it may allow the feet to rest firmly on their support with the back of the thighs properly supported by the seat. The seat height should also be measured in relation to any associated work surface, or more precisely the work being performed on it, to allow the forearms to be approximately horizontal. Where a backrest is included, the seat may be slightly inclined to prevent the person from sliding forward, although this does depend upon the nature of the seat surface.

The backrest should also be inclined, to form an angle with the seat slightly in excess of a right-angle. It should provide the most positive support to the middle back at about waist height.

When arm rests are provided, their height should be such as to allow the forearm to rest along their length with the shoulders relaxed.

One further consideration in seat design concerns the nature of the occupation of the seated person, and this, together with those already outlined, may be related to the following examples.

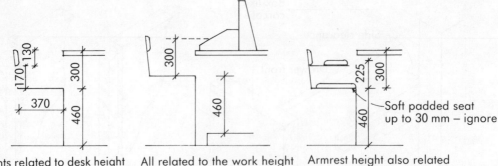

Heights related to desk height   All related to the work height   Armrest height also related

Fig. 7.21
Office seating

Offices. In this situation the seated person is required to be both physically and mentally active so as to work effectively, with the minimum of fatigue. Where the work of the occupant is principally physical, the seat may justifiably be designed for the individual, or have adjustment facilities. The surfaces are often slightly resilient, to overcome minor design deficiencies. Fig. 7.21 shows that the seat height dimension is dictated largely by the height of the work performed and points to the value of an adjustable seat if the work is variable. The user should be comfortably in contact with the floor (or footrest), the seat and the work. The armrests should give support when the user is in a relaxed position, and the backrest should give lumbar support.

Dining Rooms. Well-established dimensions relate chair and table heights, which are generally the same as those in the last example. The standard dining table height is 750 mm, but where high-level dining surfaces are employed the seat height must be adjusted accordingly and a footrest provided.

Lecture Rooms, Churches and Waiting Rooms. In these, the seated person is required to be physically inactive, though not lounging, and to remain mentally alert. As a result of the wider range of people likely to use the seat in some of these situations it may be slightly lower than those already illustrated. In many cases there is no attempt to soften the surfaces, and little attempt to provide comfort and it is sometimes suggested that this is an attempt to achieve enforced alertness, though this could be counter-productive. Fig. 7.22 shows the principal dimensions of communal seating of this kind, and details beyond this will be concerned with various properties including strength, durability and appearance. The capacity of continuous seating may be taken from the fact that four persons shoulder-to-shoulder will occupy not less than 2 m, or approximately 0.5 m per person.

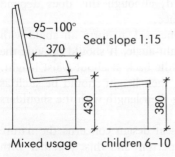

Mixed usage   children 6–10

Fig. 7.22
Public indoor seating

Public Outdoor Seating. For this, the dimensions and many of the characteristics are as in the last example, with the principal

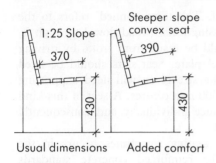

Fig. 7.23
Outdoor seating

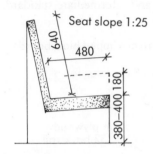

Fig. 7.24
Lounge seating

difference that there is a need for weather resistance and as far as possible proofing against vandalism. Selected hardwoods probably offer the most suitable qualities, and are often used in the form of slats supported by reinforced concrete. Fig. 7.23 shows the typical dimensions and includes an example which would give additional comfort and would suit certain situations.

Lounge. For seating in this situation, the accent is on comfort and relaxation, but there should still be consideration in the design for the correct and adequate support of the person. The lower seat height follows the intention that the feet will not rest firmly on the floor but that the legs will be extended. Associated furniture will also be to lower dimensions so as to be used comfortably by the seated person, but this work is not generally within the scope of joinery. Sometimes the seating in waiting rooms produced as joinery is made to the dimensions of lounge seating and these are indicated in Fig. 7.24. The height of the upholstered seat is shown as 380 mm, and this is likely to compress to about 330 mm in use and this affects the height of the arm rest, which is unlikely to compress and so accounts for the smaller figure than those given in Fig. 7.19. The height of the back is suitable where it is intended to serve as a headrest.

Fig. 7.25 shows a traditional seat for outdoor situations and made from Iroko. Joints are generally morticed and tenoned,

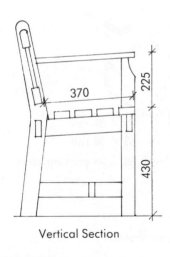

Vertical Section

Fig. 7.25
Traditional outdoor bench

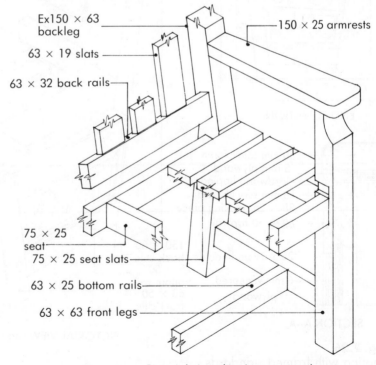

Pictorial view showing construction

glued (BS 1204) and pinned. The term 'pinned' refers to the securing of the tenon by passing a hardwood dowel through it, and in this case the pin could be made from Iroko by driving the material through a dowel plate. Seat slats should be fixed with brass screws, and in the size given will need supporting cross-rails at not more than 500 mm centres. A seat of this kind would be expensive to produce individually and consequently is most often mass-produced.

Joinery work in outdoor seating sometimes occurs in the production of formwork for reinforced concrete standards designed to support hardwood seat slats. A wide variety of seat designs are produced this way, and the formwork will be required to be used repetitively in producing concrete to a high standard of finish.

An example of continuous seating for a dental waiting room is given in Fig. 7.26, where the end and intermediate standards

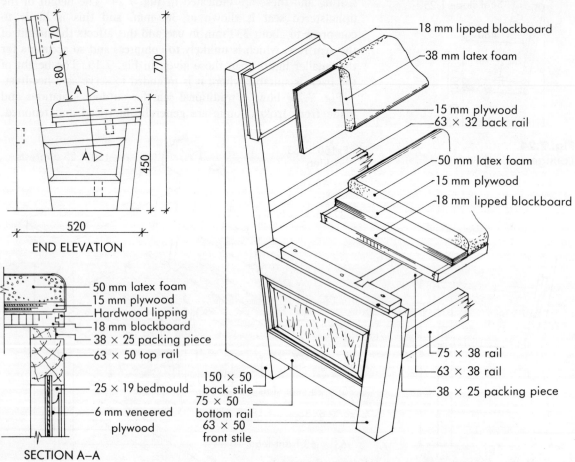

END ELEVATION

50 mm latex foam
15 mm plywood
Hardwood lipping
18 mm blockboard
38 × 25 packing piece
63 × 50 top rail
25 × 19 bedmould
6 mm veneered plywood

SECTION A–A

150 × 50 back stile
75 × 50 bottom rail
63 × 50 front stile

18 mm lipped blockboard
38 mm latex foam
15 mm plywood
63 × 32 back rail
50 mm latex foam
15 mm plywood
18 mm lipped blockboard
75 × 38 rail
63 × 38 rail
38 × 25 packing piece

PICTORIAL VIEW showing construction

Fig. 7.26
Seating with framed standards
(waiting room – dental practice)

are framed and panelled. There are three longitudinal rails which serve to tie the whole seat together, and therefore continue through the intermediate standards which are at 0.900–1.000 spacings. The rail beneath the seat gives it additional support, and the back rail provides a means of fixing to the wall if required. Both the seat and the back are upholstered around 15 mm plywood, then fixed by screws through the supporting lipped blockboard.

Another approach to the construction of seat standards is to use plywood, glued to softwood frames to achieve the obvious advantages in clean unobstructed surfaces, and in the added strength that this form of construction produces. This strength, as compared with that of framed solid timber, allows the designer to produce shapes that would otherwise be impracticable and evidence of this is seen not only in some joinery items but in examples of structural engineering in timber.

Fig. 7.27 shows an example that employs that approach in a design for internal public seating where the degree of comfort demands the proportions described earlier for lounge seating.

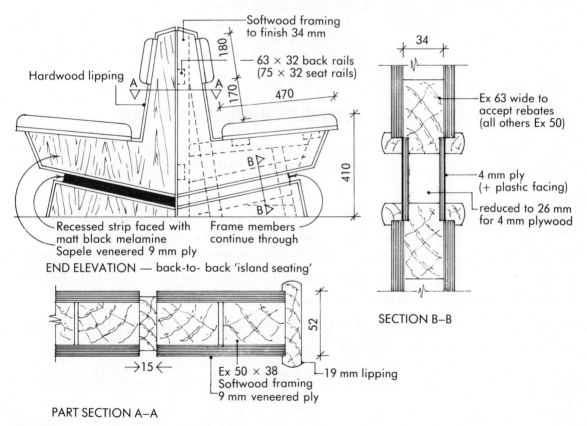

Fig. 7.27
Seating with flush standards
(lounge dimensions)

The seat and backrest are upholstered in the same way as that shown in the previous example, and each standard consists of a simple softwood frame that gains its strength from the glued plywood faces. The figure illustrates in detail a plastic-faced recessed feature that appears to separate the upper portion of each standard from the lower. For strength reasons the framing continues through this feature but is reduced in thickness to produce the effect required. The plywood faces are thicker than would normally be necessary, but are a convenient way of achieving the change of thickness at this point.

As illustrated in the figure, the design allows the seats to be fixed back-to-back to produce 'island seating', or alternatively they may be employed as wall seating as shown later in *Joinery Project No. XVI*.

Within the subject of continuous seating, reference must be made to church pews, although their manufacture is not commonly experienced in joinery and is becoming less so with the growing practice, particularly in new churches, of using portable seating to allow the church to be used for a range of activities throughout the week.

A church pew has much in common with other forms of continuous seating in its structural design, but traditionally there is less concern for comfort and there is usually no upholstery involved.

JOINERY PROJECTS XVI–XX

The five Joinery Projects that complete the chapter, to give applied examples of work related to fitments and seating are listed as follows:

No.	Item	Drawings
XVI	Seating to reception area	XVI.1, XVI.2, XVI.3
XVII	Enquiry hatch with sliding doors	XVII.1
XVIII	Refectory tables	XVIII.1
XIX	Credence table	XIX.1
XX	Wall-mounted cross	XX.1

Project No. XVI
Seating to Reception Area

This Project concerns the second of two items of joinery involved in the development of a waiting area in a commercial office building. The first involved the making and fixing of wall panelling, and was the subject of *Joinery Project No. XI*.

Continuous wall seating to those panelled walls and the provision of two small matching tables are the subjects of this project. The seating is intended for the convenience of visitors who are waiting for attention and is designed to offer the degree of comfort associated with lounge seating. The two tables are to allow the provision of light reading matter associated with the business ventures conducted within the building.

Specification

The seating is to be constructed to conform to the details illustrated in Fig. 7.27 and Drawing XVI.1, and will provide continuous upholstered seats with upholstered backrests to two adjoining panelled walls. The upholstery work will be produced elsewhere, finished in the same materials as used in the panelling, over 15 mm plywood boards produced by the joinery manufacturer.

Supporting framework will consist of four common standards and one special standard at the angle, tied together by two back rails and two seat rails. The upholstered seats and backrests will be supported by hardwood lipped 18 mm blockboard.

Standards are to be of 'flush' construction, consisting of 9 mm Sapele-faced plywood over softwood framed cores, and each will include a recessed feature finished in matt black laminated plastic so that the lower portion appears as a separate plinth. For strength reasons, the softwood framing must be continuous throughout the height of the standard. All exposed edges of standards are to be finished with a twice-nosed hardwood lipping.

Two 63 × 32 mm hardwood backrails provide fixings to the wall panelling and two 75 × 32 mm hardwood seat rails give support and fixing to the lipped blockboard seat panels. The lipped blockboard backrest panel will allow the upholstered backrest to be fixed from behind.

The two tables, illustrated in Drawing XVI.3, each 685 × 685 × 410 mm high are also to be of matching materials and will comprise vinyl faced 18 mm plywood tops within 63 × 38 mm mitred hardwood frames, resting on 63 × 63 mm legs framed to 112 × 25 rails. The framing is to be properly mitred and tongued. The vinyl tops are to be capable of being removed for re-covering when necessary.

The work throughout is to be properly executed, with close-fitting joints, well glued and cramped together and brought to a high standard of finish. Hardwood is to be clear selected Brazilian Mahogany having a moisture content in the region of 12–15%. Any necessary screws are to be of brass.

Interpretation – Seating

An early requirement will be to prepare the 15 mm plywood boards for the seat and backrest to be sent to the upholsterer, and before these can be produced some workshop geometry must be carried out to determine their shapes. Some geometry will also be involved in finding the overall shape of the special standard at the angle.

By close reference to the Drawings and Specification, and following the site checking of dimensions, the workshop rods will be produced and these will be in the form of:

(a) The elevation of a common standard with the positions of softwood core members shown. This will enable the marking-out of core members, most of which have bevelled shouldered joints.

(b) Preferably on the same rod, the plan at the angle showing the special standard with its centre line in alignment with salient features on the common standards. On this rod, the outline shape of the special standard may be developed as shown on Drawing XVI.2, then the core members may be inserted. This is shown separately here for clarity.

The shaped ends of the seat boards, to mitre together at the angle, could also be developed on this rod. This angle will be so close to 45°, due to the shallow slope of the seat, that it would not be clearly seen here to such a small scale and is therefore omitted. These edges will also be slightly bevelled in their thickness. The upper edge of this standard should be twice bevelled to provide true bearing surfaces to the seat boards, although in this case the bevels are so slight as to be safely ignored. The geometry for this, and for the backrests, is the same as for the surface shapes, dihedral and backing angles in hipped roofs (and described earlier in Chapter 4).

(c) A length rod for each of the two walls, showing the positions of the standards within the overall lengths of the seats. These rods need only be on pieces of narrow batten.

The jointing of the softwood in the standards will as far as possible be of mortice and tenons to ensure that they come together accurately, although some halving will be appropriate where members cross each other. The assembled cores must be checked for constant thickness before the veneered plywood faces are applied, since no adjustment can be made afterwards. The machining of the grooved lipping could be delayed, to advantage, until the standards have been faced and are ready for lipping.

The recesses which will receive the 4 mm plywood could be produced by router, after the cores are assembled, and before the plywood faces are applied.

Drawing XVI.1 shows some features of the assembled work and particularly the seat rails joined to the standards. It should be noted that to gain maximum strength from the rails, their entire section is supported by the plywood faces.

Most of the framework will be fitted together in the workshop, then taken apart (or reduced to two assembled straight portions) for ease of handling. Exceptions may be in the mitres to the seat boards and backrest boards, which may best be left for final fitting on site.

Interpretation – Tables

Reference to Drawing XVI.3 and to the Specification allows the collection of all necessary information for the making of the tables, and there will be no need to produce a workshop rod.

Material provided by the upholsterer will allow the tops to be produced entirely in the joinery workshop. The mitred frames may be cramped and tongued as shown in the drawing and the tongues being 'diminished to nothing' at the outer edge will simplify the cutting of the housings. The triangular cramping blocks may be offcuts from the mitre cuts. The vinyl covered top panel may be inserted after varnishing is completed, and the beads fixed with brass screws.

Tenons to the rails are mitred together to achieve maximum penetration, and the diminished haunches are employed to give a neat effect in the exposed upper surfaces.

The shaping of the rails which leaves a space below each corner of the table top purely for visual effect, does reduce the width available for tenons but the well-fitted and glued joints should be adequate. There will be very little leverage on the joints owing to the shortness of the table legs. The tops will be fixed to the frames by 'pocket screwing', using two brass screws per rail.

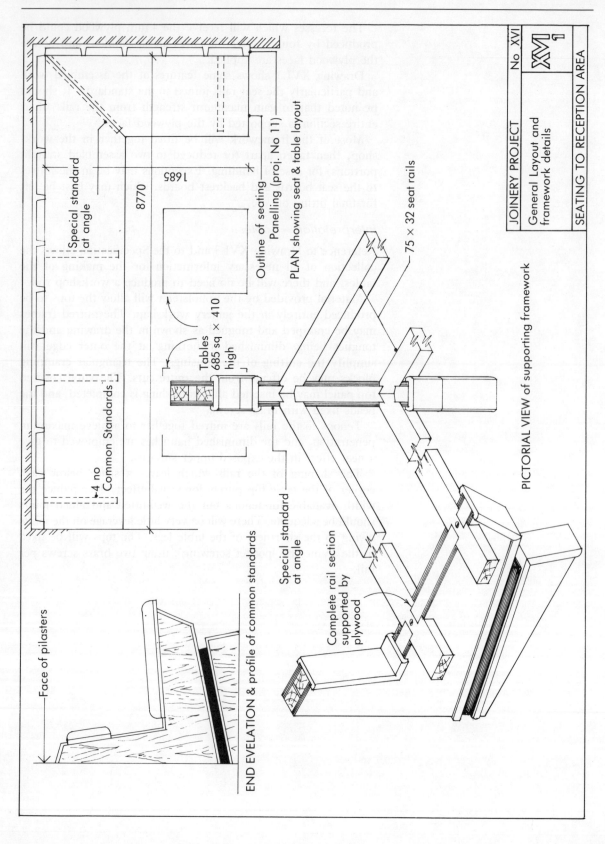

Face of pilasters

END ELEVATION & profile of common standards

Special standard at angle

4 no Common Standards

Special standard at angle

8770

1685

Outline of seating

Panelling (proj. No 11)

PLAN showing seat & table layout

Tables 685 sq × 410 high

75 × 32 seat rails

Complete rail section supported by plywood

PICTORIAL VIEW of supporting framework

| JOINERY PROJECT | No XVI |
| General Layout and framework details | XVI 1 |

SEATING TO RECEPTION AREA

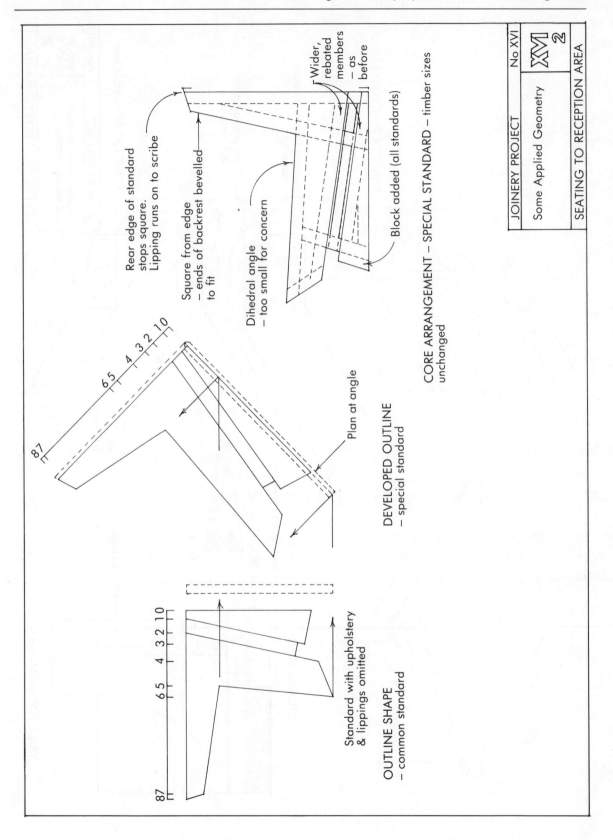

Rear edge of standard stops square. Lipping runs on to scribe

Square from edge – ends of backrest bevelled to fit

Dihedral angle – too small for concern

Wider, rebated members – as before

Block added (all standards)

CORE ARRANGEMENT – SPECIAL STANDARD – timber sizes unchanged

Plan at angle

DEVELOPED OUTLINE – special standard

Standard with upholstery & lippings omitted

OUTLINE SHAPE – common standard

JOINERY PROJECT   No XVI

Some Applied Geometry   XVI
                          2

SEATING TO RECEPTION AREA

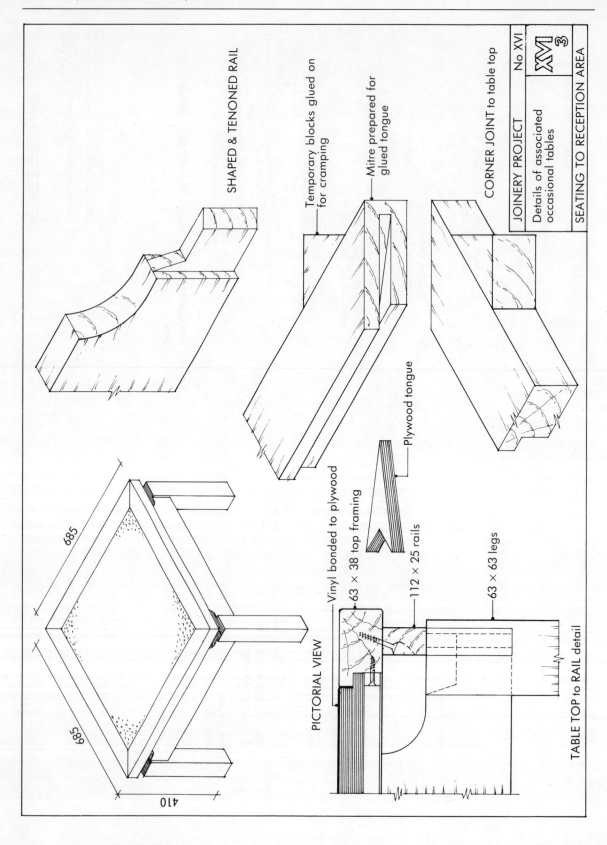

SHAPED & TENONED RAIL

Temporary blocks glued on for cramping

Mitre prepared for glued tongue

CORNER JOINT to table top

No XVI

XVI 3

JOINERY PROJECT

Details of associated occasional tables

SEATING TO RECEPTION AREA

685

685

410

Plywood tongue

Vinyl bonded to plywood

63 × 38 top framing

112 × 25 rails

63 × 63 legs

PICTORIAL VIEW

TABLE TOP to RAIL detail

Project No. XVII
Enquiry Hatch with Sliding Doors

Specification

The hatch is to provide a clear opening 1.000 m wide and 0.750 m high within an existing 100 mm plastered block wall, for the purpose of dealing with enquiries. The work is to conform to Drawing XVII.1, and useful reference may be made to Fig. 7.13.

The opening is to be lined with 150 × 25 mm tongued and mitred hardwood linings with projecting bevelled front edges grooved to receive plaster at 'making good' stage.

The working surface of the hatchway is to be of 18 mm block-board faced with laminated plastic, the front edge having a segmental curve and the width extending into the service side where the length is to conform to that of the door frame. All exposed edges of the work surface are to be hardwood lipped.

The door frame, situated on the service side, is to accommodate two bi-parting doors and is to be of 75 × 50 mm hardwood generally, with two 50 × 38 mm mullions grooved to receive the hardwood linings. The head of the frame is to be grooved to receive the sliding door track and is to have a detachable fillet, brass cupped and screwed so as to allow the insertion of the doors, with sliders, into the track.

Doors are to be of 18 mm hardwood veneered blockboard, lipped all round and with meeting edges rebated together. The lippings to the outer edges are to project inward from the door faces so as to locate into the frame mullions to serve as door stops.

Hardwood is to be African Utile, and the blockboard doors Sapele veneered both sides. Laminated plastic is to be of Formica to approved colour. Sliding door gear is to comprise an extruded aluminium top track, with nylon sliders and bottom guides, and with satin anodised aluminium circular finger pulls.

The work throughout is to be neatly executed, properly framed together and brought to a standard of preparation suitable for a clear, high gloss finish.

Interpretation

The drawing presented to the joiner is likely to show only the small-scale elevation, horizontal and vertical sections with some larger-scale sectional details. Drawing XVII.1 includes a pictorial view showing the joiner's interpretation and intentions as to a suitable approach to its construction. In this Project there is a considerable proportion of benchwork for the joiner in the making and fitting of joints which cannot be economically produced by machine.

The dovetailed and mitred joints to the upper angles to the frame will be at high level, so that the resulting end grain is acceptable. The features of these joints are set out to align with the track position to avoid further complication. It is not necessary to mitre the lower joints, because the frame is interrupted by the lippings continuing across them.

It is considered that the work should be assembled fully in the workshop and delivered as a complete unit. The frame will be assembled first and will include the tenoned mullions which are recessed, before assembly, to receive the work surface.

The Formica faced blockboard, ready shaped and tongued for the linings, can now be fixed to the frame by screwing and pelleting from beneath.

The lining jambs followed by the head will then be fixed, followed by the fixing of lippings to all exposed edges of the work surface.

In their fully open position, the doors will be stopped by the frame jambs (exposing half of each lower guide). To stop them centrally as a pair, when closed, the lippings to the outer edges of the doors must project so as to locate in the rebated mullions. These lippings must be adequately fixed. It is anticipated that the doors will need to be secured when closed and this can be achieved by fixing a barrel bolt to each door, selected to match the circular finger pulls.

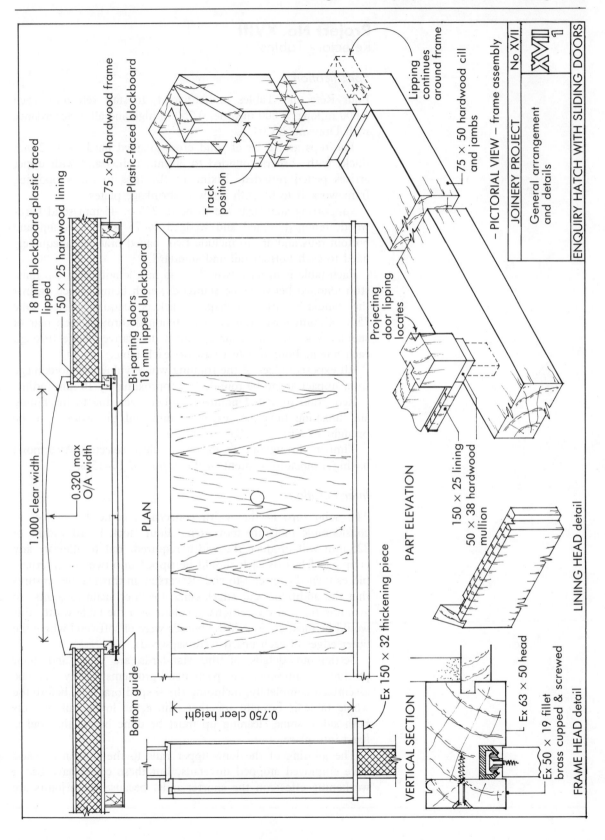

18 mm blockboard-plastic faced lipped

75 × 50 hardwood frame

Plastic-faced blockboard

150 × 25 hardwood lining

1.000 clear width

0.320 max O/A width

Bi-parting doors 18 mm lipped blockboard

Bottom guide

PLAN

Track position

Lipping continues around frame

75 × 50 hardwood cill and jambs

– PICTORIAL VIEW – frame assembly

JOINERY PROJECT   No XVII

XVII 1

General arrangement and details

ENQUIRY HATCH WITH SLIDING DOORS

Projecting door lipping locates

PART ELEVATION

150 × 25 lining

50 × 38 hardwood mullion

Ex 150 × 32 thickening piece

0.750 clear height

VERTICAL SECTION

LINING HEAD detail

Ex 63 × 50 head

Ex 50 × 19 fillet

brass cupped & screwed

FRAME HEAD detail

Project No. XVIII
Refectory Tables

Specification

Four Refectory Tables in hardwood, to staff refectory, each 1.600 m long, 0.800 m wide, 0.750 m high and all in accordance with Drawing XVIII.1.

The tops are to be of solid cross-tongued hardwood 32 mm thick, with corners rounded to 30 mm radius and with upper arrises pencil rounded. Fixing of the tops to the supporting framework is to be with screwed shrinkage plates.

Supporting standards are to be of 225 × 45 mm solid hardwood, tenoned, glued and wedged to 75 × 45 mm top and bottom rails and are to include two shaped brackets adequately fixed to each bottom rail and standard.

Each table is to have two 75 × 45 mm longitudinal top rails, stub tenoned between the standards, each being braced against the standards with two shaped brackets adequately fixed. One 75 × 45 mm lower rail is to be tenoned through each pair of standards glued and secured with a decorative wedge through each tenon. Four pad feet support each table.

All exposed edges of the framing where vulnerable to damage from impact are to be rounded to approximately 10 mm radius.

Reduction in stated nominal timber sizes due to machining and finishing must not exceed 5 mm and the work is to be brought to a high standard of finish.

Timber throughout is to be of clear selected Afrormosia having a moisture content in the region of 10–15%.

Interpretation

The solid top, in the width concerned, could be subject to considerable moisture movement. Four stock board widths of 225 mm will produce the width required, but to alleviate any cupping of boards each should be ripped into two and alternate pieces turned over end-to-end. Reversing in this manner ensures that the additional cut edges come together again as joints, so avoiding too many variations in colour over the table width (this would be most obvious if the boards were of softwood where the outer edges of each board were sapwood).

Setting-out details of the standards are clear and their production presents no particular problems. They can be assembled completely, including the shaped brackets, before the whole table is brought together. Since the lower rail projects both sides, some cleaning up must be done before that rail is fixed into place.

The jointing of the long upper rails to the standards could have employed stopped dovetails, but these could have had a weakening effect on the shorter rails, because these joints are so close to the tenons shown. Properly glued stub tenons, with the glue blocks rubbed into place, and with the support of the shaped brackets, will be adequate. Note that the lower ends of glue blocks are cut at 45° to allow the placing of the shaped brackets.

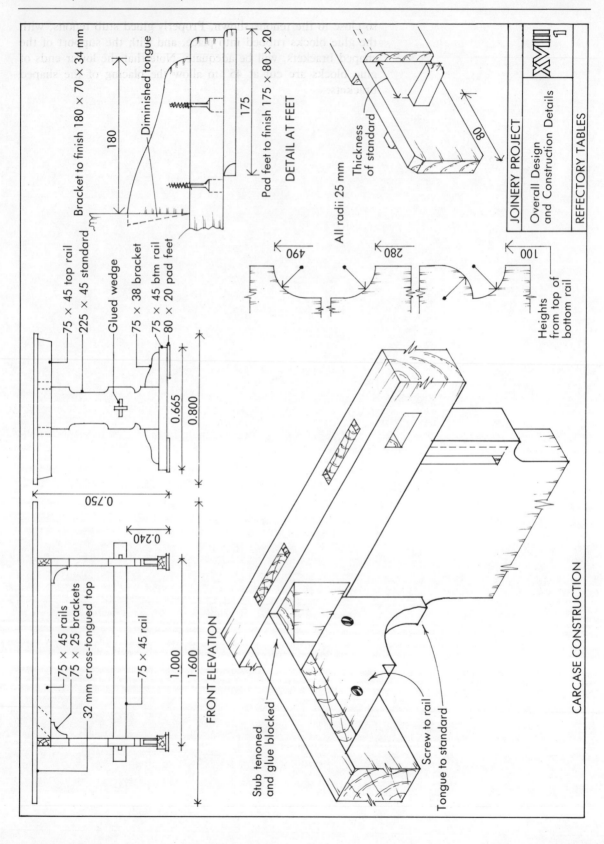

Bracket to finish 180 × 70 × 34 mm

Diminished tongue

180

175

Pad feet to finish 175 × 80 × 20

DETAIL AT FEET

Thickness of standard

80

All radii 25 mm

490

280

100

Heights from top of bottom rail

JOINERY PROJECT

Overall Design and Construction Details

REFECTORY TABLES

XVIII 1

75 × 45 top rail

225 × 45 standard

Glued wedge

75 × 38 bracket

75 × 45 btm rail

80 × 20 pad feet

0.665

0.800

0.750

0.240

75 × 45 rails

75 × 25 brackets

32 mm cross-tongued top

75 × 45 rail

1.000

1.600

FRONT ELEVATION

Stub tenoned and glue blocked

Screw to rail

Tongue to standard

CARCASE CONSTRUCTION

Project No. XIX
Credence Table in Oak

Introduction

A recently built church requires two additional items of joinery to conform to the general aesthetic lines of an altar and a free-standing lectern produced earlier. The new items are a Credence Table and a Cross, both to be made from European Oak. The Credence Table is the subject of this Project, and Drawing XIX.1 shows three designs A, B and C from which Design B has been selected.

Specification

One Credence Table 480 mm × 340 mm × 780 mm high as Design B in Drawing XIX.1. The work, following the general lines of the existing free-standing altar, is to comprise an Oak veneered 18 mm plywood top within a solid oak apron tongued and mitred together in box form and supported on four 75 × 38 mm legs with 75 × 38 mitred framed rails at low level.

Full attention must be given to achieving maximum stability through well-designed and accurately fitted joints thoroughly glued and cramped together.

All framing including glue blocks is to be of selected and matched European Oak having a moisture content of 10–12% and all surfaces are to be brought to a flat, blemish-free finish with arrises lightly removed with fine glass paper.

The applied finish is to consist of not less than three coats of clear polyurethane varnish in semi-matt over a light stain in 'fumed oak' to match as closely as possible that of the existing furniture.

Intrepretation

The drawing sheet shows a number of construction details that would be devised by the joiner to satisfy the specified requirements.

The veneered plywood top could be produced by bonding Oak-faced plywood to other plywood to achieve the necessary thickness. For a more positive matching of materials a better approach will be to bond a facing of European Oak in a reasonable thickness to the plywood one side at a time, to be reduced by passing through the thicknesser planer.

The mitred and tongued angles to the apron can be prepared at least in part on the tenoner and the housings for the legs will also be worked before assembly. To avoid difficulties in assembly due to distortion in the materials, assembly of the top should take place as soon as possible after the planing process. The glue blocks shown in the boxed top will add considerable strength to the joints concerned.

Also shown in the drawing are the bottom rail joints which have two stub tenons within each mitre to locate the joints accurately during assembly and for strength reasons. The design of these bottom rails is largely for visual effect and is not the best structural solution, but the stresses that could be felt by the mitred joints will be adequately carried by the joint shown.

Assembly of the bottom rails to the legs will be followed by the positioning of the boxed top. Most surfaces must be prepared to a high standard before assembly, since they will not be accessible afterwards.

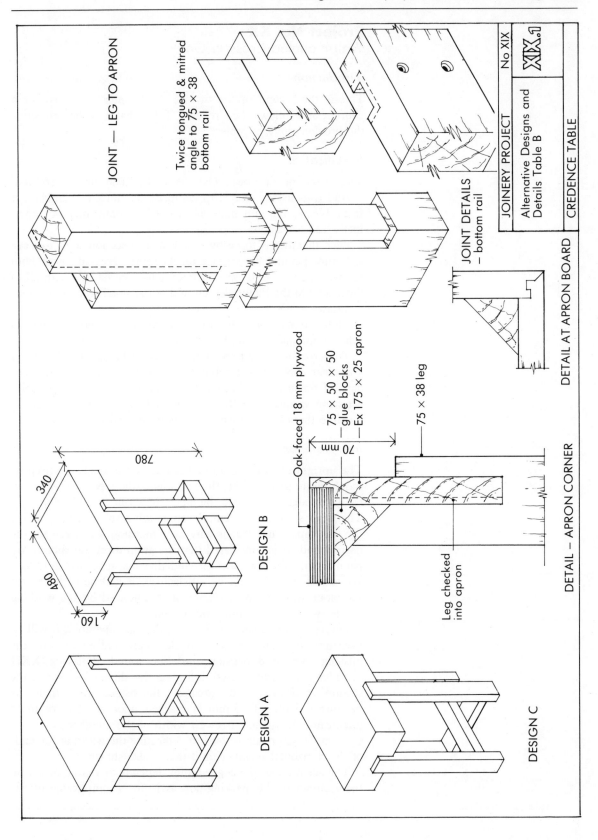

JOINT — LEG TO APRON

Twice tongued & mitred
angle to 75 × 38
bottom rail

JOINT DETAILS
– bottom rail

DETAIL AT APRON BOARD

Oak-faced 18 mm plywood

75 × 50 × 50
glue blocks

Ex 175 × 25 apron

75 × 38 leg

Leg checked
into apron

DETAIL – APRON CORNER

DESIGN A

DESIGN B

DESIGN C

780

340

480

160

JOINERY PROJECT   No XIX

Alternative Designs and
Details Table B

XIX.1

CREDENCE TABLE

Project No. XX
Wall-mounted Cross in Oak

Introduction

This is the second of the two items of joinery required for a church, and follows the Credence Table that was the subject of the previous joinery project.

Specification

The cross, of European Oak, is to be 1680 mm × 860 mm overall dimensions and is to comprise an upright member cut from 175 × 100 mm material and a horizontal member nominally 125 × 75 mm.

Each member is to be twice bevelled in section so as to leave a 28 mm parallel flat surface on its front edge, and with both the width and the thickness dimensions tapered in length all as illustrated in the Pictorial View and in the small scale projections in Drawing XX.1.

The two members are to be accurately joined together to achieve adequate strength with the best visual effect.

The cross is to be fixed with concealed fixings at a height of 4 m clear above floor level and is to be brought to a high standard of finish employing not less than four coats of clear polyurethane varnish over 'fumed oak' stain to match as closely as possible the adjacent furniture produced earlier.

Interpretation

The upright member could be brought to the shape required by moulding to section first, then removing the tapered waste from the back edge to produce the taper shown in the side elevation. The taper seen in the front elevation will result from producing the first taper, and that is why no dimension was given for the narrow end. It is considered that the grain direction should run parallel with the wall surface, and that the approach described above will therefore not be satisfactory. It will be better to cut the taper seen in side elevation first, followed by the working of the two bevels forming the section.

Before cutting away the waste in this last operation it will be necessary to mark-out the cutting lines, and to do this the missing narrow dimension must be found. Drawing XX.1 includes the geometry used in finding this dimension, where the section is drawn to its greatest dimensions first, then the narrowest depth of 75 mm is marked upon it. The required dimension 'X' is the narrowest width of the member.

A similar approach is used to determine the width at the ends of the horizontal member, and this is also shown.

The accuracy of the cogged joint depends to a large extent on the accuracy of the marking-out, and this is complicated by the fact that the material is now tapered. Centre-lines along the rear surfaces will form the basis of much of the marking-out, and the bevels seen on the side surfaces must be carefully transferred from each member to the other.

The joint will be well glued and cramped together, possibly aided by a pelleted screw driven in from the rear.

Bevelled cuts at the ends of members are parallel to the bevelled sections seen in the same view.

Heavy gauge brass 'keyhole' fixing plates will be purpose-made to be fitted flush into the back of the cross to provide concealed fixings to the wall, and three will be required. Their positions can be transferred to the wall by the use of a cardboard template.

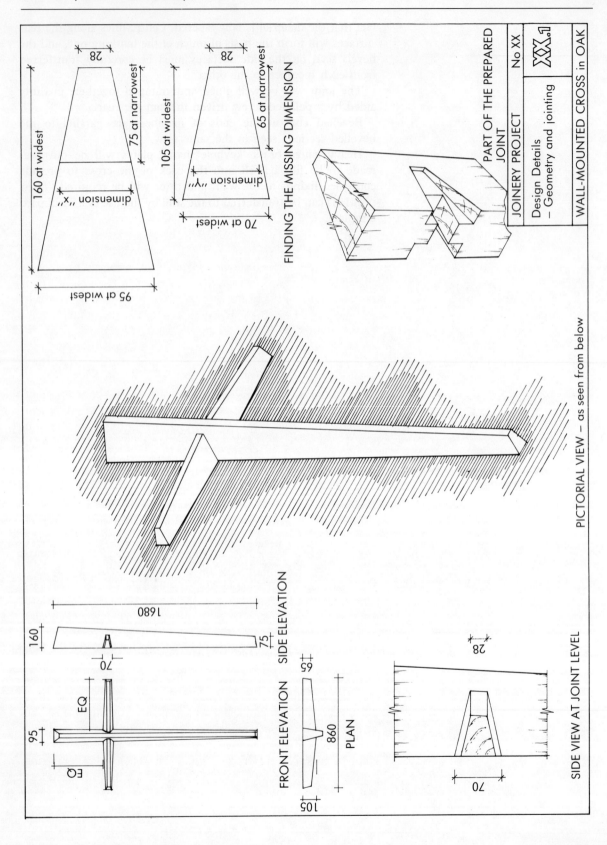

FINDING THE MISSING DIMENSION

28

160 at widest

75 at narrowest

dimension "x"

95 at widest

28

105 at widest

65 at narrowest

dimension "y"

70 at widest

PART OF THE PREPARED JOINT

JOINERY PROJECT   No XX

XX.1

Design Details
– Geometry and jointing

WALL-MOUNTED CROSS in OAK

PICTORIAL VIEW – as seen from below

SIDE ELEVATION

1680

160

75

70

FRONT ELEVATION

EQ

EQ

95

65

PLAN

860

105

SIDE VIEW AT JOINT LEVEL

28

70

Chapter 8
STAIRS

FUNCTION AND DESIGN

The main functional requirement in stair design is that of providing access from one floor level to another in as comfortable and safe a manner as possible, and traditional craft practices have long been concerned with these aims, recognising that comfort and safety in the use of a staircase are very much dependent on each other. Sometimes, to achieve economies in space within a building, too little attention has been given to comfort and safety but the current Building Regulations exercise close control in this respect and very largely dictate the functional design of any staircase.

The aesthetic design of a staircase may also be very important when the work occupies a prominent position in a building and is intended to attract attention through its overall geometry and details of construction. Work of this kind may demand a high level of craft skills in both setting-out and manufacture. In other cases, stairs may be almost entirely functional, when the demand for craftsmanship lies more in the setting-out than in the production.

The plan arrangement of a staircase comes as a result of several considerations, including the need to divide it into more than one flight, the need to change direction and the demands on floor space adjoining it at the top and bottom.

A staircase in one single flight contains a number of steps determined by the number of equal risers necessary to achieve the floor-to-floor height. It is supported by the lower floor and rests against the edge of the 'trimmed opening' in the upper floor or landing. The extent of the floor overhead, above the foot of the stairs, where the aim is generally to achieve as much floor area as possible, is limited by the headroom or clearance required beneath it. Fig. 8.1 shows a single flight and indicates the trimmed opening in the upper floor. The flight may be against a wall on one side as shown or it could be so enclosed at both sides. In some cases neither side is against a wall, then both strings are said to be 'open'. The open or outer string generally terminates and is supported by a newel at the upper end as shown and similarly at the bottom as shown in Fig. 8.2.

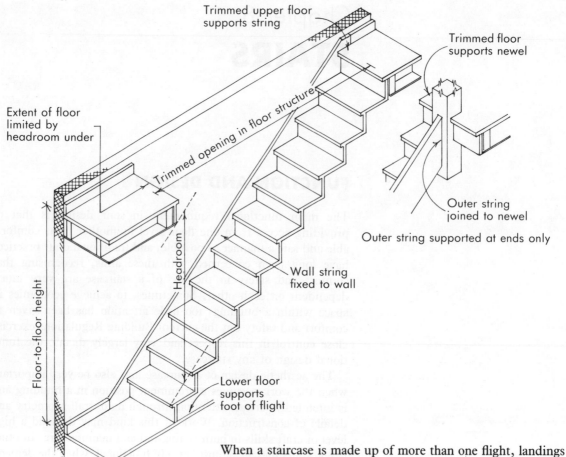

Fig. 8.1
Single flight – general
arrangement and support

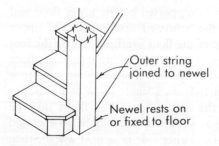

Fig. 8.2
Support at lower end of outer
string

When a staircase is made up of more than one flight, landings are introduced between them, either to serve as a rest point or to facilitate the change of direction. Fig. 8.3 shows an intermediate landing which merely restricts the number of risers in each flight, and it also shows a 'quarter-space' landing which provides a 90° turn between flights. The broken lines shown at each landing indicate the direction of supporting joists so that the boarded surface runs in the same direction as the treads of the lower flight. The joists are supported by the newel in each case, so the newel must pass down to the floor below.

Turns of 180° may be achieved in a number of ways, the most economical by using the dog-leg stair in which the upper and lower flight are supported by a common newel. Fig. 8.4(a) shows an example of such a staircase having a half-space landing. This could have been divided in two by the introduction of another riser in the centre, then either the upper or lower flight could have been shortened by one step. Open newel stairs use two newels at this point, and this is also shown in Fig. 8.4, firstly at (b) with a half-space landing, which usually depends on one of the newels for some support so that the joists may be kept down to an economical depth, usually 100 mm. Also shown

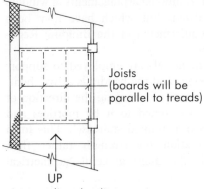

Joists
(boards will be
parallel to treads)

UP

Intermediate landing

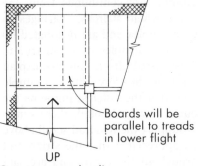

Boards will be
parallel to treads
in lower flight

UP

Quarter-space landing

Fig. 8.3
Landings between flights

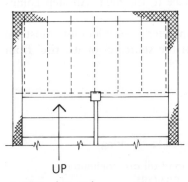

UP

(a) Dog-leg stair

Fig. 8.4
180° turns on plan
(a) Dog-leg stair
(b) Open newel stair with half-space landing
(c) Open newel with two quarter-space landings

in the figure is a similar staircase (c) with two quarter-space landings where two additional risers have been introduced, so that two steps may be eliminated from the plan dimensions. In both examples of the open newel stair, the newel at the top of the lower flight would be taken down to the floor below, and the next newel finished just below the soffit as a 'drop' or 'pendant'.

'Winders' or tapered steps are sometimes used instead of landings to negotiate turns on plan, with the advantage that the introduction of risers where the landing would have been allows a saving in plan space. Winders are, however, potentially dangerous in use, due to the narrowness of treads on the inside of the turn; there are some well established craft principles intended to minimise these dangers:

(a) Rise dimensions of the tapered steps are the same as those in adjoining flights;
(b) 'Going' dimensions, measured on the normal path of travel or 'walking line' which is measured 450 mm from the centre line of the handrail, should be as near as possible to those in adjoining flights;
(c) Winders should not occur immediately at the top of a flight, but should be above a floor or landing;
(d) There should be adequate hand support where the winders occur.

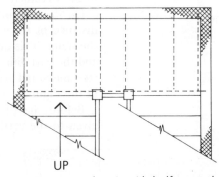

UP

(b) Open newel stair with half-space landing

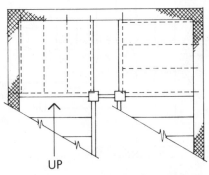

UP

(c) Open newel stair with two quarter-space landings

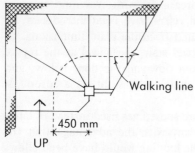

Walking line

450 mm

UP

At the bottom of a flight

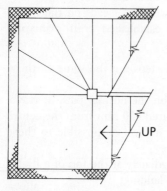

UP

Above a landing

Fig. 8.5
Traditional winders

Fig. 8.5 shows examples of traditional arrangements of winders to illustrate the principles listed, but which have now been largely superseded by the requirements of the Building Regulations which are shown later.

In the stairs already shown, newels are employed to support and to terminate the outer strings and the handrails above them. The newel is also used as a means of changing the direction of strings and handrails which are joined to it by mortices and tenons in what is often termed a 'framed staircase'. This form of construction has a reputation for strength rather than elegance, as compared with the more graceful 'geometrical stairs'.

A geometrical staircase has no newels at the changes in direction, and the strings and handrails are continuous from one flight to the next throughout the whole staircase. Changes in direction are in some cases quite complex and are negotiated by curves which are set-out by rigid principles of geometry, to produce flowing lines to the best visual effect. Curves on plan are usually circular curves, and in the very simple example shown in Fig. 8.6 it will be seen that the outer string joins the riser of the curtail step without a newel, although there sometimes is a turned newel here to support the handrail scroll above it. At the 180° turn, it will be appreciated that the string and the handrail are 'climbing' throughout the curve, and are said to be 'wreathed'.

On the plan of any flight of stairs can be seen the horizontal distance of travel, or forward progress of the person climbing the stairs. This dimension, overall, is the *total going* of the stairs, and the part dimension representing one step is the 'going' of the step measured from one riser face to the next. All step goings in the flight are equal.

Before the plan can be completed, consideration must be given to the vertical function of the staircase, or its 'rise' from

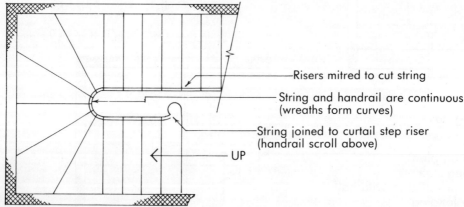

Risers mitred to cut string

String and handrail are continuous
(wreaths form curves)

String joined to curtail step riser
(handrail scroll above)

UP

Fig. 8.6
Geometrical stair

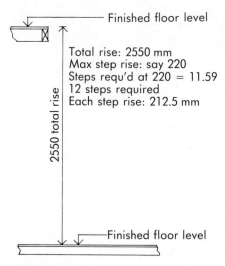

Finished floor level

Total rise: 2550 mm
Max step rise: say 220
Steps requ'd at 220 = 11.59
12 steps required
Each step rise: 212.5 mm

2550 total rise

Finished floor level

Fig. 8.7
Riser calculation

floor to floor. The total rise is measured 'finished floor to finished floor', and with a predetermined maximum figure for each step rise, all of which must all be equal, and simple division will determine the number of risers required. In Fig. 8.7 a total rise dimension of 2550 mm is to be achieved with a step rise dimension not exceeding 220 mm. With a 220 mm rise dimension, 11.59 steps would be required, so 12 steps will give a rise dimension not exceeding 220 mm. On the drawing sheet this division would of course be carried out by geometry, and on the bench, full size, by the use of dividers.

In considering now the 'going' dimensions, it must first be appreciated that the number of treads will usually be one less than the number of risers, because there is generally no tread to the top riser. Fig. 8.8 outlines the common situation at this point, where it will be seen that the top riser is close to the trimmer of the floor. The floor finish above this merely has a matching nosing and no tread is required. The wall string shown in the figure is cut round, and rests against the trimmer.

It is important to realise at this stage that all rise and going dimensions so far discussed, including the subdivisions for steps, concern the face of the members in each case, and that the thickness of materials has no bearing on the geometry of the staircase. The only consideration for this now is that an allowance must be made at the top riser to accommodate the riser thickness, and some clearance, between the riser face and the trimmer face. An allowance of 40 mm would be reasonable for a riser thickness of 19 mm with packings.

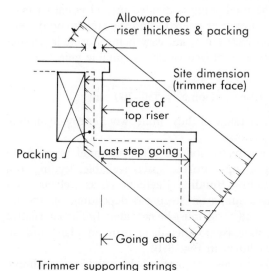

Trimmer supporting strings

Fig. 8.8
Geometry at upper step –
traditional strings or supporting
carriages

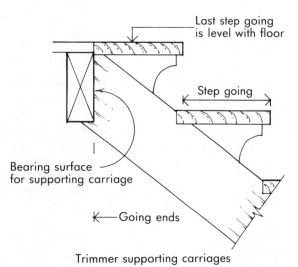

Trimmer supporting carriages

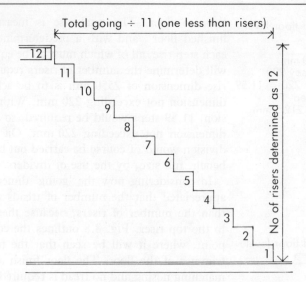

Total going ÷ 11 (one less than risers)

No of risers determined as 12

Fig. 8.9
Determination of goings

An exception, where there are as many treads as riser divisions, is in the modern staircase which has supporting carriages beneath it, instead of the more common strings, need a trimmer support 'further on' than is usual, and this would be considered at the trimming stage. Consequently a tread is required at the upper floor level and the trimmer is located one step going dimension beyond its normal position and this is also shown in Fig. 8.8.

Fig. 8.9 shows the determination of the step goings, related to the stairs shown in Fig. 8.7, where it was seen that 12 risers were required. The total going is divided into 11 equal parts or one less than the number of risers to find the step going dimension. If there is no restriction, an 'easy going' formula relating rise to going may be employed to find a suitable going dimension, and this is

$$(2 \times \text{Rise}) + \text{Going} = 550\text{–}700 \text{ mm}$$

A figure in the lower range of those limits would provide an easy going staircase, as shown.

Should there be a restriction, an attempt would be made to fit the eleven step goings into the space available, leading to a steeper flight of stairs. Building Regulations, as well as good craft practice, place limits on steepness depending on the location of the stairs and these must be considered. The alternative is to design the staircase to include a turn on plan, and an example of this is shown in Fig. 8.10.

Widths of stairs are also required to be not less than limits set by the Building Regulations, and these depend on the location and nature of use. There is a tendency to design near to these lower limits, to avoid waste of space within the building.

Before looking into the principal requirements of the Building Regulations concerned with stairs, although this cannot be separated from those aspects of planning already discussed, there will be some value in relating the rise and going geometry to the practical approach of setting-out the stair strings. The trimmed opening will have been prepared as determined by the designer, and the joinery producer is required to relate his work with that existing on site. He must take accurate site dimensions, particularly the finished floor-to-floor height, the overall going, and overall widths where these are in any way restricted. From the point of view of setting-out, the two most important are the going and rise dimensions, which are shown on lengths of batten, to be divided into the required number of equal parts. Fig. 8.11 shows the going rod, where the clearance at the trimmer face is deducted before the length is divided accurately into the 11 equal parts for the step going dimension. The height rod shows the accurate floor to floor height, divided into 12 equal parts for the rise dimensions. From these rods a 'pitchboard' is made from 5 or 6 mm plywood.

The pitchboard has an accurately prepared right-angle, and the rise and going dimensions are made to conform precisely to those on the rods. It will be used for marking out the strings and any bevel lines related to the pitch of the stair. It is easily handled and to most joiners is preferred to the steel square for

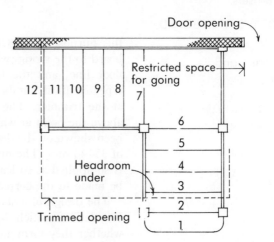

Fig. 8.10
Necessary turn on plan

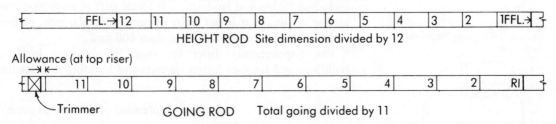

Fig. 8.11
Step dimensions from site dimensions

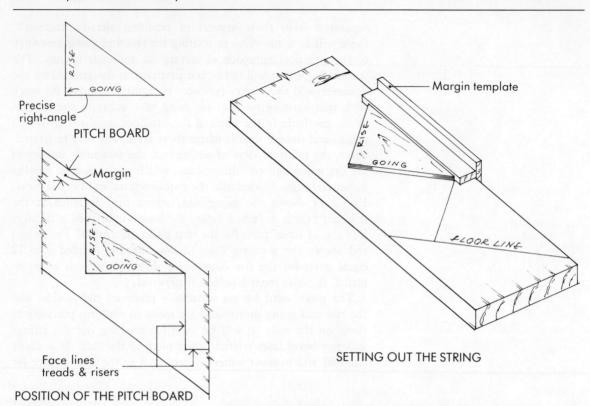

PITCH BOARD

POSITION OF THE PITCH BOARD

SETTING OUT THE STRING

Fig. 8.12
The pitch board and its
application

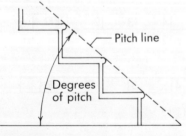

Fig. 8.13
Degrees of pitch

this purpose. Fig. 8.12 illustrates the application of the pitch-board to the string, where the device has already established the floor line, and the face lines of the first step. This will be repeated until number 12 is reached, this being the riser face at the trimmer. The 'margin' is the projection of the string, above the point at which riser and tread faces meet; it will have been shown on the detail drawings and is generally in the region of 35–40 mm. The margin template ensures that the pitchboard is so applied as to leave the required margin. It must therefore be made to the correct width and perfectly parallel.

The design of a stairway is closely controlled by the Building Regulations which lay down specific requirements for stairs whether they form an internal or external part of the structure. The Regulations are concerned with the whole of any stairway, including flights and landings, if it forms part of an escape route in case of fire, or if it has a rise of more than 600 mm, or from which it is possible to fall more than 600 mm.

The requirements differ for stairs in different kinds of building, and for this reason the types of building are classified as:

- *Private*   A building intended for use as one dwelling
- *Common*   A building intended for use as two or more dwellings;

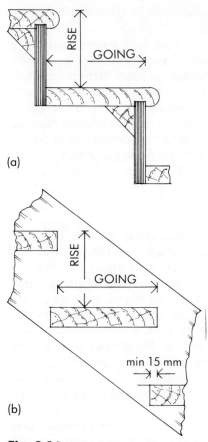

(a)

(b)

Fig. 8.14
Rise and going
(**a**) Conventional stair
(**b**) Open-riser stair

- *Institutional*   Except where used only for staff, or an assembly building having an area of 100 m² or more;
- *Others*   Any not within the above descriptions.

Limits to the pitch or steepness of stairs, expressed in degrees of pitch:

- *Private stairs*   Must be no greater than 42°;
- *Common stairs*   Must be no greater than 38° (see Fig. 8.13).

Further limitations are in the permissible rise and going dimensions, where maximum figures are given for the rise of steps, with minimum figures for goings, to be applied as shown in Figs 8.14(a) and 8.14(b) and listed as follows:

	Max Rise (mm)	Min Going (mm)
Private stair	220	220
Common stair	190	240
Institutional	180	280
Others	190	250

It should be noted that for Private and Common Stairs, to keep within the degrees of pitch already stated, it is not possible to work to both rise and going limits in the same staircase.

In addition to the limits placed on pitch or steepness, it is required that the ratio of rise to going is kept within certain bounds to ensure comfort and safety in the use of the stairway. Satisfactory ratios in any stairway are where twice the rise plus the going produces a figure between 550 and 700 mm.

As a quick route to finding a going dimension that may be used with any particular rise dimension, the Regulations offer the following additional information:

Private Stairs

Any rise between 155 and 220 mm can be used with any going between 245 and 260 mm.

Within the above range, any rise between 165 and 200 mm, may be used with a wider range of goings, 220 to 305 mm.

Common Stairs

Any rise 155 to 190 mm requires a going between 240 and 320 mm.

This information is helpful not only in the design of straight flights, but also as a guide to suitable going dimensions in tapered steps, as described later.

If the lowest step adjoins a sloping paving or floor, then the

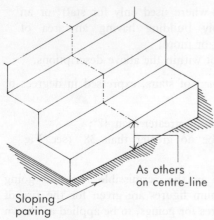

As others
on centre-line

Sloping
paving

Fig. 8.15
Step at sloping paving

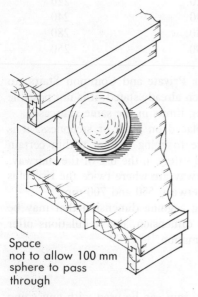

Space
not to allow 100 mm
sphere to pass
through

Fig. 8.16
Restriction in open risers –
certain buildings

rise dimension of the step is measured on the centre-line of the stairway as shown in Fig. 8.15.

A further requirement in the open-riser stairway referred to earlier concerns the possibility of users, and most particularly children, slipping partially through the space between treads. In stairs classified as Private or Common, or intended for use in Institutional buildings where children under 5 years of age are likely to use the stairway, or for any other residential building, the space between the treads must be so restricted as to prevent a 100 mm diameter sphere from passing through it. One solution to this is shown in Fig. 8.16 where a part riser has been introduced to restrict the space.

Rise and Going Dimensions – Tapered Steps

The craft principles regarding the design of 'winders' or tapered steps, described earlier in association with Fig. 8.5, required consecutive steps to be all to the same taper, and that rise dimensions were to be the same as the steps in adjoining flights. The measurement of goings in tapered steps is more specifically covered by the Building Regulations. The limiting figures, already given, concerned with the pitch or steepness of the stair, apply also to tapered steps and the Regulations show at what points in the length of the step these figures are to be applied.

Figure 8.17 gives two examples of 90° turns employing tapered steps, the first having a stair width in excess of 1 m and the second a width less than 1 m.

Where the width is 1 m or more, the going dimension must conform between two points measured 270 mm from each edge of the stair, and shown in the Figure as a shaded area.

Where the width of the stair is less than 1 m then the going dimension is measured on the centre line.

Check calculations may be applied to the two examples as follows. Taking the first as a Common Stairway having a stair width of 1.100 m, a rise of 180 and a going of 250 mm, then:

Checking the Ratio of Rise to Going

2R+G = 360 + 250 = 610 mm, which is within the specified limits.

Checking the Goings of the Tapered Steps

The list given earlier showed that for this rise dimension in a Common Stairway, the going may be as little as 240 or as great as 320 mm. Fig. 8.18 shows firstly that if this 90° turn is negotiated by three equal steps in the conventional manner, then the goings conform to the limits laid down by the Regulations for a short distance within the 270 mm points. The second diagram illustrates the effect of dividing the turn into four equal steps, where a greater part of the length of each step is seen to conform.

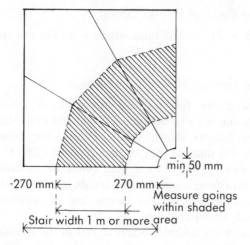

Fig. 8.17
Goings to tapered steps

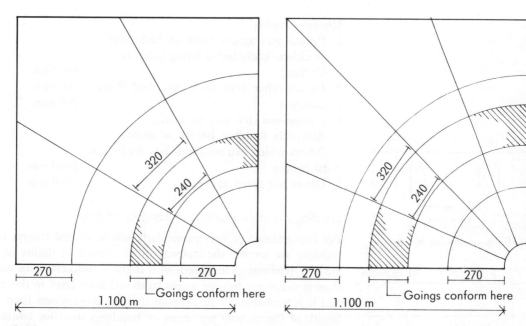

Fig. 8.18
Going limits to tapered steps

It is seen that the more parallel the shape of the step, the more of its length can be made to conform. In a typical framed stair it would be very difficult to satisfy the going limits to the full extent, and the example with four steps would reasonably be deemed to satisfy.

Geometrical stairs on curves of larger radius could be expected to satisfy the requirements completely.

Taking the second of the two examples in Fig. 8.17 as a Private Stairway having a stair width of 950 mm, a rise of 210 and a going of 245 mm, then:

Checking the Ratio of Rise to Going

2R+G = 420 + 245 = 665 mm, which is within the specified limits.

Checking the Goings of the Tapered Steps

The list showed that for this rise dimension in a Common Stairway the going must be between 245 and 260 mm. Measured on the centre line as shown in the Figure, the goings are approximately 320 mm, so they do not conform (2R+G would produce 740 mm). The solution here could be to divide the quarter-turn into four equal tapered treads instead of three to give a going dimension on the centre line of approximately 230 mm, which would conform.

Widths of stairways referred to above, and in the following list of minimum widths, may be defined as the *clear unobstructed width between walls, balustrading, handrails,* or *newels,* but ignoring the thickness of skirtings and strings.

Minimum widths

1. *Private* serving one room or bathroom or closet (excluding a living room or kitchen) 600 mm
2. *Private* other than those described above 800 mm
3. *Common* 900 mm
4. *Institutional* (not just for staff) Assembly building 100 m² or more Others which can accommodate more than 50 people 1000 mm
5. *Others* not listed above 800 mm

Landings and Limitations in Lengths of Flights

For convenience of use, particularly where several storeys of a building are served, the stairway often consists of flights separated by landings. The length of a flight is unlikely to be more than is necessary to give access from one floor level to the next and it is probably for this reason that the Regulations limit the length of flights only for shops or buildings used for assembly purposes, where the number of risers must not exceed 16. In these situations, landings may be introduced to serve only as rest points, with consecutive flights continuing in the same direction as in Fig. 8.19(a). It is required that the number of risers in consecutive flights is limited to 36 without a change of direction of at least 30° on plan, and this minimum requirement is shown in Fig. 8.19(b).

Landings between consecutive flights are most often intended partially to introduce a change of direction, because most stairways must be designed to fit into a limited space within the building. Examples were given in Figs 8.3, 8.4, and 8.5.

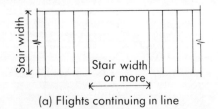

(a) Flights continuing in line

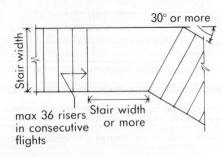

(b) Required change in direction

Fig. 8.19
Intermediate landings
(a) Flights continuing in line
(b) Required change in direction

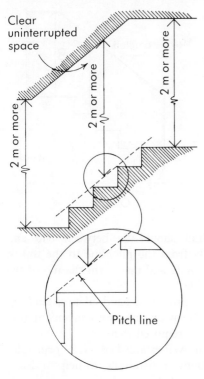

Clear uninterrupted space

2 m or more

2 m or more

2 m or more

Pitch line

Fig. 8.20
Headroom – stairs and landings

Headroom

This concerns principally the structural work in the floor above the staircase and most particularly the size of the trimmed opening prepared to receive the stairway.

Usually it is important not to lose more area from the upper floor than is necessary, and the trimmed opening is likely to be restricted as far as is permissible. The requirement for clear headroom above the stairs and associated landings determines how far the floor may extend over the stairs, and this must be determined as an integral part of the stair design. Fig. 8.1 earlier in the chapter illustrates the relationship between headroom and the size of the trimmed opening. The Building Regulations require at least 2 m clear headroom over the whole width of the stair and measured vertically from the pitchline or from the floor level at landings as shown in Fig. 8.20.

Guarding and Handrails

The guarding of stairs and landings is a requirement of the Building Regulations, irrespective of the kind of building concerned, and require the provision of walls, screens or balustrades at the sides of flights and landings where there is a drop of more than 600 mm.

The guarding must be of adequate strength and figures are given in the Regulations for the magnitude of force that the guarding should withstand, per metre length at handrail height. Any glazing forming part of the guarding below that height must be of glass blocks, toughened glass or laminated safety glass, and not of wired glass.

For Private, Common, Residential or Institutional buildings where children under 5 years of age are likely to use the stairway, the guarding must be so constructed as to prevent a 100 mm sphere from passing through it. Its design should be such that children would find difficulty in climbing up it.

The required minimum heights of the guarding related to the use of the building are as follows, and as illustrated in Fig. 8.21.

		Minimum Heights
Private	Flights	840 mm
	Landings	900 mm
Common	Flights	900 mm
	Landings	1000 mm
Others	Flights	900 mm
	Landings	1100 mm

Handrails are specifically required by the Building Regulations which demand that there should be a handrail on at least one side of a flight less than 1 m wide, and on both sides if the flight is wider. It need not extend to the bottom two steps of the stairway.

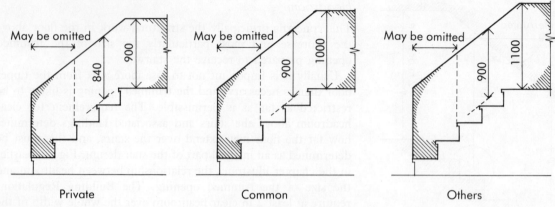

Private   Common   Others

Fig. 8.21
Guarding stairs and landings –
minimum heights

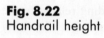

Handrail at landing
(not requ'd by Building Regulations)

Fig. 8.22
Handrail height

The height of the handrail should be between 840 and 1000 mm, measured vertically from the pitchline to the top of the handrail as shown in Fig. 8.22 and may form the top of the guarding if the heights coincide.

There is no requirement to provide a handrail to a landing, but it is common practice to provide one as a convenient way of capping the guarding that is required there.

There are some additional well-established craft principles that complement the Regulations on handrails, to help to determine the construction details, and these include:

The handrail should be easily and comfortably grasped. This should influence the chosen sectional size of material, and its moulded shape.

It should give adequate support and reassurance to the user, so the strength of material and its jointing to newels, or its fixings to the wall must be adequate.

It should, as far as is practicable, be continuous throughout the stairway. Interruptions by newels are common, but gaps, particularly at tapered steps, should be avoided.

At tapered steps, the location of the handrail at the outer edge of the turn will encourage the user to avoid the narrower parts of the treads.

There is some value in providing a positive feature as a 'stop' at the end of a handrail to remind the user of the end of the support provided. This is effectively achieved by the newel that commonly occurs at this point, otherwise some form of shaping to the end of the handrail may be employed, both as an aesthetic and as a safety feature.

Construction Details and Features

Step Details

The earlier part of the chapter has been concerned with the general design criteria used in the planning of a stairway, and this leads to the construction details that might be employed.

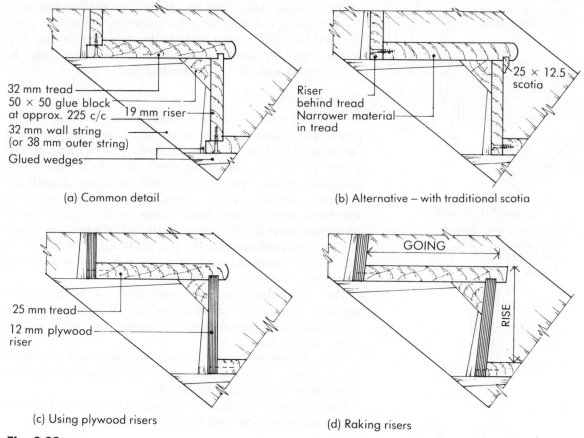

32 mm tread
50 × 50 glue block
at approx. 225 c/c   19 mm riser
32 mm wall string
(or 38 mm outer string)
Glued wedges

(a) Common detail

Riser
behind tread
Narrower material
in tread

25 × 12.5
scotia

(b) Alternative – with traditional scotia

25 mm tread
12 mm plywood
riser

(c) Using plywood risers

GOING

RISE

(d) Raking risers

Fig. 8.23
Alternative step details
(**a**) Common detail
(**b**) Alternative with traditional
        scotia
(**c**) Using plywood risers
(**d**) Raking risers

Fig. 8.23 shows four alternative sectional details that might be used to build up the steps

(a) Shows a common detail which allows the 'boxing-up' of the individual steps by tonguing together the tread and riser, with glue blocks rubbed into place. The section allows the final adjustment of tread and riser widths as each step is fitted to the string;

(b) The traditional scotia is a decorative feature that eliminates the need to tongue the riser to the tread. Another detail that is a popular alternative to the first example is in allowing the riser to pass down behind the tread as shown, so reducing the width of material required for the tread;

(c) The use of plywood for risers goes some way toward eliminating problems such as opening joints, and creaking under load, that can result from shrinkage in solid material. In this example the tread thickness is shown as 25 mm which is adequate for Private Stairways;

(d) Shows raking risers as a feature that may be introduced for visual interest as an alternative to the usual outline shown

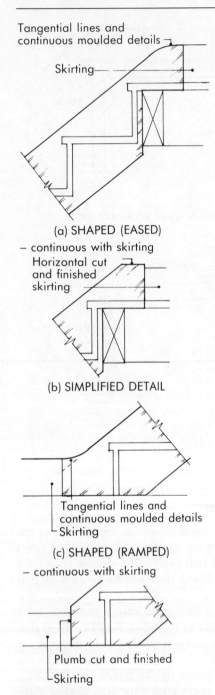

Tangential lines and continuous moulded details

Skirting

(a) SHAPED (EASED)
– continuous with skirting

Horizontal cut and finished skirting

(b) SIMPLIFIED DETAIL

Tangential lines and continuous moulded details
Skirting

(c) SHAPED (RAMPED)
– continuous with skirting

Plumb cut and finished
Skirting

Fig. 8.24
End details – wall strings
(a) Shaped (eased) – continuous with skirting
(b) Simplified detail
(c) Shaped (ramped) – continuous with skirting

in the other three. This has no effect on the rise and going dimensions and the main effect on setting-out will be in the need for a pitch board made to the appropriate shape. It is also unlikely that the housings in the strings can be machined with the aid of standard jigs.

String Details

Since the function of a string is largely a structural one, because it must resist bending stresses when under load, the stiffness of the material and its sectional dimensions are important. The string will be of considerable depth in order to accept the dimensions of the steps joined to it, and the structural needs will be largely satisfied for that reason. Wall strings are subject to less stress because they have fixings to the wall at points throughout their length, consequently their thickness is usually less than the thickness of other strings. Board widths of 250 or 275 mm are commonly used, in thicknesses of 32 mm for wall strings and 38 mm for outer strings.

The upper exposed edge of a wall string may be moulded to match skirtings at the adjoining landings. Where the stairs are to be fixed before plastering, plaster rebates may also be worked in one or both edges.

Outer strings may carry features associated with the balustrading above, or the spandrel panel below, or possibly the stair soffit where there is no spandrel panel.

Fig. 8.24 shows details at the upper and lower ends of the wall string, where skirtings will normally come into contact.

(a) The upper end of the string is shaped so that its straight lines are tangential to the curve, with any moulded features following through to meet the skirting;

(b) Shows a more common approach which eliminates much of the work that occurs in the first example, together with much of its visual appeal;

(c) Shows the lower end where the traditional treatment requires an additional piece to be glued to the edge of the string, at setting-out stage, to allow the shaped 'ramp' to be produced with any associated moulding. This leaves only the plumb cut to be made on site to join to the matching skirting;

(d) Shows the simplified approach used as an alternative at the lower end.

The outer string will normally connect to a newel at each end by the use of a mortice and tenon joint. The setting-out of both members will require them to relate to each other, because the joint must conform to tread and riser positions. The string will be set out first, as far as fixing the tread and riser positions all of which will be numbered. In most cases the riser face will align with the centre of the newel as shown in two plans in Fig. 8.25,

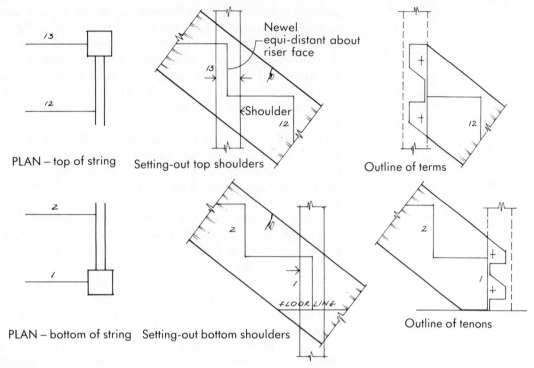

Fig. 8.25
Setting-out, string to newel

where risers numbered 1 and 13 conform to this. The shoulder positions are found by placing the newel dimension equally about the appropriate riser line, then marking the shoulder by use of the pitchboard with a parallel rule. The tenons will penetrate about two-thirds into the depth of the newel and will be draw-bored and pinned. Surplus material can be cut from the length of the string before passing through the tenon machine. In high class work the tenon shoulders may be lengthened by 6 mm to be recessed, full thickness, into the newel. This practice is to conceal any shrinkage of material that would result in an open shoulder.

The tenon width should be separated into two smaller tenons to minimise the loosening of the joint due to shrinkage as would be more likely to occur if the tenon were left as one. The outlines of the tenons are shown in the last two diagrams, where the principle is to avoid any weak 'short grain' and to avoid undercutting at the end of any mortice. These outlines should be determined at the same setting-out stage so as to arrive at the mortice positions on the newel. The handrail, which is usually the same length as the string, and with the same bevel to the shoulders, is set-out at the same time.

Shaped Steps

These usually occur at the bottom of a stairway, and are intended to give more open access to it by eliminating the guarding or balustrade to the bottom one or two steps. A second reason for their use may be seen by referring again to Fig. 8.25 where the plan shows riser number 1 entering the newel and the resultant joint is seen to be of reduced width because some of the string is lost at floor level. This joint would have been stronger if the whole width of the string could have been in contact with the newel, as would occur where shaped steps are introduced.

Fig. 8.26 shows firstly alternative plans at the foot of a flight of stairs where either one or two shaped steps are incorporated. Using one such step, a bullnose and a D-end step are shown, resulting in riser number 2 dictating the shoulder position seen in side elevation.

Where two shaped steps are included then riser number 3 is seen to determine the shoulder position. In both cases the joint will be the same, and will as illustrated employ the full width of the string to give the best possible strength result.

The construction of shaped steps such as those shown, involves a good deal of skill when produced by the traditional craft methods. The curved riser is produced by reducing it to a veneer, no more than 2 mm thick over part of its length to enable it to be bent around a block, as shown in Fig. 8.27. The block is laminated to minimise distortion due to moisture changes, then cut accurately to shape. By rolling its curved surface along the riser the length of the reduced portion is found. The riser must be of clear, selected material with straight grain, and must be carefully worked to avoid any weak points

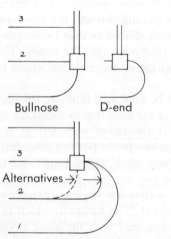

Bullnose   D-end

Alternatives →

Plans – one or two shaped steps

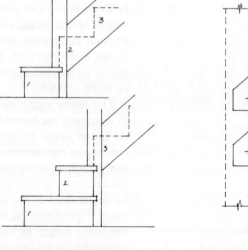

Side elevations

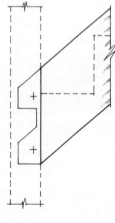

Full-width tenoned joint

Fig. 8.26
Shaped steps – and the string to newel joint

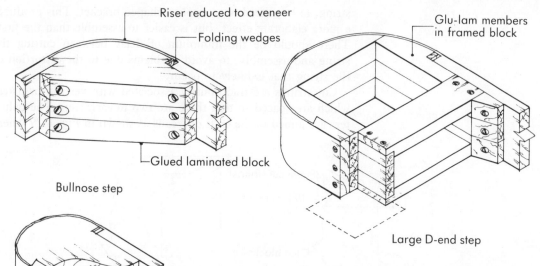

Riser reduced to a veneer

Folding wedges

Glued laminated block

Bullnose step

Glu-lam members in framed block

Large D-end step

Small D-end step

Fig. 8.27
Shaped steps

in the veneer. Water is applied to the outer face as the riser is glued and bent around the block to be tightened by the folding wedges. The larger step shown in the Figure employs a framed block for economy and stability, and its larger members are of glued laminated material.

Alternative methods of manufacturing shaped steps are sometimes possible. The shaped riser can be produced by gluing 3 mm plywood to the straight riser material, which is omitted where the curve occurs. The plywood should have the grain of its face veneers running vertically to allow easier bending.

Shaped risers made entirely from glued and pressed laminates cannot be produced economically in small numbers, but some standard shapes have been produced by specialist manufacturers for the trade.

Less attractive but sometimes used as an alternative to curved shapes are risers that are mitred together to produce shapes such as the 45° 'bullnose' step where the joints are glue-blocked at the back to ensure that no movement occurs.

Cut Strings

These are used in staircases as a form of construction that will produce a more elegant visual effect than those already discussed. The work will be considerably more expensive as a result of the proportion of bench work in fitting and assembly. This kind of string is most often associated with geometrical stairs where the absence of newels, the continuous handrails and strings, and the exposed profile of the steps can combine to produce a very attractive staircase. Fig. 8.28 shows the two kinds of cut string. In the first, the risers are mitred to the string itself and the differing thicknesses allow the square recess to each mitre, to make a useful 'location' in assembly. In the second example the risers are allowed to pass beyond the face of the string, to be mitred to an applied shaped bracket. This produces a more elaborate effect, but is easier to assemble than the first. There should be the minimum of delay between cutting the string and assembly, to avoid problems due to the distortion of the string that is likely to occur.

Cut strings are traditionally associated with vertical balusters which are spaced so that there are two to each step. The balusters are joined to the ends of treads as shown in Fig. 8.29 where

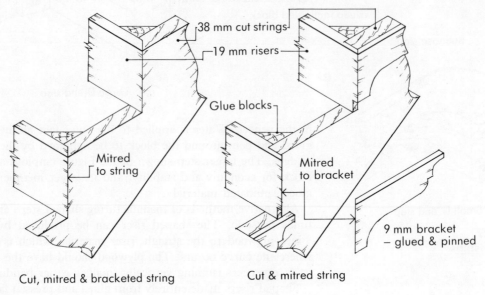

Fig. 8.28
Cut strings

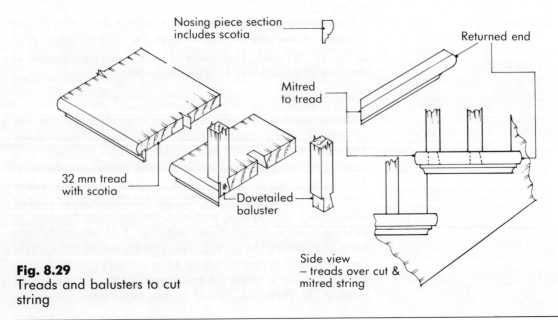

Fig. 8.29
Treads and balusters to cut
string

it will be seen that the dovetailed joints are finally concealed by an applied nosing piece fixed to each tread. The fixing of the nosing piece is by slot-screwing.

Wall Strings at Winders

It is necessary to develop the shapes and resulting material needs in the tapered treads and wall strings, and this is achieved initially by producing a scaled layout as in Fig. 8.30. This geometrical development will enable the production of the cutting list for the material in the tapered steps and in the shaped portions of the wall strings. A workshop rod showing the full-size plan layout of the winders will also be produced as a necessary aid to marking out.

In Fig. 8.30 the plan shows firstly a possible solution to the problem of achieving a minimum of 50 mm going at the

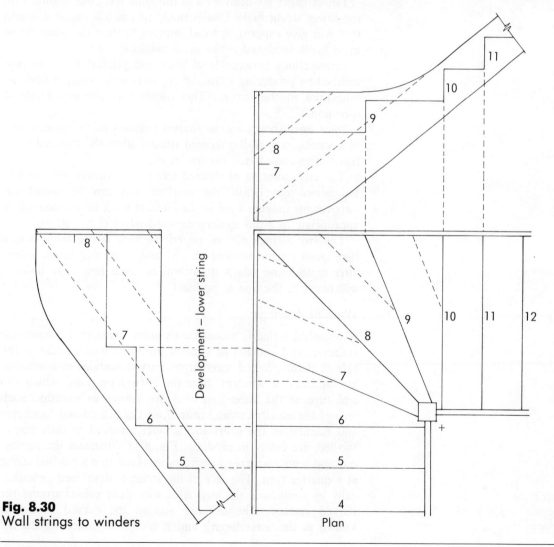

Fig. 8.30
Wall strings to winders

Development – lower string

Plan

narrowest ends of the treads, by allowing the riser faces to radiate from a point outside the strings.

The material needed for each tread is determined by showing the stock width where the broken lines indicate joints between boards. Account should be taken of the use of reversed triangular offcuts in making up the width required.

The strings are developed on the drawing by firstly projecting the riser faces to combine with rise dimensions to draw the face outlines of the numbered steps in each flight. Allowing for the margin, the width of each wall string is then shown.

The shaped upper edge of the upper string is now shown to finish level, or horizontal, with a margin above step number 9. The lower string is then also made to finish level, and to coincide with the upper string, by checking heights against numbered tread faces.

Lower edges are dealt with in the same way, but dealing with the lower string first. This is made to finish level, at a height that will give support to tread number 6, then the other string must finish level and at the same height.

Intersections between level lines and pitched lines are now finished by producing a circular arc so that the straight lines are tangential to the curve. (This avoids any abrupt change of direction.)

Joint lines shown on the shaped portions of the strings will, in a similar way to the tapered treads, allow the material to be listed after considering the use of offcuts.

The edge jointing of tapered treads and strings will need to be carried out before the marking out can be completed. Grooves for tongues used in the jointing must be stopped where appropriate to avoid spoiling exposed edges of the strings.

The two strings will be joined together at the angle with a bare-faced tongue worked on one and a housing in the other, after considering which flight will be fixed first. The housing will occur in the first to be fixed.

Wreathed Strings

A wreathed string is a continuous outer string to a geometrical staircase, and consists of straight portions, which occur at the side of flights, joined together by curved portions at intermediate landings or winders. It is the curved portions, which rise and turn at the same time that are known as wreaths. Such strings are usually cut and mitred, or cut mitred and bracketed and because of the skills and labours involved in their manufacture, are costly to produce. Fig. 8.13 illustrates the setting-out and manufacturing principles involved in a wreathed string at a quarter turn. The face of the string is developed geometrically by combining the step rises with their goings around the curved surface. The distance around the curved surface is known as the 'stretch-out', and is found by projecting the 60°

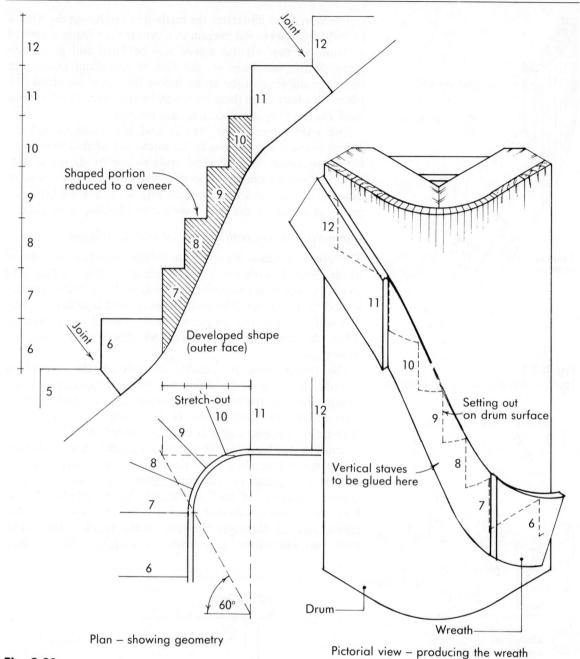

Fig. 8.31
Wreathed string

line as shown, to meet the tangential line across the crown of the curve. In this case the stretch-out is then divided into four equal parts to produce the goings of the tapered steps at the curved surface. The curved portion is shown hatched, and the wreath will include one full step profile at each end before the joints occur in the string.

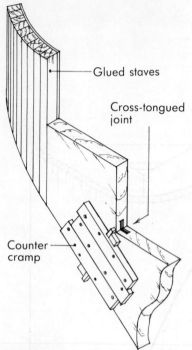

Fig. 8.32
Joint – straight string to wreaths

The figure also illustrates the method of producing the wreath by reducing the curved portion to a veneer then fixing it around a 'drum' so that vertical staves may be fitted and glued into place. Setting-out lines on the face of the drum ensure the correct positioning of the string before the staves are glued into place. At a later stage these lines may be transferred to the string itself for the purpose of cutting and mitring.

The joint between the wreath and the adjoining straight strings is cut at right angles to the pitch, and located in position by the inclusion of a plywood cross-tongue as shown in Fig. 8.32. A counter cramp, otherwise known as counter keys as described earlier and illustrated in Fig. 6.16, is used here as a means of cramping the joint together and holding it in place.

Open-Riser Stairs with Strings or with Carriages

The most common form of open-riser stairway consists of treads, possibly with part risers (referred to earlier in Figs 8.12 and 8.14) which are supported at their ends by being securely jointed to the strings. The joints must be held together in a way that will not spoil the appearance when viewed from above or below the tread, so the conventional glued wedges are not appropriate.

The treads must be capable of resisting the stresses of everyday use without the support of risers, although part risers properly fixed to the treads will contribute substantially to their strength. Material used for the treads is likely to be thicker than in stairs with risers, and it is often of hardwood.

Stairs of this kind may be noisy in use, and abrasion damage to the applied finish is very likely to occur. There is also a danger of slipping on the uncarpeted treads and for these reasons a number of applied features may be employed. Fig. 8.33 shows some details that may result from the above considerations, and (a) illustrates the joint of the tread to the string, with two alternative approaches to wedging. The wedged

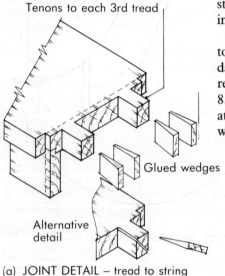

(a) JOINT DETAIL – tread to string

Fig. 8.33
Tread details – to open riser stairs
(**a**) Joint detail – tread to string
(**b**) Safety nosings
(**c**) Carpeted tread

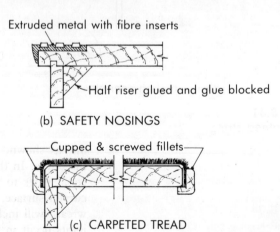

(b) SAFETY NOSINGS

(c) CARPETED TREAD

tenons, exposed on the face of the string may not be considered acceptable, then pelleted screws may be employed, although screws into end-grain are not very effective. Tie rods appropriately spaced, and located beneath the treads, are sometimes used, with decorative covers concealing the ends of the rods. Part (b) illustrates a proprietary safety nosing that is fixed by screws through the coloured fibre inserts, to be concealed with matching fibre pellets. Part (c) shows a method of concealing the edges of carpet by using rebated hardwood fillets, cupped and screwed into place. An example of an open riser stairway, with strings as described appears later as a Joinery Project.

Open riser stairs on carriages instead of strings appear to be lighter and more elegant. Fig. 8.8 made reference to these, and Fig. 8.34 shows some typical details of a stairway having two substantial carriages of hardwood, with shaped brackets tenoned into them. The sectional sizes of the carriages will depend upon

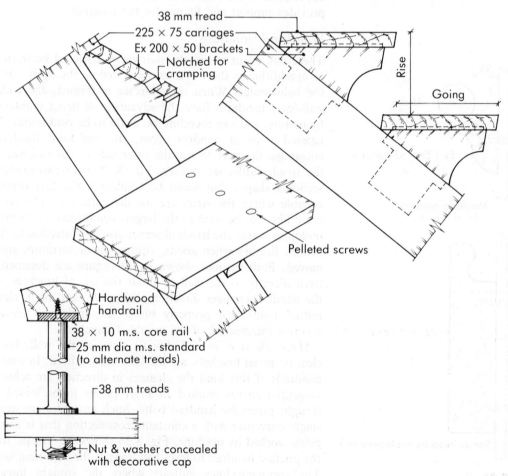

Fig. 8.34
Open-riser stairs on carriages

their inclined span and the stiffness of the material but the sizes given are typical. Carriages are sometimes of glued laminated material for its extra potential strength, and in some cases to allow it to be bent to achieve curves on plan.

The tenoned joints of brackets to carriages must be close-fitting and thoroughly glued to avoid the need for any mechanical aid in the form of pins, which would be unsightly, and the notches shown in the upper edges of the brackets are to enable cramping. The treads are glued, screwed and pelleted to the brackets to ensure that no movement occurs in the joint.

Handrails in these stairs do not have the support of newels and will depend largely on the balustrade, which must be securely connected to the treads. The given detail shows the principal members of the balustrade as round mild-steel standards at alternate treads. Further lateral support would be gained by end fixings to walls, and by any turns on plan. The upper edge of the balustrade features a mild steel core rail which provides support and fixings for the handrail.

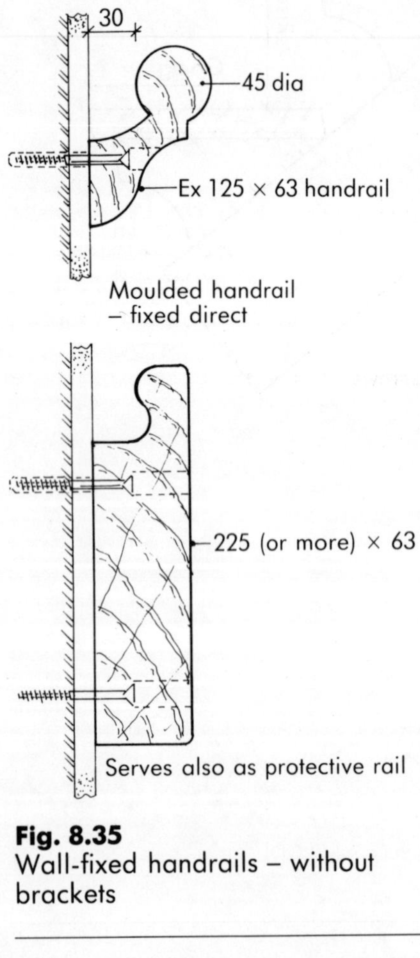

Wall-fixed Handrails

These will occur where the stairway is enclosed between walls, or in addition to those that are provided on the open side above the balustrades. When the staircase is framed, the additional wall-fixed handrails have the advantage of being uninterrupted by newels, and can therefore be made to be continuous. Where tapered steps or winders occur, the wall-fixed handrail will encourage the user to use the safer side of the stairway where the tread widths are greater. Fig. 8.35 gives two examples of sectional shapes that could be employed, the first being most suitable where the stairs are for domestic use. The second is more likely to be used in the larger, commercial or institutional buildings where the handrail serves also as protection to the wall and its finishes when goods, equipment or furniture are being moved. Both sections shown in this figure are designed to be fixed directly to the wall, without the use of brackets. Where the handrail changes direction, either on plan, or in elevation, mitred joints that properly bisect the angle will ensure the accurate intersection of the moulded members.

Handrails that are not directly fixed to the wall, but stand clear on metal brackets, are unlikely to be mitred. In continuous handrails of this kind the changes in direction are achieved by tangential curves worked in short pieces to be joined to the straight pieces by handrail bolts. Such examples are usually in single curvature with a constant cross-section that is capable of being worked by machine. Fig. 8.36 shows the 'ramps' that join the pitched handrail to level handrails at the adjoining landings. The springing lines indicate where the straight lines make tangential contact with the circular curves, and if the joints are made to occur at these points then the side bevels may be

30

45 dia

Ex 125 × 63 handrail

Moulded handrail
– fixed direct

225 (or more) × 63

Serves also as protective rail

Fig. 8.35
Wall-fixed handrails – without brackets

worked over a saddle on the spindle moulder. The curve on plan also shown, is achieved by a 'quadrant' or a quarter of the full circle. If the joints are made to coincide with the springing lines then the curved member will itself include no straight portion and will therefore be capable of being worked partially over a saddle. In this case it is the curved upper surface that can be worked in this manner.

Handrail Scrolls

The end of a handrail that is not joined to a newel may be finished with a spiral scroll, largely as a decorative feature but also for safety reasons by making the user aware that the end of the handrail has been reached. The scroll may occur in the vertical plane to be seen in elevation as a 'drop scroll', or more often in the horizontal plane, to be seen on plan.

There will be some geometry involved in producing a scroll that is workable, pleasing in appearance, and conforming to the

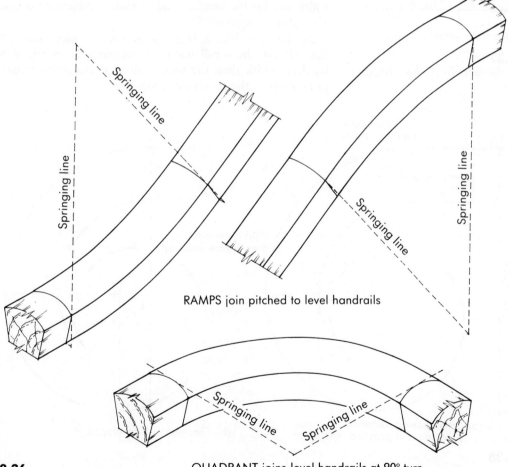

RAMPS join pitched to level handrails

QUADRANT joins level handrails at 90° turn

Fig. 8.36
Handrails in single curvature

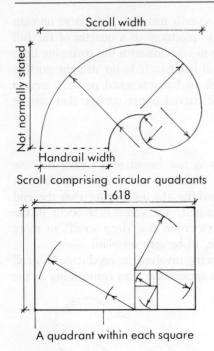

Scroll width

Not normally stated

Handrail width

Scroll comprising circular quadrants
1.618

A quadrant within each square

Fig. 8.37
Scroll derived from the golden
section

required dimensions. For practical reasons the spiral outline is produced as a number of circular quadrants, tangential to each other and of progressively smaller radius.

Fig. 4.5(d) in Chapter 4 described the 'Golden Section' which can be used as a basis for producing the outline of a scroll and this is developed in Fig. 8.37 where in the series of decreasing squares, each contains a circular quadrant. The method requires that the largest rectangle is drawn first with its largest dimensions equal to the scroll width and the smaller dimension such that the ratio of the sides as 1:1.618. The second side can be found by calculation. The shape produced may satisfy some situations, but the method does not allow any flexibility in the design of the scroll.

Fig. 8.38(a) shows a scroll shape that is more pleasing in appearance and has practical advantages. The inner curves continue to just beyond the first quadrant where it is possible that a joint may occur, and the space at 'X' can be varied by the geometry employed. Dimensions are given for the scroll width and for the handrail width, then a judgement is made for a suitable dimension 'X'.

As shown in Fig. 8.38(b) the geometry commences with the line AB for the scroll width. Dimension 'X' is added to the handrail width then the total is divided into eight equal parts to be used in the following construction.

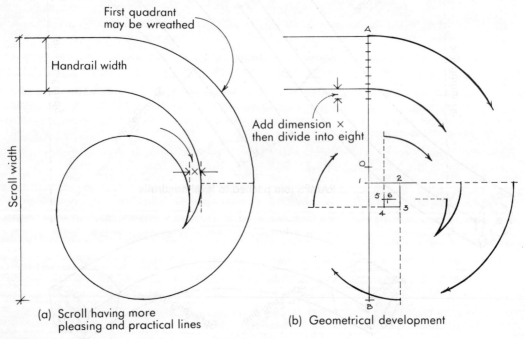

First quadrant
may be wreathed

Handrail width

Scroll width

Add dimension x
then divide into eight

(a) Scroll having more
pleasing and practical lines

(b) Geometrical development

Fig. 8.38
Handrail scroll and its practical
geometry

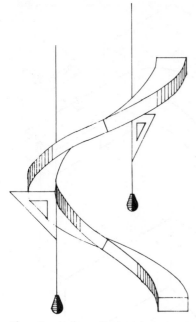

Elevation – the cylindrical concept

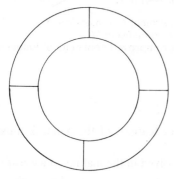

Plan – four separate wreaths

– GEOMETRICAL BASIS

Fig. 8.39
Wreaths – geometrical basis

AB is bisected at O, then O–1 is equal to two parts. 1 is the centre of the first inner and outer quadrants. 1–2 is equal to four parts, then 2 is the centre of the second outer quadrant and the shorter, inner arc. 2–3 is equal to three parts, 3–4 equal to two parts, 4–5 equal to one part and 5–6 equal to half of a part. Consecutive numbers to 5 are the centres of consecutive quadrants, and 6 the centre of the final arc.

Note that the whole of the scroll may be in a single, flat plane when the first quadrant will be merely a curved extension of the straight handrail all to the same cross-section. In other cases the first quadrant is required to be wreathed so as to commence the 'climb' of the stair as it turns, as part of a geometrical handrail.

Wreaths in Geometrical Handrailing

Changes in the direction of geometrical handrails are achieved by the inclusion of wreaths which combine the turn on plan with the associated rise of the stairway at that point. In most cases the turn is confined to a local position and occurs at the end of, or between, the handrails of straight flights.

Plan shapes of wreaths usually consist of circular curves which when combined with the rise may be visualised as climbing around a cylinder. Ignoring any moulded feature in the handrail, a vital aspect of its geometry is that the side faces continue to be plumb throughout their length, and the top and bottom faces continue to be level across their width when measured normal to the curve. Fig. 8.39 illustrates these characteristics in a handrail that is wreathed around one complete circular turn.

An individual wreath made from one solid piece of material must be limited in size for practical reasons, and most commonly will produce a 90° turn on plan and will include a straight portion or 'shank' of 100 to 150 mm where it is to be joined to a straight handrail.

Fig. 8.40 shows a pictorial view of the wreath to a quarter turn where the raking handrail to a flight joins the level handrail at the landing above. The Figure illustrates that the wreath forms part of a quadrant on plan, and has a shank at each end. At planning stage it may be possible to adjust dimension 'X' to achieve the best possible lines to the handrail, and similarly dimension 'Y' the height of the level handrail may be adjusted within limits set by the Building Regulations (if, as is usually the case, it caps the balustrade or 'guarding' of the landing).

To achieve smooth flowing lines in the handrail, the centre lines which run through the lengths of adjoining members must be made to come together tangentially both in plan and in elevations. These centre lines are known as 'tangents', and they should be examined firstly at planning stage when it may be possible to adjust the layout of the handrail or features of the stairs themselves to achieve the best results. The tangents will also be used in the setting-out and manufacture of the wreath

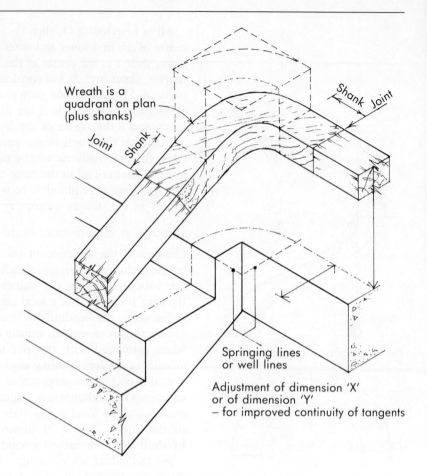

Wreath is a
quadrant on plan
(plus shanks)

Shank Joint

Joint Shank

Springing lines
or well lines

Adjustment of dimension 'X'
or of dimension 'Y'
– for improved continuity of tangents

Fig. 8.40
Pictorial view – wreath at
quarter turn

to serve as datums to which other features of the handrail must conform.

The following processes are involved in the making of a wreath:

1. *Determine the minimum size of material required*, and bring it to a constant thickness;
2. *Cut and 'shoot' the ends or joint faces* to length and to the bevels required. These cannot be checked again when further shaping has taken place;
3. *Cut to the plan outline shape* to conform to face moulds or templates. Relative to the surface of the plank, some of these cuts will be bevelled and the shape will appear distorted. Circular curves become elliptical;
4. *Square the wreath*, by cutting the top and bottom curved faces to their 'falling lines'. The surfaces produced must meet the rectangular ends marked on the end or joint faces, and will be 'twisted' through their length;
5. *Fit joints together*, using handrail bolts and dowels, then work the moulded section to match the adjoining straight handrails.

To allow these processes to be carried out, applied full-size geometry must be used to determine:

(a) The minimum thickness of material required;
(b) Bevels at joints, and in sections, measured against the face of the material;
(c) Face moulds or templates, showing shapes as projected to the faces of the material;
(d) Location of tangents to ensure continuity between members and to be used as datums for related measurements.

Fig. 8.41 shows the geometry that would be necessary in the setting-out of the wreath shown in the previous Figure. Firstly,

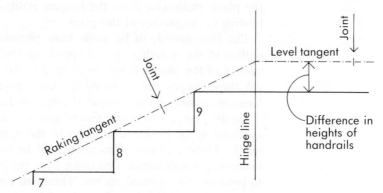

DEVELOPMENT OF TANGENTS

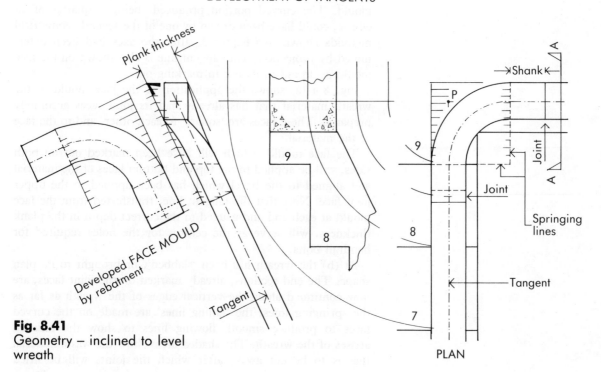

Fig. 8.41
Geometry – inclined to level wreath

PLAN

the plan shows the wreath and the adjoining handrails located over the upper steps and landing. The tangents are shown as running through the centres of the three members. The side views of the tangents are developed above, where the pitch of the flight is found by rebatement about point 'P' (the hinge line) to relate the goings of the steps with their rise. The tangents of pitched and level handrails meet at the hinge line and show the difference in heights of the two. This is an ideal relationship for the tangents, but if the height of the level handrail had been predetermined it may have been necessary to 'ease' or modify the fall of the wreath.

Section A-A is projected from the plan and shows the handrail thickness and width located around the tangents to determine the plank thickness. Note the tangent position and the bevel, relative to the surface of the plank.

The face mould, to be made from plywood, will show the outline of the wreath as it will appear on the upper and lower surface of the plank. It will be applied to the material to mark out these shapes and to locate the exact positions of the rectangular outlines on the prepared end joint faces.

On the plan, conveniently spaced ordinates are drawn over the quadrant to be projected through to the upper surface of the plank. These increased dimensions will be combined with the unchanged width dimensions taken from the plan of the wreath to produce the elliptical curves. These are completed freehand and the shanks added to show the finished outline of the face mould. The curved portion produced, being a quarter of an ellipse, could have been drawn by one of the several geometrical methods shown in Chapter 3, after the axes had been determined by projection. The tangent line is also shown on the face mould as an aid to its use in marking out.

Fig. 8.42(a) shows the application of the face mould to the wreath material that has already had its joint faces accurately prepared. These faces are 'square' to each other, and to the face of the material.

The face mould, which will have been marked out on both sides, will be applied to the top and bottom faces of the material and aligned to the bevel which has been applied to the upper joint face. Note that the tangent line, transferred from the face mould at each end and gauged to the correct depth in the plank thickness, will serve as the centres for the holes required for handrail bolts.

At (b) the wreath has been 'slabbed', or brought to its plan shape. The end sections, already marked on the joint faces, are now continued along the vertical edges of the wreath as far as the springing lines, the 'falling lines' are made on the curved faces to produce smooth flowing lines to show the finished arrises of the wreath. The shaded areas show the waste material that is to be cut away, after which the joints will be fitted

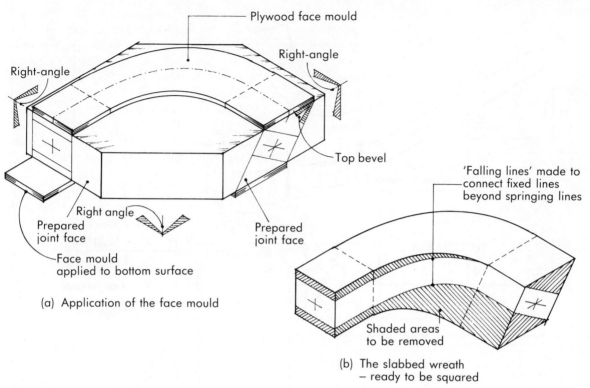

Plywood face mould

Right-angle

Right-angle

Top bevel

Right-angle

Right angle

Prepared
joint face

Prepared
joint face

Face mould
applied to bottom surface

(a) Application of the face mould

'Falling lines' made to
connect fixed lines
beyond springing lines

Shaded areas
to be removed

(b) The slabbed wreath
– ready to be squared

Fig. 8.42
Principal stages in making the
wreath
(**a**) Application of the face
mould
(**b**) The slabbed wreath – ready
to be squared

together, then the wreath moulded to match the adjoining
straight pieces.

Fig. 8.43 shows another example of a wreath to a quarter-
turn, in this case at the foot of an upper flight of stairs, adjoining
a half-space landing.

Handrail heights have been predetermined at 910 mm above
the pitch line for the raking handrail, and 100 mm above the
floor for the level handrail, giving a difference of 90 mm. The
centre of the balustrade is also fixed, at 100 mm from the edge
of the stairway. The continuous handrail must be made to
conform to those dimensions. The going of the steps is 280 mm
and the rise is 160 mm.

The plan shows the wreath, which has 100 mm shanks over
steps numbered 9 and 10 and part of the landing.

The tangents are developed by rebatement, and are drawn to
accommodate the 90 mm difference in height, and it is found
that in order that the two lines may meet at the 'hinge line' it
is necessary to 'ease' the raking tangent upward with a tangential
curve. This easing takes place before the well line, or springing
line, in order to leave a straight shank.

In Section A-A the handrail and wreath are drawn as seen in
that direction, then the plank thickness needed for the wreath
is shown. Note that in this example, where the shaping is more
pronounced, the plank is shown as not being parallel to the

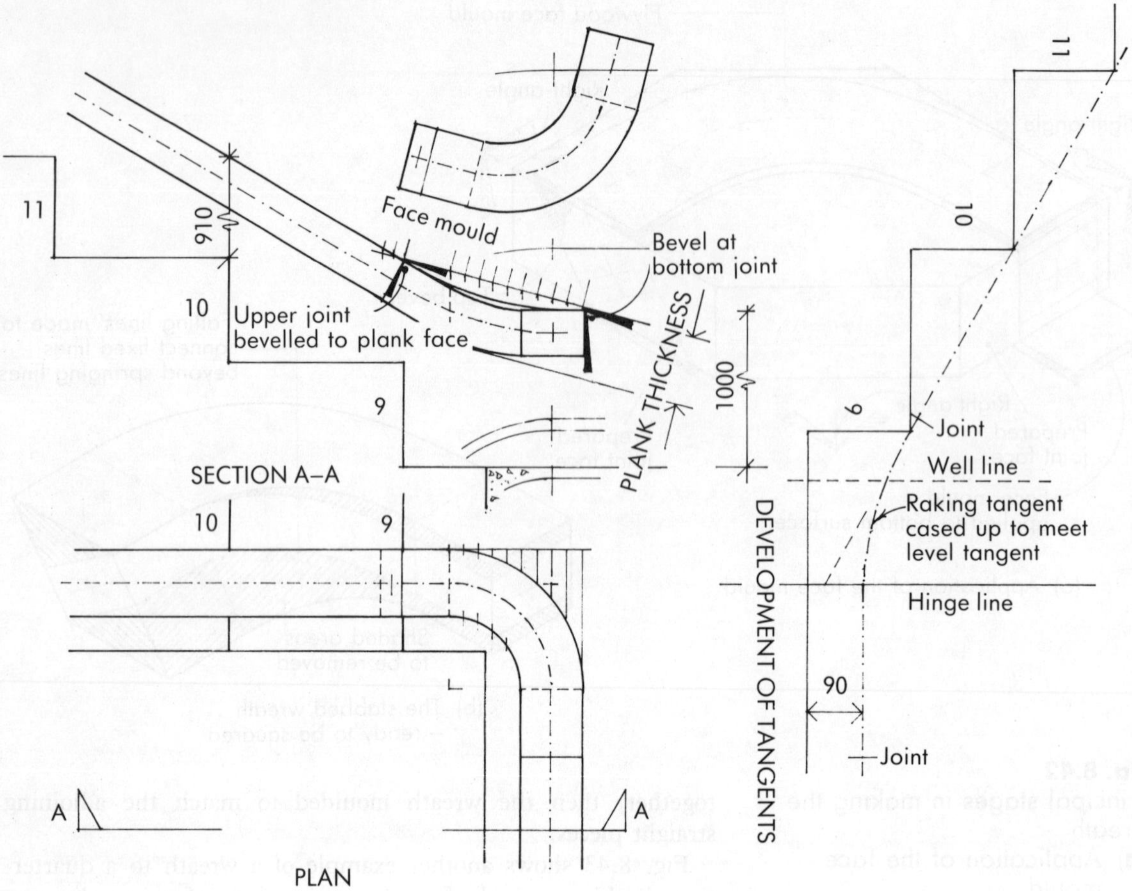

Fig. 8.43
Geometry – level to inclined wreath (handrail positions and heights not adjustable)

raking handrail to ensure that 'short grain' is kept to a minimum and that the plank thickness is not wasteful. The upper joint face is cut at a bevel to the plank face and the bevel is seen in this view. The lower joint face will be square from the plank face and, as before, the handrail section when drawn upon that face will be inclined to the upper surface, and this bevel is also seen.

JOINERY PROJECTS XXI–XXII

The remainder of the chapter is devoted to two related Joinery Projects which are listed as follows:

No.	Item	Drawings
XXI	Open-riser Domestic Stairway	XXI.1, XXI.2, XXI.3
XXII	Glazed balustrade to domestic stairs	XXII.1, XXII.2

Project No. XXI
Open-riser Domestic Stairway

Specification

The stairway required for a new private house is to comprise two flights separated by a quarter-space landing and will be situated against one wall which is parallel to the upper flight. The stairs, which will be fixed after plastering, will be of clear selected European Oak throughout, with the exception of the concealed structural timbers to the quarter-space landing, which will be of softwood.

The total rise from finished floor to finished floor is designed as 1.568 m in thirteen equal steps with other dimensions as shown in Drawing XXI.1. Dimensions are to be checked on site.

Nominal timber sizes are to be as listed below, and these must not be reduced by more than 2 mm for each prepared face when measured in the finished product. The moisture content of the material at the time of assembly is to be within the range of 10–14%.

Newels	100 × 100 mm	European Oak
Half newels	100 × 50 mm	European Oak
Outer strings	250 × 38 mm	European Oak
Wall strings	250 × 32 mm	European Oak
Treads	250 × 32 mm	European Oak
Nosing pieces	100 × 32 mm	European Oak
Half risers	100 × 25 mm	European Oak
Boards to landings	100 × 25 mm	European Oak
Handrails	75 × 63 mm	European Oak
Joists (Quarter-space landing)	100 × 50 mm	Swedish Redwood
Landing soffit & trimmer facing	12 mm	Oak-faced Birch multi-ply

Construction details are to be as shown in Drawings XXI.1 and XXI.3 and the work is to be properly framed together with close-fitting, well-glued joints and brought to a high standard of preparation ready for a clear gloss finish.

Note – some details have been omitted from this project for reasons of clarity. Features such as mouldings to strings, skirtings and handrails, and finishes to upper and lower ends of newels are variable and largely a matter of taste. An example of balustrading to suit this project, or other, appears as Project No. XXII.

Interpretation

It is noted that the stairway is to be fixed after plastering, and in order to achieve neat close contact the plaster must be accurately finished. The fixing of softwood grounds to the wall before plastering would ensure this.

Under-surfaces of the stairs will be visible and must be finished accordingly. Glue blocks must be properly finished and accurately positioned. All surplus glue must be removed to avoid spoiling the following applied finish.

Treads and half-risers must be neatly housed into the strings and alternate treads tenoned through and wedged.

Setting-out procedures will be as for stairs having full risers, and the normal pitch board will be applied to strings, handrails and newels.

Particular care must be taken to reduce the unsightly effects of shrinkage in work of this kind where wide boards are employed and where bevelled shoulders will exaggerate the problem.

Hardwood pins used in draw-bored tenons must be of matching hardwood or alternatively counter-bored and pelleted.

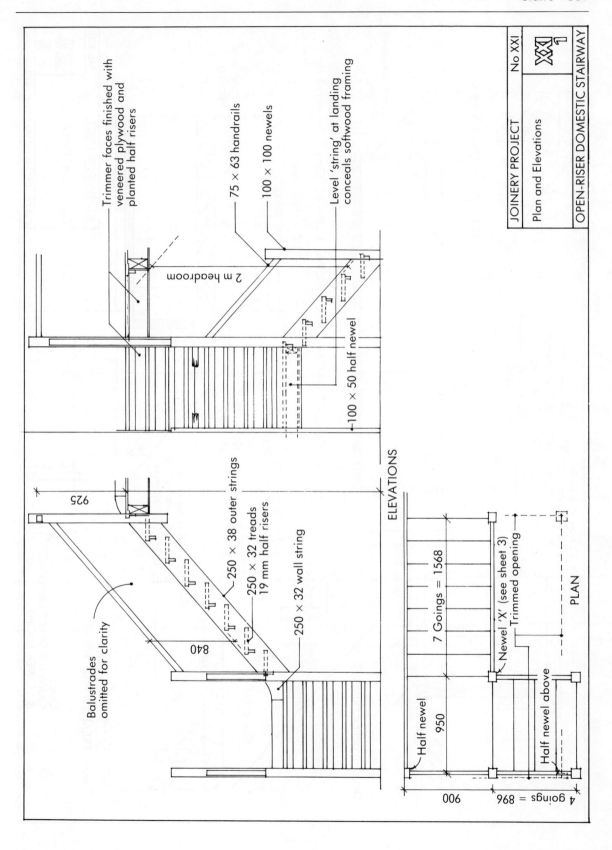

Trimmer faces finished with veneered plywood and planted half risers

75 × 63 handrails

100 × 100 newels

Level 'string' at landing conceals softwood framing

2 m headroom

100 × 50 half newel

Balustrades omitted for clarity

925

250 × 38 outer strings

250 × 32 treads 19 mm half risers

250 × 32 wall string

840

ELEVATIONS

7 Goings = 1568

Newel 'X' (see sheet 3)
Trimmed opening

Half newel

950

PLAN

Half newel above

900

4 goings = 896

JOINERY PROJECT   No XXI

XXI
1

Plan and Elevations

OPEN-RISER DOMESTIC STAIRWAY

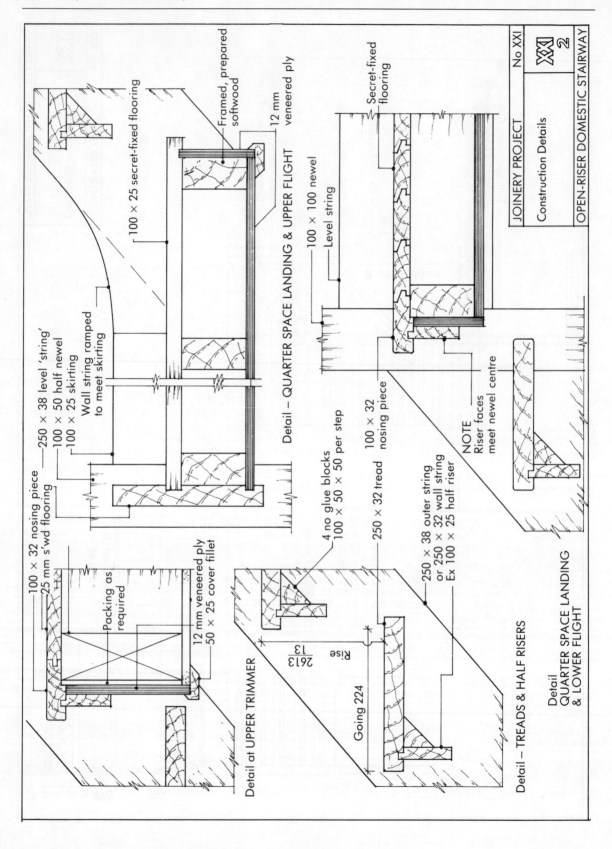

Detail – QUARTER SPACE LANDING & UPPER FLIGHT

Framed, prepared softwood

12 mm veneered ply

100 × 25 secret-fixed flooring

250 × 38 level 'string'
100 × 50 half newel
100 × 25 skirting

Wall string ramped to meet skirting

100 × 32 nosing piece
25 mm s'wd flooring

Packing as required

12 mm veneered ply
50 × 25 cover fillet

Detail at UPPER TRIMMER

4 no glue blocks
100 × 50 × 50 per step

100 × 32 nosing piece

250 × 32 tread

250 × 38 outer string
or 250 × 32 wall string
Ex 100 × 25 half riser

Rise 2613⁄13

Going 224

Detail – TREADS & HALF RISERS

Secret-fixed flooring

100 × 100 newel
Level string

NOTE
Riser faces meet newel centre

Detail
QUARTER SPACE LANDING
& LOWER FLIGHT

JOINERY PROJECT   No XXI

Construction Details   XXI / 2

OPEN-RISER DOMESTIC STAIRWAY

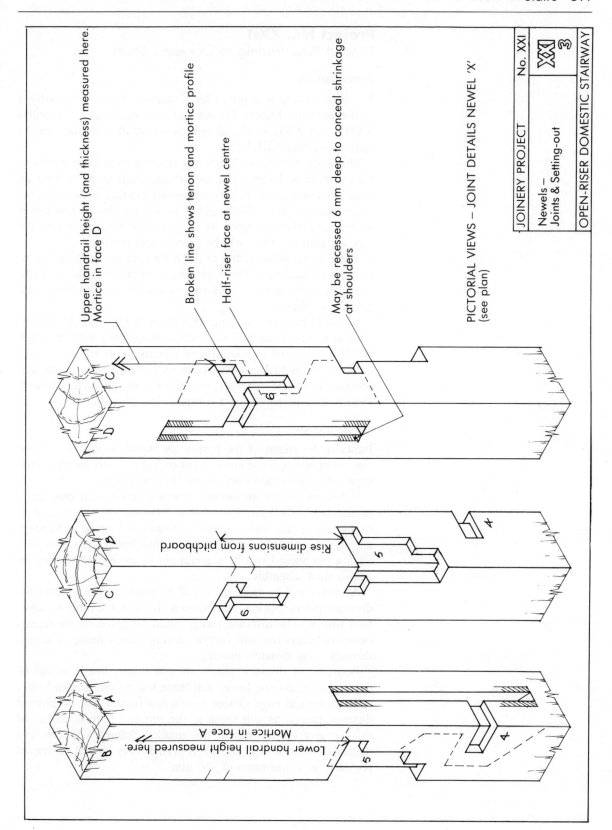

Upper handrail height (and thickness) measured here.
Mortice in face D

Broken line shows tenon and mortice profile

Half-riser face at newel centre

May be recessed 6 mm deep to conceal shrinkage at shoulders

PICTORIAL VIEWS – JOINT DETAILS NEWEL 'X'
(see plan)

Rise dimensions from pitchboard

Lower handrail height measured here.
Mortice in face A

JOINERY PROJECT   No. XXI

XXI 3

Newels –
Joints & Setting-out

OPEN-RISER DOMESTIC STAIRWAY

Project No. XXII
Glazed Balustrading to Domestic Stairs

Specification

The balustrading is required for a stairway that was the subject of the previous Joinery Project and is to conform to Drawings XXII.1 and XXII.2. Useful reference may also be made to the earlier Drawing XXI.1.

The work consists of hardwood framing to contain panels of 6 mm toughened glass, and each frame made so as to leave an open margin around its perimeter with locating distance pieces where fixings occur. Each glazed panel is to be in two pieces with a central open space as a decorative feature, where the exposed edges of glass will be ground and polished.

Three rectangular frames of differing sizes are required, to be situated at landings. Three pitched frames (one pair and one single) are to be made to conform to the stair pitch, to be situated at the stair flights.

It should be noted that the sizes given in Drawing XXII.1 are close approximations and that before proceeding with the work it will be essential to take precise dimensions from site.

The work is to be of European Oak throughout, neatly and accurately framed together to conform to the given Joinery Details, and prepared for a natural, clear gloss finish.

Interpretation

Joints at the angles of the frames are shown as mitres, and for reasons of strength the given detail includes a dovetail. A similar approach will be necessary at the 'square' angles.

When taking site dimensions it will be good craft practice to prepare a plywood pitchboard of as large dimensions as is practicable, to fit the angle between a newel and string (a handrail may not be perfectly straight and could lead to inaccuracies). Such a pitchboard will be a useful aid in setting out the frames and in their assembly.

Accuracy will be vital, yet it will be good practice to leave the distance pieces thicker than shown, by about 2 mm, to allow final fitting. The distance pieces could be glued to the frames before delivery, this will simplify fitting. Screw fixings will pass through these distance pieces.

Positions of distance pieces are not given, but it would be reasonable to assume firstly that there will be one at mid-height to each vertical edge. Those to pitched frames will be pitched distance pieces, as will those to the top and bottom edges. At the top and bottom edges, the smallest frames will have two distance pieces, and to the larger frames they should be spaced regularly at a maximum of 450 mm.

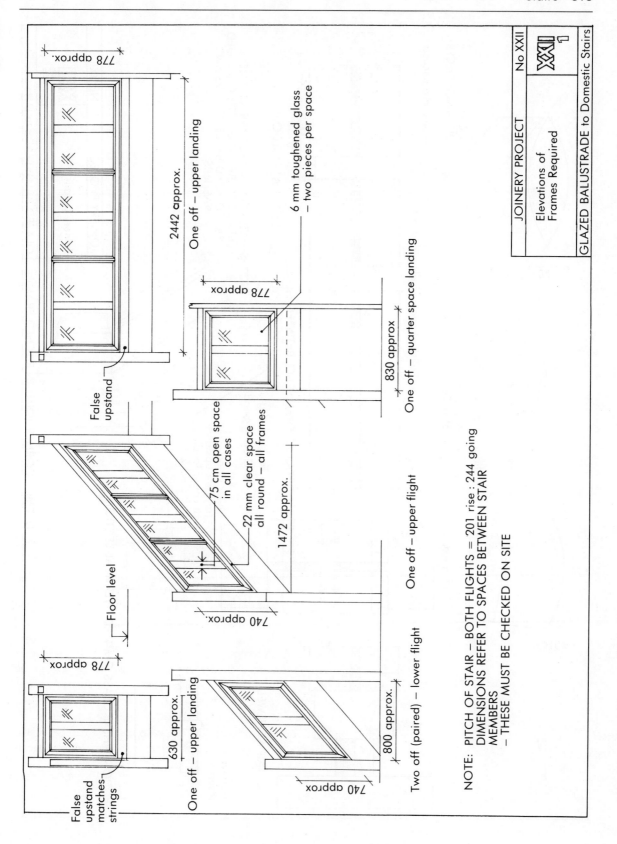

778 approx.

2442 approx.

One off – upper landing

False upstand

75 cm open space in all cases

22 mm clear space all round – all frames

Floor level

778 approx.

One off – upper landing

630 approx.

False upstand matches strings

6 mm toughened glass – two pieces per space

778 approx.

830 approx

One off – quarter space landing

1472 approx.

One off – upper flight

740 approx.

One off – lower flight

800 approx.

740 approx.

Two off (paired) – lower flight

JOINERY PROJECT   No XXII

XXII
1

Elevations of Frames Required

GLAZED BALUSTRADE to Domestic Stairs

NOTE: PITCH OF STAIR – BOTH FLIGHTS = 201 rise : 244 going
DIMENSIONS REFER TO SPACES BETWEEN STAIR MEMBERS
– THESE MUST BE CHECKED ON SITE

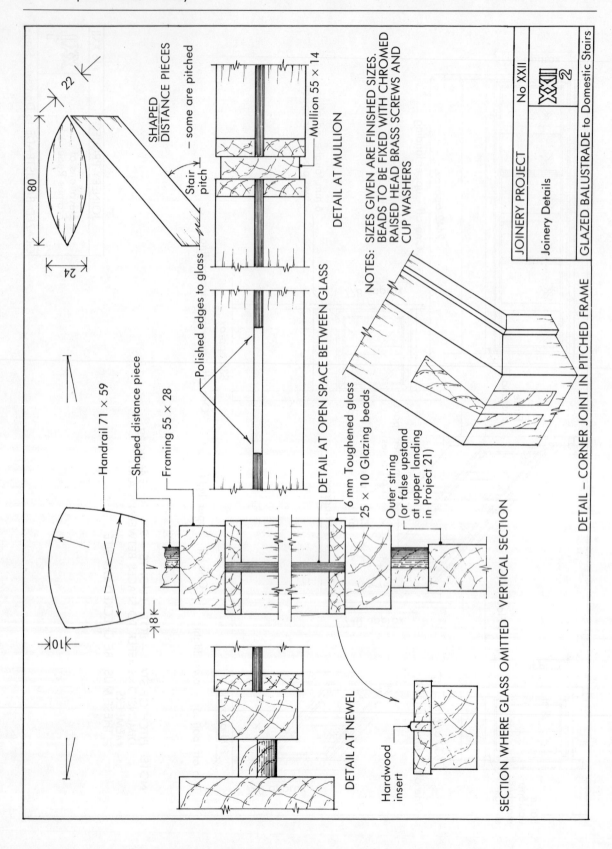

22

80

24

SHAPED DISTANCE PIECES
– some are pitched

Stair pitch

Mullion 55 × 14

DETAIL AT MULLION

Polished edges to glass

Handrail 71 × 59

Shaped distance piece

Framing 55 × 28

DETAIL AT OPEN SPACE BETWEEN GLASS

6 mm Toughened glass

25 × 10 Glazing beads

Outer string (or false upstand at upper landing in Project 21)

8

10

NOTES: SIZES GIVEN ARE FINISHED SIZES. BEADS TO BE FIXED WITH CHROMED RAISED HEAD BRASS SCREWS AND CUP WASHERS

DETAIL AT NEWEL

Hardwood insert

SECTION WHERE GLASS OMITTED   VERTICAL SECTION

DETAIL – CORNER JOINT IN PITCHED FRAME

JOINERY PROJECT   No XXII

XXII
2

Joinery Details

GLAZED BALUSTRADE to Domestic Stairs

Index

Many of the subject topics indexed below are not entirely confined to the pages indicated, and further applications may be found elsewhere in the general text, or perhaps more readily in the JOINERY PROJECTS. Where this is particularly so, the reader has been advised to relate the topic to one or more of the projects.

Aesthetics in joinery   22, 99, 102

Bay windows   112, 126
Bolection mouldings   162, 164, 201
Bow windows   142
Bullseye windows   60, 108, 137

Circular work   60, 72, 106, 108
Communications
   Bill of Quantities   58
   cutting lists   61, 177
   external   49
   internal   52
   patterns   65
   scaled drawings   54
   specifications   56
   workshop rods   59
Conversion of timber   7, 38
Counters   212, 234
   clamped ends   209
   counter keys   209, 296
   curved counter   234
   doors and flaps   214
Credence tables   267
Cross-wall mounted   270
Cupboard fitments   13, 236
Curtain walling   120

Design
   aesthetic   22
   functional   3
   production   37
Dihedral angle   129
Door frames and linings   44, 150

combination frames   152, 175
   door linings   154
   interior door frames   154
   projecting frames and linings   156
Doors
   emergency exit   186
   fire-resisting   170
   flush   166
   framed, ledged and braced   11, 160, 189, 192
   glazed   164, 175
   industrial, with Wicket   192
   panelled   161, 183, 186
   sliding   192, 261
   stable   189
   swing   169, 175
Door seals   172
Double glazing   118
Drawers   245

Elliptical work   74, 80, 140
Enquiry hatch   261
Ergonomics in joinery   3, 211, 248

Finishes to joinery (see also JOINERY PROJECTS)   25, 40, 42
Fire-resisting doors   170
Flush doors   166

Geometry in
   aesthetics   25
   angles   70
   circle   72, 142

continuous handrails 299
development of surfaces 78, 80, 127, 143
dihedral angle 129
ellipse 74, 140
golden section 102, 300
intersecting mouldings 76
louvres 104, 147
mitre developments in counter 219
mitre developments in seating 256
mouldings 44, 73, 163
orthographic projection 76
pictorial drawing 77, 128, 130
pivot-hung windows 103
polygons 71
raking mouldings 225
roofing 80, 128
scaled drawings 54, 76
spiral glazing bars 137
swing doors 169
tangents and normals 73
tapered steps and wall strings 282, 293
wreathed strings 294
Glazing (see also JOINERY PROJECTS) 15, 100, 118, 164, 312
Glues 20

Hatch for enquiries 261

Intersecting mouldings 44, 71, 76
Isometric projection 77, 128

Joints in framed joinery 14, 29, 44, 112, 116, 122
Joinery projects
  I.   Splayed bay window with hipped roof 126
  II. Bullseye window with spiral bars 137
  III. Elliptical borrowed light 140
  IV. Bow window with flat or pitched roof 142
  V.   Louvred frame with sloping head 147
  VI. Swing doors and glazed vestibule frames 175
  VII. Hardwood doors with enriched panels 183
  VIII. Emergency exit doors and frames 186
  IX. 'Stable' doors and frame 189
  X.   Industrial sliding doors with wicket 192
  XI. Wall panelling to reception area 221
  XII. Strip panelling to isolated pier 225
  XIII. Table-mounted lectern (I) 228
  XIV. Table-mounted lectern (II) 231
  XV. Curved bar counter 235
  XVI. Seating to reception area 255
  XVII. Enquiry hatch with sliding doors 261
  XVIII. Refectory tables 264
  XIX. Credence tables 267
  XX. Wall-mounted cross 270
  XXI. Open riser stairs 307
  XXII. Glazed balustrading 312
Labour costs 63
Laminated work 108, 137, 140, 143, 234
Lecterns 228, 231
Linings 150, 154, 157, 261
Louvres 104, 147

Machine shop layout 41
Manufactured boards 18
Moisture in timber 5
Mouldings 44, 73, 163

Occasional tables 257
Open-riser stairs 277, 281, 282, 307
Orthographic projection 76

Panelled doors 11, 28, 161, 183
Panelling to walls 195, 221
Patterns 65, 142
Pitched roof details 130, 143
Preparation for finishes (see also

JOINERY PROJECTS)
25, 40,42
Preservatives   15
Production design   37
Production sequence   41, 53
Projecting frames and linings   9

Raking mouldings   225
Refectory tables   264
Roofing and geometry   128

Saw kerfing   109
Scaled drawings (*see also*
JOINERY PROJECTS)   54,
76
Scribing to walls and floors   34
Seating   248, 255
Secret fixings   197, 221, 270
Sliding doors   192, 241, 261
Sliding sashes   114
Softwood grounds   36, 141, 196,
221
Sound insulation   99, 119
Specifications (*see also* JOINERY
PROJECTS)   56
Splayed windows   126
Stable doors   189
Stairs
construction details   286
continuous handrails   298
cut strings   291
design and setting-out   273
glazed balustrading   312
newels   289, 309, 311
open risers   296, 307
shaped steps   289
tapered steps   282
wall strings at winders   293

wreathed strings   294
Storage and display fitments
cupboard doors   239
drawers   245
shelving   237
Swing doors   169, 175

Tables   257, 264, 267
Tangents and normals   72, 109,
137, 140
Terotechnology   3
Thermal insulation   99, 143
Timber calculations   63
Timber sizes available   38
Transporting and handling   34

Wall panelling   195, 221
Waste   39, 61, 109, 177
Weathering details   15, 98, 100,
122, 158
Wicket door   192
Windows
bay windows   112, 124
bow windows   114, 142
bullseye   137
curtain walling   120
curved members   108
double-glazed   118
elliptical   140
louvred   104, 147
performance
requirements   97
pivot-hung   103
sliding sashes   114
Workshop rods (*see also*
JOINERY PROJECTS)   59
Work surfaces   12, 207, 228,
231, 257, 264, 267